KT-237-155

1927

1872

The Brown & Sharpe Mfg. Co. occupies at the present time ten fireproof manufacturing buildings, having a floor area of over 1,397,000 square feet, or approximately 32 acres. This plant is the outgrowth of the small shop in which the business started in 1833 and which it outgrew in 1872. The works are located but a short distance from the business centre of Providence and visitors are always welcome. All styles of our milling machines may be seen at the plant in the course of construction or actually at work under manufacturing conditions.

Practical Treatise
on
Milling
and
Milling Machines

Brown & Sharpe Mfg. Co.
Providence, R. I., U. S. A.
1927

Printed in U. S. A. 2M-4-29

PREFACE

It is our purpose in publishing this book to present, in as non-technical a manner as possible, information that will assist the beginner and practical man to a better understanding of the care and various uses of modern milling machines of the column and knee and manufacturing types.

CAUTION

Do not order parts from numbers shown in cuts in this book. Send for Milling Machine Separate Parts Book stating the size and style of the machine for which the parts are desired.

CONTENTS

The Original Universal Milling Machine

The original universal milling machine was designed primarily for the purpose of forming the flutes in twist drills. Its wonderful capabilities, however, were quickly recognized, and its use soon spread to other lines, until today we find that there is an unusually large variety of machine shop jobs that can be done on a modern machine of this type. Straight and angular pieces, and surfaces of an endless variety of irregular contours, together with spur, bevel and spiral gears, twist drills, etc., can be produced. Also such work as drilling, boring, planing, rack cutting, slotting, cam cutting, graduating, etc., can be successfully accomplished. In fact, the full variety of work that can be done on a universal milling machine is still unknown, for new ways of using it are being constantly discovered.

INTRODUCTION

Milling is the process of removing metal with rotary cutters. It is employed extensively in machine shops today for forming parts of machinery, tools, etc., to required dimensions and shapes. A machine designed especially for this purpose was in existence as early as 1818, but little progress was made in the process until after the invention of the universal milling machine (shown on the opposite page) in 1861–62 by Mr. Joseph R. Brown, of J. R. Brown and Sharpe. This was owing chiefly to the difficulties of obtaining satisfactory cutters and of sharpening them. Shortly after this, however, improvements in the methods of making cutters, the invention by Mr. J. R. Brown of the formed cutter which can be sharpened without changing the cutting contour, and the introduction of the grinding wheel for sharpening cutters removed the obstacles that had so seriously hindered the early development of milling.

As the field of milling widened, the demands upon the machine increased accordingly, and it became necessary to make certain improvements to adapt it to the new conditions. But it is a noteworthy fact that in all of the changes in design leading up to the modern heavy type of universal machine, shown on page 44, none of the fundamental ideas of the original machine have been lost. Parts have been strengthened to better withstand heavier service, and radical changes have been made in the method of driving the spindle and feeds to accommodate the machine to modern requirements.

From a comparison of the original machine with a modern type, the important changes that have been made are readily noted.

The column has been carried well above the spindle, and an overhanging arm with a support for the outer end of cutter arbor has been added. To further stiffen the arbor, arm braces have been devised by the use of which the overhanging arm, cutter arbor, and knee are all rigidly tied together. These braces on the smaller sizes of machines consist of long slotted cross arms, while on the larger, or heavy service machines, a different and heavier type is employed.

The table feed has been changed from the end of the feed screw and carried up through the centre of the knee and saddle, thus allowing the table to be swiveled through a much greater arc. Power feeds have been applied to the transverse and vertical table movements, and on large machines a power fast travel for the table has taken the place of the hand quick return. The old-style elevating screw for the knee that required cutting a hole through the floor has been replaced by a telescopic screw.

Improvements have been made on the spiral head to make it more rigid and convenient to operate; differential indexing largely replaces the compound method, and refinements such as graduated index sectors, and an adjustable index crank have been added.

Such conveniences as permanent handwheels instead of cranks, adjustable dials reading to thousandths of an inch on the feed shafts, and other improvements have been added from time to time.

When the milling machine came into more general use, and its possibilities in removing metal began to be appreciated, the demand arose for the ability to make heavier cuts. These demands soon demonstrated that the method of driving the feeds through belts and cone pulleys from the spindle of the machine to the feed mechanism, was inadequate. The first improvement was to substitute chain and sprockets for the belt and pulleys and to use removable change gears to provide a variation in the rate of feed. The next step was to place all the change gears in a feed box wherein by simply shifting levers, a wide variation of feeds could be obtained.

The main spindle drive has undergone radical changes. The original machine had a four-step cone pulley mounted directly on the spindle, and many of the smaller sizes of machines today are similarly built. In order to get more power and a greater range of speeds, back gears similar to those of a lathe were added.

Following these improvements came a radical change in the whole driving mechanism of the machine. The value of feeds that were independent of the spindle speeds had become well recognized, and with the introduction of high speed steel, from which cutters could be made that would take much heavier cuts at faster speeds, and coarser feeds than had ever before been the practice, there arose a demand for more powerful machines. The constant speed type of drive was therefore originated. In this type of machine any combination of table feed and spindle speed is available, because both spindle and feeding mechanisms are driven from the main shaft of the machine, which revolves at a constant high velocity at all times. The table feeds are therefore entirely independent of the spindle speeds. A powerful drive is also transmitted to the spindle from the driving pulley of large diameter and wide face on the main shaft of the machine through a train of heavy spur gearing in which are certain change gears that can be manipulated to give a wide range of spindle speeds.

At the same time that the constant speed type of drive was evolved, the machine was redesigned and made stronger throughout in order to better fit it for the heavy cuts that had become the practice.

Later improvements have been the extension of the flat bearing surface on the front of the column to the top, the application of a friction clutch in the driving pulley with levers at the sides of the machine for operating it, the power fast travel for quick movement of the table, the double or capped overarm, the motor-in-the-base, and other improvements of lesser importance.

It is not to be assumed that the constant speed type of drive has been developed to the exclusion of the cone type, for there are many pieces of work that can be done to good advantage on this machine. The modern cone type of machine embodies many of the previously mentioned improvements, and there is still, and probably always will be, a steady demand for this machine.

Two other types of machines known as Plain and Vertical Spindle Milling Machines have kept pace with the development of the universal machine.

Milling Machines of the Planer and Manufacturing types have also come into extensive use, the former producing a wide range of work that is of too large dimensions for the previously mentioned machines, and the latter manufacturing in large quantities, small duplicate parts of machinery, tools, etc.

Automatic Milling Machines are also economically used for large quantity production where the loading time is somewhat less than the cutting time. This condition permits the machine to cut almost continuously, as the operator can load the work in one fixture while that in the other is being milled. They are made in column and knee, manufacturing and duplex types.

With the improvements that have been made on the machines and their equipment, milling has become indispensable in the modern shop. Interchangeable pieces can be easily made, and work is produced at a low cost because of the continuous operation and inexpensiveness of cutters for a given amount of production. We, therefore, recommend the milling machine to manufacturers desirous of obtaining the best results at the lowest cost on all classes of work to which

Column and Knee Milling Machine of the Universal Style, Cone Drive

the machine is adapted. And we trust that a careful reading of the following chapters will be of material assistance in understanding the process of milling and how to use the machines.

CHAPTER I

Classification of Milling Machines

The existing types of milling machines are so numerous, and their designs merge into one another to such an extent, that it is very difficult to classify them definitely. But, taken as a whole, they may be said to consist of two distinct groups, those adapted to a variety of work, and those restricted to the performance of a single operation, such as gear cutting, bolt head milling, thread milling, etc. While this latter group embraces some valuable and interesting machines, the class of work done is of a more or less special character, and little can be learned from it of the general process of milling. For this reason, and also from the fact that it would be practically impossible to treat of every type in the limited space of this book, the first group alone will be considered. The machines of this group are classified in a variety of ways by different writers. We prefer to divide them, according to general appearance and design, into three classes, comprising the column and knee type, manufacturing type, and planer type. Such a classification brings out the characteristics of the different machines, and their relation to one another.

Column and Knee Milling Machines

An illustration of a representative example of the column and knee type of milling machine is shown on the opposite page. This machine is the most recent of the three types named, having been in existence about sixty years. The rapid strides, however, that have been made within the past few years in the process of milling are largely due to its versatility and convenience. Even with the most expert cutter making, milling could never have obtained its important position in the field of machinery and tool manufacture had it not been for the column and knee type of construction.

The name, column and knee, is derived from the high, column-like design of the main casting, and the likeness of the bracket which supports the table to a knee or angle iron. The knee is adjustable on the column so that the table can be set at different heights to accommodate work of varying size. It can also be fed upward, thus enabling vertical cuts to be taken. Provision is made for movement of the table horizontally in two directions: one, longitudinally, at right angles to the axis of the spindle; and the other, transversely, parallel to the axis of the spindle. The combination of these three movements is found only in the column and knee machine, and it is due to the advantages derived from this construction that the machine is superior to the manufacturing or planer type for general milling purposes.

Several more illustrations of column and knee machines are shown on succeeding pages of this chapter, where a further classification is given.

Manufacturing Milling Machine

This type of milling machine is shown in the illustration on the opposite page. It is a development of one of the earliest forms that was built particularly for use in the manufacture of small parts of firearms, and has since been successfully adopted for machining parts of sewing machines, typewriters and other machines and tools. The advantages it offers for this class of work are due to the stiff construction and convenience with which it can be operated. These make possible an exceptionally large production of first quality work — factors of great importance in commercial manufacturing.

There are many minor variations of this type of milling machine, but the general features are similar in all. In that shown on the opposite page, the spindle is supported in bearings located in an adjustable head that can be raised and lowered. The capacity of the machine is rather limited as regards work of widely varying heights. Furthermore, there is no transverse table feed, the only movement transversely being obtained by a slight adjustment of the spindle. These, however, cannot be considered disadvantages, as provision for work of widely varying heights is not required, because all work done is of comparatively small dimensions, and there is seldom any necessity for a transverse table movement.

The longitudinal movement of the table is at right angles to the axis of the spindle. This movement is accomplished either automatically or by hand by means of a rack and pinion on the under side of the table. The pinion is driven from the spindle through a train of change gears and a worm and wheel when the automatic feed is in action.

A larger and improved style of manufacturing machine is shown on page 88. It embodies all the features of the machine illustrated

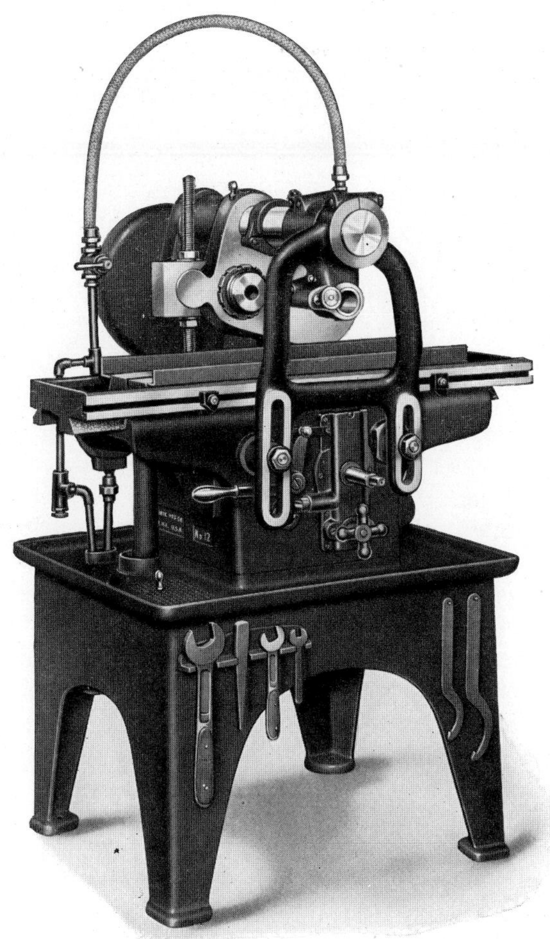

Milling Machine of Manufacturing Type

on page 13, but in addition is designed so that the spindle is more powerfully driven and has a greater vertical adjustment. The table is also provided with a transverse movement. This machine is therefore adapted to a somewhat wider range of work than the one previously described.

Planer Milling Machine

The planer milling machine is designed for the heaviest classes of slab and gang milling. It bears a marked resemblance to the planer, from which it derives its name. The spindle is mounted in bearings carried in a vertically adjustable slide similar to that of a planer, and the table is in a corresponding position. This brief reference will enable one to easily distinguish these machines. And, as the class of work preformed is identical in character, only heavier than that done on the column and knee type of machine, the same principles are involved.

Returning to the column and knee type, we can subdivide it into three classes, known as Plain, Universal, and Vertical Spindle Machines. In the first two the spindle is supported in horizontal bearings that are fixed in the main casting of the machine instead of being adjustable vertically, as in the case of both manufacturing and planer types of machines. This is one of the points where the column and knee machine is radically different from either of the other types. As we have already explained, vertical adjustment in this type is obtained by the movement of the knee upon the column. In the vertical spindle machine, the spindle is supported in vertical bearings, vertical adjustment being obtained by the movement of both the knee and spindle.

Plain Milling Machine. The word **plain** when applied to any milling machine is used to designate one in which the longitudinal travel of the table is fixed at right angles to the spindle. Both manufacturing and planer types are therefore essentially plain milling machines.

An illustration of a plain milling machine of the column and knee type is shown on page 20. In this machine, the table has the three movements, longitudinally, transversely, and vertically, that have already been mentioned. Some machines have both power and hand feeds for all three of the movements; others have longitudinal and transverse movements so controlled and the vertical is operated by hand; or the longitudinal movement alone is operated both by power and by hand, and the transverse and vertical movements are made only by hand. Lead screws are used for operating all of the table movements in many of the smaller sizes and all of the larger machines, but in some of the smaller ones a rack and pinion are employed for the longitudinal movement. The smallest sizes of machines have no power feeds at all, and are called hand milling machines. (See illustration on page 46.) In these, the table and knee are moved by means of racks and pinions operated by levers. They are convenient for manufacturing purposes on some classes of small work, as they can be operated very rapidly.

It is the practice in the classes of work to which the medium and larger sizes of plain milling machines are adapted to take heavy cuts at fast speeds and coarse feeds. The rigid construction of the machine enables this to be successfully done, and it is in this ability that the chief value of the plain machine is found.

Universal Milling Machine. The Universal milling machine is justly regarded by many to be the most important machine tool employed today; for with it much of the work of the planer and shaper — heretofore considered indispensable machines in every shop — can be done with an appreciable saving of time. Spur, bevel and spiral gears, twist drills, and all kinds of straight and taper milling can also be economically produced.

It was first patented February 21st, 1865, by Mr. J. R. Brown, of the firm of J. R. Brown & Sharpe, who designed it for the purpose of milling the grooves in twist drills, but adopted it shortly after for producing small spirals used in the manufacture of sewing machines. (An illustration of the original universal milling machine is shown on page 6.)

The cuts on pages 10 and 44 are representative of modern universal milling machines. This style of machine is essentially the same in construction as the plain milling machine, and the table has the same movements. But, in addition, the table swivels upon the saddle and can be set at an angle to the spindle in a horizontal plane. Also, it is fitted with a mechanism known as a spiral head, for use in spiral milling and indexing to obtain any required spacing on the periphery of work. The introduction of the swivel renders the table a little less stable than that of the plain machine, though in common practice heavy cuts are taken. It is apparent, however, that the offices of the two machines are in a way distinct. A universal machine is the better for general shop purposes, but where continuous heavy milling of straight cuts is to be done the plain machine is preferable.

Vertical Spindle Milling Machine. The vertical spindle milling machine embodies the principles of a drilling machine. The spindle and table are similarly located, and the cutter is mounted at the end of the spindle. The table on the milling machine, however, has a

Vertical Spindle Milling Machine of Constant Speed Drive Type

series of movements that are not found on the drilling machine. For such work as face milling, die-sinking, profiling, etc., the vertical spindle machine offers many advantages over the horizontal style. Some work can be fastened directly to the top of the table, eliminating the use of special fixtures necessary for the same kind of work on a horizontal spindle machine. Furthermore, the operator is enabled to see his work at all times during operation and more readily follow any irregularities in outline. This feature is especially valuable in profiling, cutting odd-shaped slots, etc.

Not all vertical spindle machines are of the column and knee type. There are several styles that have no provision for vertical adjustment of the table. Also some vertical spindle machines have two spindles instead of one, but these are more generally known as profiling machines.

But the combination of the vertical spindle and column and knee constructions has given the mechanical world an exceptionally valuable machine tool. With it, all of the advantages of the vertical spindle, together with those of the column and knee, are acquired. A modern example of this style is shown in the cut on page 16. A further convenience of this machine is found in the spindle head, which is adjustable vertically, and can be fed by power, thus enabling drilling to be conveniently done. With the adjustable spindle head and column and knee construction, it is apparent that work of a wide range of heights can be accommodated. Another style of vertical spindle machine, where the spindle is driven by a belt, is shown on page 36.

Automatic Milling Machine. This type of machine (see cut on page 18) does not differ materially from the general design of the plain and manufacturing types except to obtain the construction necessary to include the automatic features. The major feature of these machines is their ability to keep non-cutting time to a minimum, which, with simplicity of operation and ready adaptation to a wide variety of work, makes them ideal production machines.

Different Methods of Driving Milling Machines

Milling machines of the column and knee and manufacturing types are either cone driven or gear driven. The latter class is more commonly referred to as the " constant speed drive."

Cone Drive. In cone driven milling machines, the belt runs directly from a stepped or cone pulley on the countershaft to one of like design fastened, either directly to, or mounted on a sleeve on the ma-

Automatic Milling Machine of Manufacturing Type

chine spindle. In one case the spindle is driven directly and only speeds that are obtained by shifting the driving belt on the pulley steps are available; while in the other an additional series of speeds is procured by the employment of back gears. The cut on page 10 is of the latter type, and the back gears referred to are enclosed at the front of the column. The feeding mechanism is driven from the rear end of the spindle by a chain and sprockets, and is subject to the speed variations of the spindle.

When the cone method of drive is employed for vertical spindle milling machines, the belt usually leads from the cone pulley on the countershaft to one on a shaft at the back of the machine. Power is transmitted thence to the spindle on the lighter machines, by means of a quarter-turn belt. An application of this method of drive is shown in the illustration on page 36. The heavier machines are fitted with bevel gears, and a vertical shaft from which the spindle is driven by a chain and sprockets.

Constant Speed Drive. This is the result of a demand for a machine in which the feeds would be entirely independent of the spindle speeds, and all speeds and feeds would be self-contained, thus doing away with complicated overhead works, or permitting the machine to be driven by a constant speed motor. More power and greater convenience in changing speeds and feeds were also important factors leading to the development of this type of drive.

Early in 1904, the Brown & Sharpe Mfg. Company placed the first constant speed drive machine upon the market. Several examples of constant speed drive machines are shown in this treatise, notably those illustrated on pages 16, 18, 20 and 44.

The general features of this drive are as follows: the belt delivers power to the driving pulley that runs loose on a sleeve on the main shaft of the machine. By means of a friction clutch on the main shaft, operated by levers at each side of the column, power is transmitted from the driving pulley to a train of hardened gears leading to the spindle, and in which there are certain change gears operated by levers at the right-hand side of the column. The belt and main driving pulley run at a constant high velocity regardless of the spindle speed. The power at the spindle is therefore constant, regardless of its speed.

The mechanism of constant speed drive vertical spindle machines is essentially like that outlined above, except that a pair of bevel gears and vertical shaft are introduced to transmit power to the spindle head, from whence it is communicated to the spindle itself by spur gearing.

The feed changing mechanism is driven from the main shaft by means of a chain and sprockets in all constant speed drive machines.

Heavy Service Plain Milling Machine of Constant Speed Drive Type

Hence it is completely separated from the spindle drive, in so far as its speeds are concerned, permitting the full range of feeds to be available for every spindle speed. Such an arrangement also permits the table feeds to be rated directly in inches per minute.

CHAPTER II

Essentials of a Modern Milling Machine

It has been previously stated that the foremost advantages attending the employment of the milling machine are, the production of a great variety of work, and the exact duplication of pieces at an economical cost. In order that these advantages may fully materialize, it is necessary that many requirements be fulfilled in the design and construction of the machine.

These requirements vary to a certain extent with the style and size of machine; taken as a whole, however, they are materially the same. The machines must all be accurate, economical to operate, and durable. Hence, these may be said to constitute the general requirements of a milling machine. Those qualities upon which accuracy is chiefly dependent are thorough workmanship, especially in aligning the working parts, and sufficient rigidity. In order to be economical in operation, a milling machine must have ample ranges of spindle speeds and table feeds, and plenty of power, so as to adapt it to the many varieties of work. Further, its efficiency must be high, and its parts must be conveniently arranged to allow quick manipulation and ready adjustment. The third general requirement, durability, is, to a great extent, dependent upon the design and quality of materials that enter into the construction of a machine. It is also influenced by several of the already-mentioned points that are essential to accuracy and economy. To particularize then, the requirements of a milling machine are thorough workmanship, correct alignment of all working parts, sufficient rigidity, wide ranges of speeds and feeds, ample power, high efficiency, durability, and convenience in design and operation.

Workmanship. It is stated above that the dependence of accuracy upon workmanship in the building of a milling machine is of greatest importance in connection with the alignments of the different working parts. Correct alignments are most essential because they establish exact positions of the various parts with relation to one another. Any error in alignments is transmitted from one part to another until it is finally communicated to the piece of work, where it is liable to be multiplied. If the work is of the coarser grade, or mere roughing cuts are being taken, a few thousandths of an inch over or under size do not matter; but when finishing a piece that must come within close limits of a pre-determined size, a very small error is often sufficient to seriously impair its quality.

All of the important alignments in milling machines are obtained by scraping, a process consisting of going over the different bearing surfaces by hand with a chisel-like tool, and removing the highest spots until a maximum number of bearing points is secured. Flat bearings are scraped to conform to master surface plates and straight edges, and the boxes of important cylindrical bearings are scraped to fit the revolving piece, which is ground. This work necessarily calls for much skill on the part of the workman, and the care with which scraping is performed largely influences the accuracy of the resultant bearings.

Principal Alignments of Milling Machines. Broadly speaking, the principal alignments of all milling machines are those of the spindle and table. They are, of course, affected by various minor alignments throughout the machine, but it is not essential to take up each of these in detail. The alignments of the table on horizontal spindle column and knee machines should be such that its upward and downward movements will be perpendicular to the spindle axis. Its longitudinal and transverse movements should be in horizontal planes, the longitudinal being parallel to the face of the column on plain machines, and on universal machines when the table is set at zero; and the transverse at right angles to the column.

On universal machines, the table should also swivel in a horizontal plane.

These alignments of the table and spindle of column and knee machines are typical, and it is easy to understand from them what the alignments of other types of milling machines should be.

While we have emphasized the importance of good workmanship in scraping bearing surfaces, in order to obtain accurate alignments, it must be understood that certain elements in design are largely responsible as to whether the alignments remain accurate or not. A bearing surface may be scraped ever so carefully, yet the lack of sufficient weight in the casting, or of ample proportions of the bearing surface itself, will quickly result in the alignments becoming inaccurate. Thus it is apparent that if alignments are to be permanent, the proportion of the different parts, including the bearing surfaces themselves, must be ample to easily support the weight brought upon them. The accuracy of alignments can be ascertained upon first operation of a machine, but their permanency can be determined only after a considerable period of service.

Rigidity. This requirement is of just as great importance to the success of a milling machine as correct alignments. Any machine tool must be rigid in order to produce accurate, well-finished work;

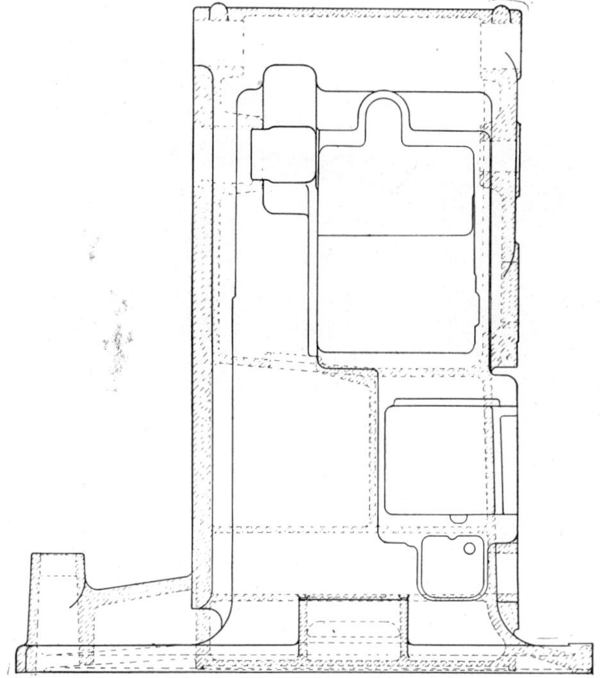

Brown & Sharpe Milling Machine, showing large base, thick walls and internal bracing. The spindle bearings are mounted directly in thick walls of column.

the milling machine must be particularly so. It is not until within the past few years, however, that the real value of this essential has been fully appreciated. This is owing to the fact that up to that time the milling machine had not become so extensively used for manufacturing purposes. In this field it must be capable of not only producing accurate work of high quality, but of producing it rapidly. The more rapidly a machine is operated, the greater is its tendency to vibrate. This is further augmented by the use of cutters made from high speed steel, for they can be made to take unusually heavy cuts at fast speeds and coarse feeds. It is impossible to eliminate all vibrations from even the very best types of machine construction, but they may be reduced to a minimum, or, in other words, to a point where they will not affect the accuracy of the work, if every part is so constructed that it is capable of resisting heavy stresses, and absorbing vibrations. Weight and well-proportioned construction are most necessary to overcome vibrations.

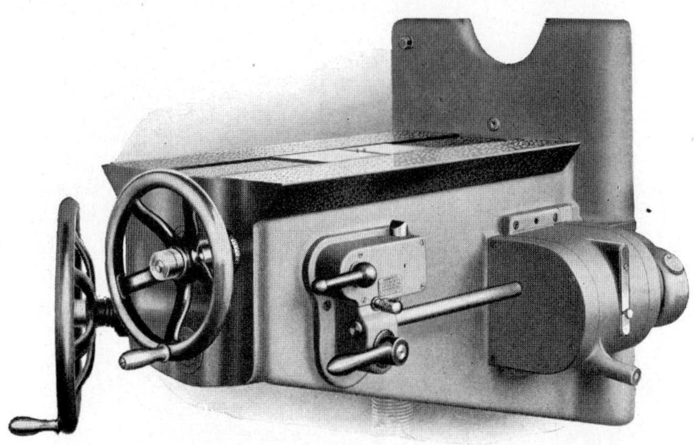

Knee of Brown & Sharpe Milling Machine illustrating the points mentioned opposite

The essentials in the design and construction of the column and knee machine that serve well to illustrate the general points that conduce to rigidity in all machines, follow:

First, the base must be large and heavy enough to provide a firm foundation, and the walls of the column must be thick and strongly braced, in order to support rigidly the weight of the working parts and withstand the strains of operation. Especially is this true of the front wall, which forms the basis of support for the table. If this is not heavy enough and well braced, it will have a tendency to buckle under the heavy loads it is required to support, which will not only admit of vibrations, but also destroy the alignments of the machine. Another point in connection with this front wall, or vertical slide, is that it should be wide in proportion to the size of the machine, as the wider a flat bearing, the more stable it is.

All shafts should be of large enough diameter to resist bending and torsional stresses, and gears should be of ample size to give strength and good wearing qualities, and to transmit the requisite power to the spindle. Cylindrical bearings should be firmly supported, and the boxes should be as long as is consistent with a high degree of efficiency. Those of the spindle are most stable when mounted directly in the thick walls of the frame.

A heavy, well-braced construction is necessary in the knee in order to overcome all tendency to vibrate or sag under the load of the saddle and table during operation. It is also well, to have the back of the knee that fits the vertical column extended above the top as this gives a larger bearing surface to resist sagging tendencies and vibrations under heavy loads.

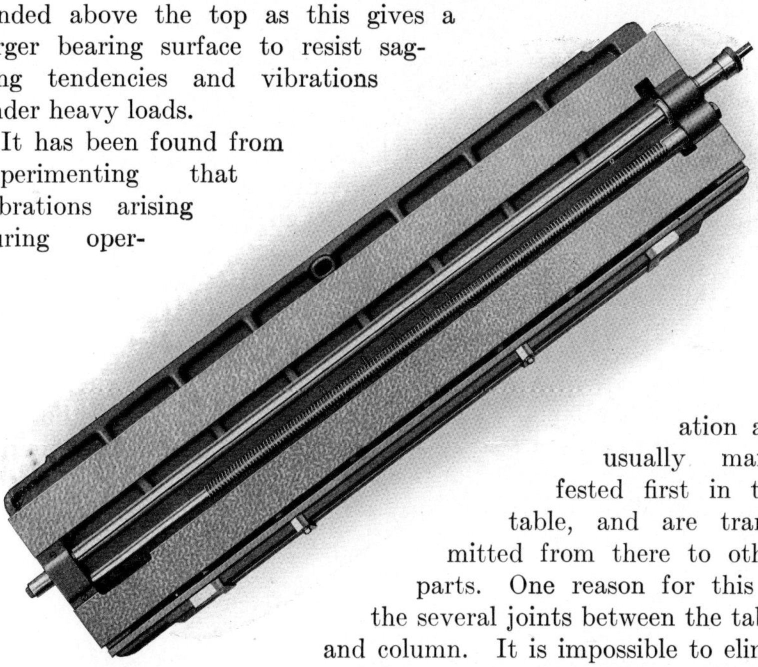

It has been found from experimenting that vibrations arising during operation are usually manifested first in the table, and are transmitted from there to other parts. One reason for this is the several joints between the table and column. It is impossible to eliminate all lost motion between the bearing surfaces, and still have the parts free to perform their different functions. But weight has much to do with the stability of the table, and in many cases vibrations have been practically overcome by simply adding more weight to this part. It is important, therefore, that both the table and saddle be of sufficiently heavy construction. Transverse braces, however, placed at frequent intervals on the under side of the table often produce the required rigidity without adding unduly to the weight. Efficient clamps on the flat bearings of the knee, saddle and table also provide means of rigidly fastening any one or two of the table movements that may not be in use, thus eliminating vibrations.

Showing Firm Support of Arbor on Heavy Job

Another point that influences largely the rigidity of the table is the size of the flat bearing surfaces in the saddle and on the knee. It is essential that the table bearing in the saddle be wide and sufficiently long to prevent too great an overhang when the table is at the ends of its traverse, and the top of the knee be of ample width to easily support the weight placed upon the table.

Other features which conduce to rigidity are: a single or double overarm with a support for the outer end of the cutter arbor, and an intermediate bearing on the larger machines, also arm braces that firmly tie the overhanging arm and knee together.

Speeds and Feeds. It is rare that the conditions surrounding any two jobs on a milling machine are the same. Sometimes the work is of the heaviest class to which the machine is adapted, requiring gangs of cutters operating at a comparatively fast speed and coarse feed; again it is of a lighter type, requiring only one cutter operating at a fast speed and fine feed. The shape of the piece sometimes demands that the cutter be fed through faster or slower than would ordinarily be done in milling a plain surface. Different materials cannot be milled at the same speeds and feeds. Cutters of large diameter are employed for some jobs, and to get the proper peripheral speed, they must be rotated at a slower rate than those of smaller diameter. A finishing cut with the same cutter is usually taken at a faster speed, and correspondingly lower rate of feed per revolution of spindle than the roughing cut, in order to obtain a smoother finish. All these, and many other conditions, make it necessary that a machine have a wide range of spindle speeds and table feeds. Furthermore, there must be many intermediate speeds and feeds between the highest and lowest in the ranges. In many cases it is also advantageous to have the speeds and feeds independent of one another, so that the spindle speed may be changed without disturbing the rate of table travel. This is possible in the constant speed driven machine,

Feed Changing Mechanism on Brown & Sharpe Milling Machine

and constitutes a particular point wherein this type of drive differs from that known as the cone drive.

The cone drive machine is admirably adapted to all classes of work where it is not necessary to use combinations of extreme speeds and feeds. In these cases, however, it cannot fulfill the requirements. For instance, it is impossible to obtain a coarse enough feed for a cutter of very large diameter, because the feeding mechanism is invariably driven from the end of the spindle, and is subject to the speed variations of this part. Consequently, when a large cutter is being used, the spindle is usually driven at its slowest speed, and the fastest feed that is then available is not coarse enough. Likewise, a correct combination of speed and feed cannot be had for a small mill, as this should run at the fastest spindle speed, and, when it does, the finest feed obtainable is much too coarse. The majority of work, however, does not require such combinations, and when medium-sized mills are used and work of ordinary classes is done, the cone drive machine is very satisfactory

Owing to the dependence of the feeds upon the spindle speeds in the cone drive machines, it is necessary to rate them as so much per revolution of the spindle. This requires that the feed being used be multiplied by the spindle speed, in order to obtain the rate of production in inches per minute — the most generally accepted standard.

With the constant speed type of drive any combination of spindle speed and table feed within the ranges of the machine can be obtained, and thus the large, medium, or small sizes of cutters can all be run at the most practical speeds and feeds. This is due to the fact that the spindle and feeding mechanisms are driven independently of each other from the same main shaft, which revolves at a constant velocity at all times. Feeds obtained in this manner can be rated directly in inches per minute a point that in itself constitutes an important advantage.

On practically all of the Brown & Sharpe constant speed drive machines, sixteen changes of spindle speed, and at least sixteen different feeds are available, while some sizes have as many as twenty feeds. Their range varies slightly in the different sizes of machines, but is such in every case that the correct combination can be had for any cutter that is used.

Power. A milling machine must have ampie power, or its use is exceedingly limited. This applies to all styles and sizes of machines, but more particularly to the larger ones that are used in commercial manufacturing, where an economical production means the taking of heavy cuts at fast speeds and coarse feeds.

In driving machine tools, the power delivered to a machine depends upon the diameters of the driving pulleys, and size and velocity of the belt. A wide belt running at a high velocity on pulleys of large and equal diameters develops the maximum power, and, as its speed and width are lessened, its pulling ability decreases correspondingly. Likewise, it transmits less power, as the pulley on the machine exceeds in diameter the pulley on the driving shaft, for, when the surface contact on the driver becomes smaller, the belt has a tendency to slip.

Hence, in the factor of power is found another important difference between the cone and constant speed drive machines, with the advantage in favor of the latter.

The cone drive machine is very suitable for light and medium work, of such as the majority of milling consists, but when it comes to driving a large cutter through a heavy cut at a slow spindle speed and coarse feed, the requisite amount of power is lacking. This is due to the belt being upon the smallest step of the driving pulley, where it runs at its slowest velocity, and has a small arc and surface of contact.

On constant speed drive machines, the pulley is of the same, or almost equal diameter to that on the overhead shaft, and runs at a constant high velocity, irrespective of the spindle speed. Furthermore, a wider belt can be employed than on cone drive machines. As a result, a maximum amount of power is delivered to the machine pulley, and is transmitted through heavy gearing to the spindle, under all conditions, thus fitting this style of machine particularly well to the heavier classes of work. Another advantage of this drive is its particular adaptation to the application of a motor. The constant speed type of motor, which is more economical, both in first cost and in the amount of power consumed, than the variable speed motor, can be employed. This is also the most simple and compact form of motor drive. When applied to Brown & Sharpe Machines, the motor is mounted on a bracket at the back of the column, where it is away from dust and chips of the table or totally enclosed in an oil-tight compartment in the base. Very simple operating controls are used — often a handy push button controls the starting and stopping of the motor (see page 168).

Efficiency. Production costs are of vital importance to the shop owner, and no one factor influences them to a much greater extent than the efficiency of the different machines employed. Where this is low, the amount of power consumed for which there is no apparent return is higher than it should be, with the result that the cost of production is increased. It is essential, therefore, that a high degree of efficiency be attained in the milling machine, so that a maximum amount of work may be produced for the power consumed.

In order to obtain the highest degree of efficiency in milling machine construction, it is necessary that the utmost care be taken in designing the different parts, selecting materials, and in the quality of workmanship in building.

All parts must be proportioned in accordance with the functions they perform. They should be heavy enough to resist any stress that would tend to cramp operating movements. For instance, cylindrical shafts should be large enough in diameter to eliminate bending tendency, for this will cramp them in the bearings, thus interfering with their free revolution. Care must be taken, however, that the different parts are not proportioned so heavy that they will be cumbersome and thus produce excessive friction, which is detrimental to efficiency. It is here that the selection of materials is of value, for often the weight of a part can be made lighter by the use of a material of greater strength.

Pointed Teeth of Hardened Change Gear

The size of bearing surfaces is of especial importance to efficiency, as well as to permanent alignment and rigidity. It is between them that friction arises in operation, and in order to reduce this to a minimum, their proportions should be such that the parts may move freely under the heaviest load.

Correct alignments of bearing surfaces are as essential to efficiency as to accuracy, in order that the working parts may move freely. Any error in alignments tends to cramp or wedge the moving parts.

Simplicity of parts and the use of spur gearing as far as possible are also elements that contribute largely to high efficiency.

Durability. The first cost of a milling machine, like any other modern machine tool, is comparatively great, and to make its employment economical, this cost must be spread over a long period of service — in other words, the machine must be durable. Strong design and the use of high quality materials throughout the machine are most essential to durability.

Thorough workmanship is also an important factor. Seemingly small details in construction should receive careful attention, for it is these that many times give rise to serious trouble. The fitting of different parts, and making of all alignments should be carefully done, and means should be provided for taking up wear at any points where it is apt to occur. In connection with the wearing qualities of different parts, the selection of materials is an important factor; parts that are subject to continuous usage, such as the change gears in constant speed drive machines, should be made of a hard material having good wearing qualities. In Brown & Sharpe machines, these gears are made of steel and are hardened.

Where change gears are being thrown into and out of mesh frequently by a tumbler arrangement, it is well to have the tops of the teeth pointed, and the ends of teeth in sliding gears chamfered. These features not only facilitate throwing the gears into mesh, but also reduce the danger of teeth becoming bruised or broken, which is apt to happen when gears with teeth of the ordinary shape are thrown into mesh.

Rigidity is as essential to durability as to accuracy, since the existence of vibrations causes very rapid wearing of parts. Hence, every part should be of stable enough construction to resist vibrations under all practical working conditions.

Beyond these points, and that of provision for lubricating all bearing surfaces, the matter of durability is more especially a question of the care devoted to the machine while in use. Its failure to be durable because of lack of proper care cannot be attributed to any faults in design or construction. The information given in the next chapter on the care of milling machines is very important to those who have charge of these machines.

Convenience. Much time is lost in operating a milling macnine that is inconvenient in any way for the workman to handle: therefore, from the standpoints of economy and efficiency, convenience is a most desirable quality. To be convenient, a machine must be so designed

All Handwheels, Operating Levers, etc., Located Where Workman Can Reach Them Handily

Handwheels and Controls on the Front of Machine

A, Transverse hand feed.
B, Vertical hand feed.
C, Longitudinal hand fine adjustment.
D, Longitudinal automatic feed trip and reverse lever.
E, Transverse automatic feed trip lever.
F, Vertical automatic feed trip lever.
G, Lever for disengaging table feed.
H, Transverse saddle clamp.
I, Vertical knee clamp.
J, Feed reverse operating lever.
K, Adjustable dials graduated to thousandths of an inch.
L, Knob for locking transverse and vertical feed operating levers.
M, Power Fast Travel control lever.
N, Centralized oiling for table and saddle bearings.
O, Table clamp.

and constructed that work and tools can be readily placed in position and removed from the table, spindle and table feed adjustments easily made, and all working parts readily accessible.

As the station of the operator is at the front of the machine, all controlling levers and hand-wheels for stopping and starting the machine and the different table movements should be within reach from this point.

The spindle speed and table feed changing levers of constant speed driven machines are placed on the left-hand side of the column by some builders, and on the right by others. This is more a matter of choice than anything else, the chief advantage being in having them conveniently grouped and so designed that the manner of operation is clear.

Arrangements for lubricating the various parts and making adjustments to compensate for wear should be such that these can be accomplished with a minimum loss of time.

Hand or Automatic Feed. It is essential that the table of all milling machines used for manufacturing purposes, with the exception of the very smallest of the plain type, be fitted with both hand and automatic feeds. In the case of this exception, the work done is of such a small character that the machine can be operated more rapidly by hand than it could be if an automatic feed were applied. By the use of automatic feeds, one operator is enabled to run several machines on the majority of commercial work.

Tool room machines, and those used for miscellaneous milling, should be fitted with both hand and automatic feeds, for, while much of the work requires careful feeding by hand, there are, nevertheless, many times when an automatic feed can be employed and the mechanic can devote his attention to some other detail of the job while a cut is being taken.

Power Fast Table Travel. On large machines it is necessary that the table be provided with a power fast travel in order that the minimum amount of time will be consumed in moving the work to and from the cutter.

Also a faster rate of travel is thereby provided than is possible by hand, and the operator is relieved of the laborious task of moving the heavy table and work many times a day. Both of these are points which materially influence increased production.

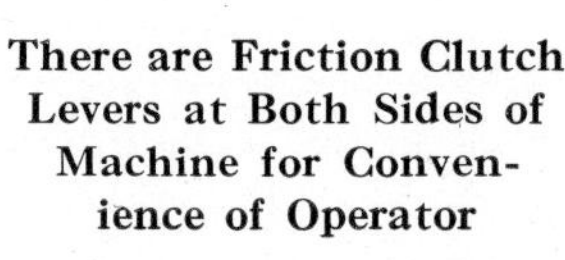

There are Friction Clutch Levers at Both Sides of Machine for Convenience of Operator

Operator Does Not Have to Go Around Table to Clamp Knee

Oil Can or Pump and Tank. Every milling machine must be fitted with some arrangement for lubricating the cutters when working on steel or wrought iron. Either an oil can or a pump and tank are employed for this purpose. For machines that are used for light work and miscellaneous milling, an oil can is found satisfactory, as the amount of lubricant used is small and a pump and tank complicate the machine and make more for the operator to care for. When heavy and manufacturing milling is being done, however, and an abundance of oil is required, both to cool the cutters and wash out chips, it is not always practical to supply it through the medium of a can, as this cannot be made large enough to hold sufficient lubricant to last long. By fitting the machine with a pump and a tank to which the used oil returns by gravity, a copious supply is available at all times. When it is not needed it can be shut off and a relief valve in the piping returns the unused oil to the tank.

Plenty of Lubricant Should Be Used on the Cutters

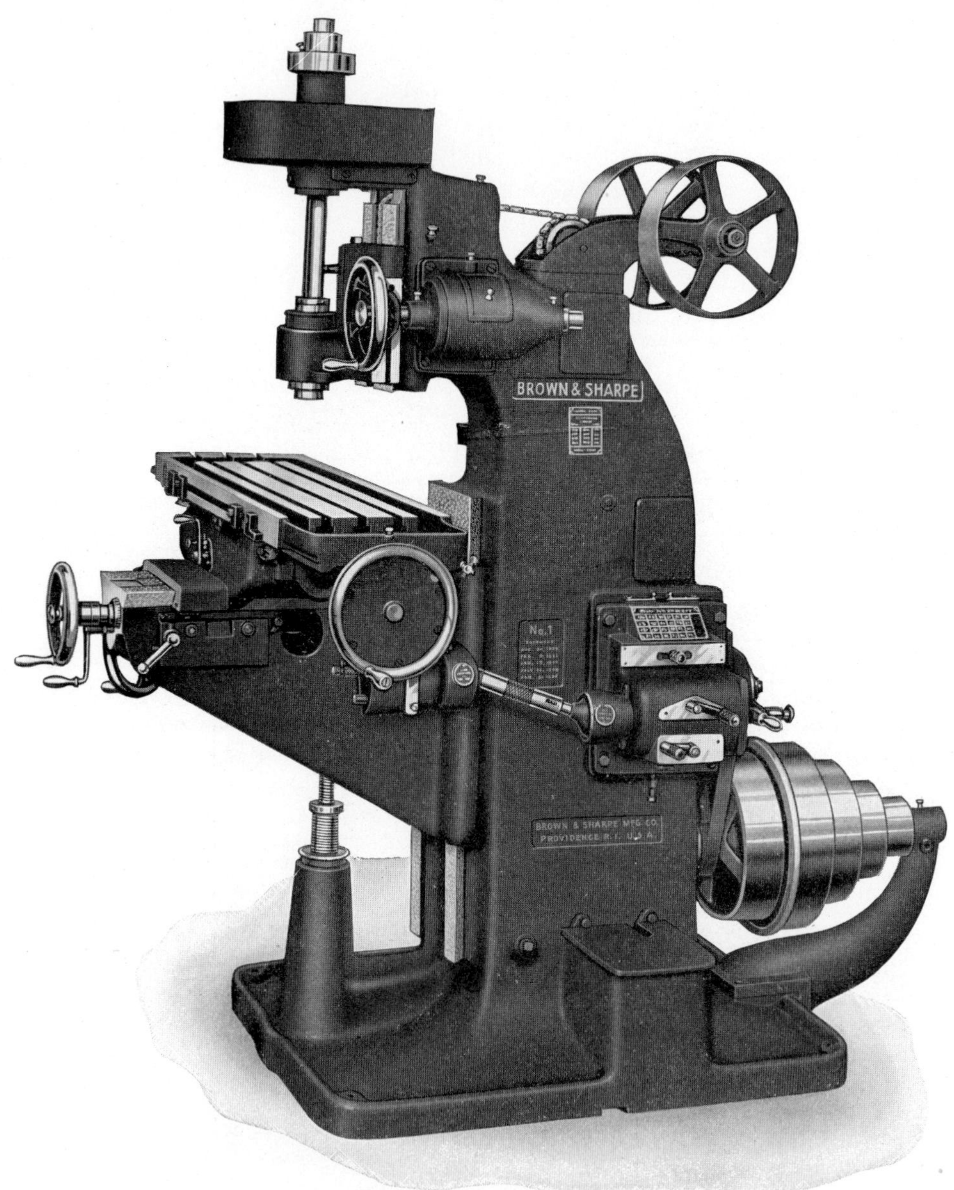

Vertical Spindle Milling Machine with Spindle Driven by Belt

CHAPTER III

Erection and Care of Machine

Erection. A machine should be placed upon a level, and, if possible, a solid floor or foundation. If the foundation is not firm, undue vibrations will exist and possibly impair its accuracy and durability. Either stone or concrete makes an excellent foundation for the larger sizes. Neither of these can be used, however, when it is desired to place a machine above the ground floor of a building, and it is best, in this case, to locate it directly over a beam; not in the middle of a bay.

Ordinary wooden shingles are commonly used in leveling a machine. When the exact position has been determined, the fastening screws or bolts should be screwed down until nearly tight. A spirit level should then be used to test the top of the table, both longitudinally and transversely. If the machine is too low at any corner, drive a shingle under the base at this point to bring it up. When the table is found to be level in every direction, the nuts, or bolts, should be brought up solidly. It is well, even after tightening the bolts, to test the surface of the table once more, as this tightening sometimes throws the machine out of level again.

Counter-shaft. Putting up the counter-shaft, when one is employed, is usually the first operation in installing a machine. It is generally placed directly over cone drive machines because of the interference of the driving belt with the upper part of the frame if it is located very far at either side. With constant speed drive machines, it is not necessary to place the counter-shaft directly overhead. It may be placed diagonally as long as the belt does not interfere with the overhanging arm when it is pushed back.

The counter-shaft should be level and accurately aligned parallel with the main, or driving, shaft. Where the beams are not uniform enough to bring the stringers to which the counter-shaft hangers are attached level, it will be necessary to shim between the feet of the hangers and the stringers to make the shaft level. The holes in the feet of the hangers are usually in the form of slots, which allow the hangers to be slightly adjusted when aligning the counter-shaft with

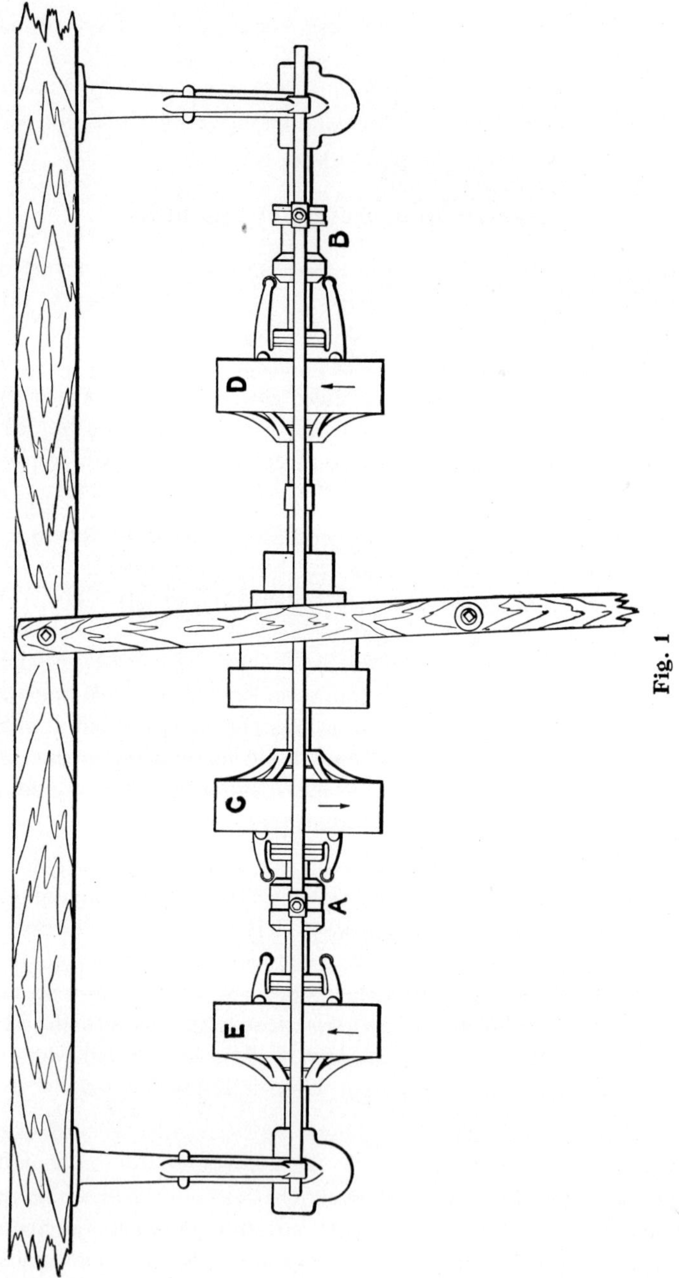

Fig. 1

the driving shaft. In leveling and aligning the counter-shaft, it is the practice to insert the bare shaft in its boxes and take measurements from it. It is afterward removed, the pulleys put on and then replaced in its bearings. When the hangers are securely tightened, the shaft should revolve freely. About an eighth of an inch end play is desirable on a counter-shaft. This can be obtained when placing the hangers.

The shipper handles are most convenient when they come within easy reach from the left front side of the machine, as this is the position commonly taken by the workman to watch the operation.

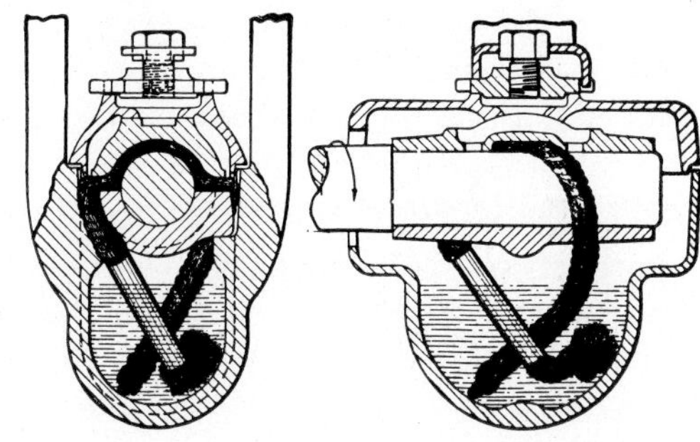

Fig. 2

Counter-shaft bearings are lubricated in various ways. In our particular type the oil is raised from reservoirs in each hanger by means of rope wicks as shown in Fig. 2.

As a rule it is not necessary to draw off and replace the oil in counter-shaft reservoirs at very frequent intervals if a good machinery oil is used. If the reservoirs are thoroughly cleaned and filled with fresh oil once every year or so they rarely need much attention. It is good practice, however, to put in a little oil every three or four months in order to insure maintaining the proper level.

The arrangement of a three-friction pulley counter-shaft is shown in Fig. 1. Its operation is as follows: A movement of the shipper to the right from the position in which it is shown, causes thimble *A* to spread the friction levers or engage pulley *C*. Throwing the shipper to the left until thimble *A* is about central between pulleys *C* and *E*, causes thimble *B* to spread the friction levers or engage pulley *D*. A further movement of the shipper to the left allows the levers of pulley *D* to slip over onto the smaller diameter of thimble *B*, disengaging the clutch of this pulley; at the same time thimble *A* spreads the levers engaging pulley *E*.

Diameter of Pulley on Driving Shaft. To find the diameter of pulley required on the driving shaft for driving the counter-shaft at a given speed, multiply the required speed of the counter-shaft in revolutions per minute by the diameter in inches of the pulley on same, and divide the product by the revolutions per minute of driving shaft. If, for instance, the speed of the main shaft in a shop is 200 r.p.m., and it is required to drive a counter-shaft, having a pulley 14 inches in diameter, 320 r.p.m., the diameter of the main shaft pulley is found as follows:

$$\frac{320 \text{ r.p.m.} \times 14''}{200 \text{ r.p.m.}} = 22.4'', \text{ diameter of pulley required on main shaft.}$$

When the counter-shaft has two or more pulleys whose speeds differ, a separate calculation is required for each. And when no counter-shaft is used, the calculation is the same as above, except that the required speed and diameter of the machine pulley are substituted for the diameter and speed of the counter-shaft pulley.

Importance of Keeping Machine Clean and Well Oiled. Many workmen fail to appreciate the importance of keeping a machine clean and well oiled, and we cannot emphasize this point too strongly. Proper attention to these details influences the accuracy and efficiency of a milling machine and prolongs its life, while neglect to attend to these matters has ruined many a good machine.

Working parts most exposed to dust, dirt or chips, should be frequently cleaned and oiled. Chips should not be allowed to collect upon the surface of the table until they fall over the sides on to the flat bearings on the top of the knee. Care should also be taken to prevent chips and dirt getting between the knee and column, causing scoring of these flat bearings and throwing the knee out of alignment.

Oil tubes and channels many times become clogged with a gummy substance, due to the accumulation of dirt in the oil, and also to decomposition of the lubricant itself. This can be effectively removed without injury to the bearing surfaces by flushing the tubes and channels with gasoline or naphtha. It is well to do this occasionally to insure free passage of oil to the bearings, for if the bearing surfaces, especially cylindrical ones, run dry, they become roughed up, which necessitates taking them apart, and entails considerable work before they can be made to run satisfactorily again.

A machine that has been in active service for a period of a year or two, should be thoroughly cleaned and inspected. To do this requires that it be taken apart to some extent, as it is impossible to ascertain the condition of some of the more important bearing surfaces in any other way. Also it is the only way in which one can make sure that some of the oil channels that are not easily accessible are not filled up.

Only good mechanics who thoroughly understand the construction of the different parts should be permitted to take apart and reassemble a machine, owing to the liability of parts being put together wrongly and alignments imperfectly made, if the work is intrusted to less responsible persons.

Arbors and collars should be kept clean and care exercised that chips do not get into the hole in the spindle or between collars.

Neatness about a machine is usually the mark of a good workman. By assigning definite places to tools and attachments and returning them immediately after using, he is able to know just where to look for any one whenever he wants it. The time required to replace tools in this way is more than offset by the advantage of being able to readily find them again; besides, the tidiness of a machine materially adds to the appearance of a shop.

It is well to remember when applying oil that ordinary bearings can hold only a few drops at a time and that this amount applied at regular and frequent intervals is far more beneficial than a flood of lubricant at irregular periods. It is a good practice to have one man attend to the oiling daily in shops where the machines are used by different workmen.

Kind of Oil. There are so many good machinery oils upon the market that it is hard to specify any one as the best to use for lubricating a milling machine. Any good coal or mineral oil can be used. Never use an animal oil, as it will gum up the bearing surfaces, oil channels and tubes, and have a tendency to retard rather than render easy the movements of the different parts. It might also be said that in buying machinery oil it is always safest to purchase a lubricant of reliable quality instead of experimenting with the less expensive brands. It is cheaper to buy good oil than to run the risk of damage to bearings from overheating or scoring.

Care of Driving Chain on Motor Driven Machines. The care of the driving chain on motor driven machines is important. It should be kept clean, well lubricated and adjusted. To clean a driving chain, remove it and immerse in a bath of kerosene or gasoline. This will loosen up the gum and dirt, and by working the joints while in the bath, foreign matter will come out. Remove the kerosene or gasoline by soaking the chain in a very hot and fairly strong solution of soda and water. Wipe dry and immerse in a bath of warm and quite thick lubricating oil for several hours. This treatment should be applied about every two or three months.

A good quality of lubricant that is free from tendency to gum should be used, and a generous quantity applied daily.

The tension of the chain is usually regulated by the adjusting screws in motor bracket. It should run at a tension that might be termed just a little too slack for a leather belt; that is, a slightly greater sag should be allowed.

Adjustments. As bearing surfaces and parts wear, it becomes necessary from time to time to make adjustments, and at all important points convenient means are provided for doing this. Flat bearings are provided with tapered gibs that are easily adjusted, and cylindrical bearings, like those of the spindle, have ready means of taking up wear. It is essential that any adjustment required be promptly

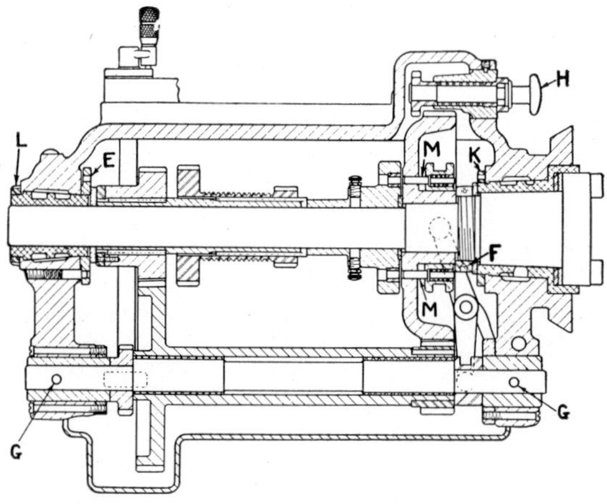

Fig. 3

made, for otherwise the accuracy of the machine is impaired. Furthermore, parts wear much more rapidly as the lost motion becomes greater. By a little examination and adjustment every now and then, the efficiency of a machine can be maintained and its life indefinitely prolonged.

Before proceeding to adjust or take anything apart, it is a good plan to carefully study its principle of construction. Many times this simple precaution will obviate considerable trouble.

The prevailing practice in designing spindle bearings is to have the front bearing on the spindle tapered and the rear bearing straight. On our machines the front bearing is adjusted by loosening the check screw and tightening nut *F*, Fig. 3. This draws the spindle back into the box, and as the bearing is tapered, the lost motion is taken up. Should it become necessary, after running a machine for a number of years, to obtain more adjustment in this front box, the spindle can be removed and the washers between the spindle collar and the front of the box can be reduced a little in thickness. The adjusting nut *F* will then take care of the wear for another long period. Nut *K* should not be disturbed, as this merely holds the box in place. The rear box is split and fits in a taper hole in the frame. It is adjusted by loosening nut *L* and tightening nut *E*.

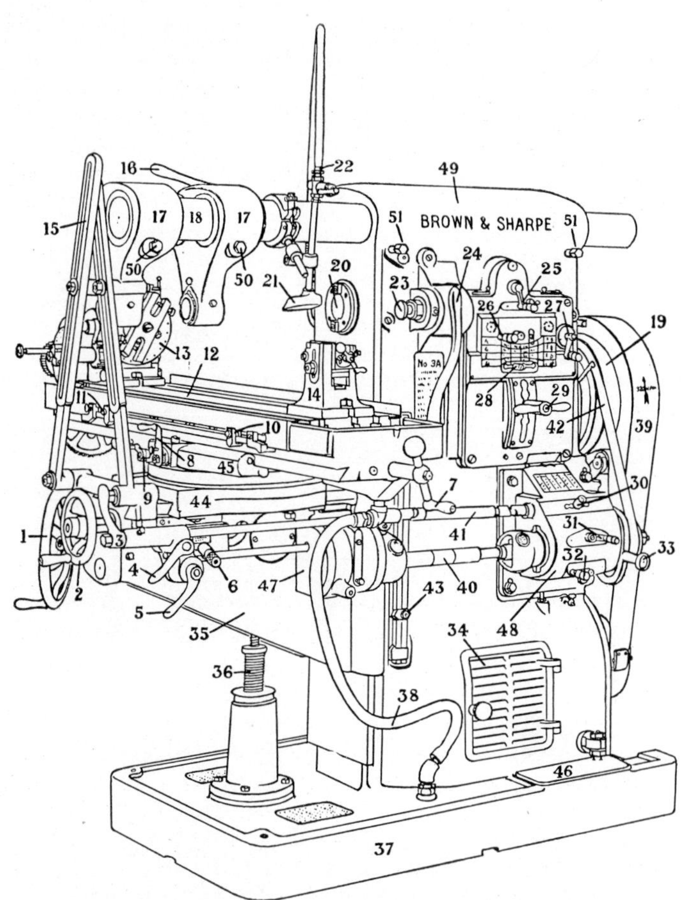

Motor Driven Constant Speed Drive Milling Machine

Explanation of Levers, Handwheels, etc., on Brown & Sharpe Constant Speed Drive Milling Machines

1. Handwheel for vertical feed
2. Handwheel for transverse feed
3. Power fast travel control lever for table
4. Power transverse feed control lever
5. Power vertical feed control lever
6. Locking device for transverse and vertical feed operating levers
7. Longitudinal table hand feed crank
8. Table feed trip lever
9. Table feed disengaging lever
10. Adjustable table dog
11. Adjustable table dog
12. Table
13. Spiral head
14. Footstock
15. Arm braces
16. Starting lever (left)
17. Arbor yoke
18. Overarm
19. Driving sprocket
20. Spindle
21. Cutter lubricant distributor
22. Flexible tube for cutter lubricant
23. Knob for fine adjustment of spindle
24. Starting lever (right)
25. Spindle speed change lever
26. Spindle reverse lever
27. Back gear operating lever
28. Knob for sliding tumbler gear
29. Tumbler gear locking lever
30. Feed index knob
31. Feed change lever
32. Feed change lever
33. Tumbler gear lever
34. Door to motor compartment
35. Knee
36. Knee elevating screw
37. Coolant tank in base
38. Flexible tube for return of cutter lubricant
39. Chain guard
40. Telescopic table feed shaft
41. Power fast travel control shaft
42. Power fast travel drive belt
43. Vertical feed trip dog
44. Clamp bed
45. Swivel
46. Cutter lubricant reservoir cover
47. Feed reverse gear case
48. Variable feed case
49. Column
50. Clamp bolt for arbor yoke
51. Overarm clamp bolt

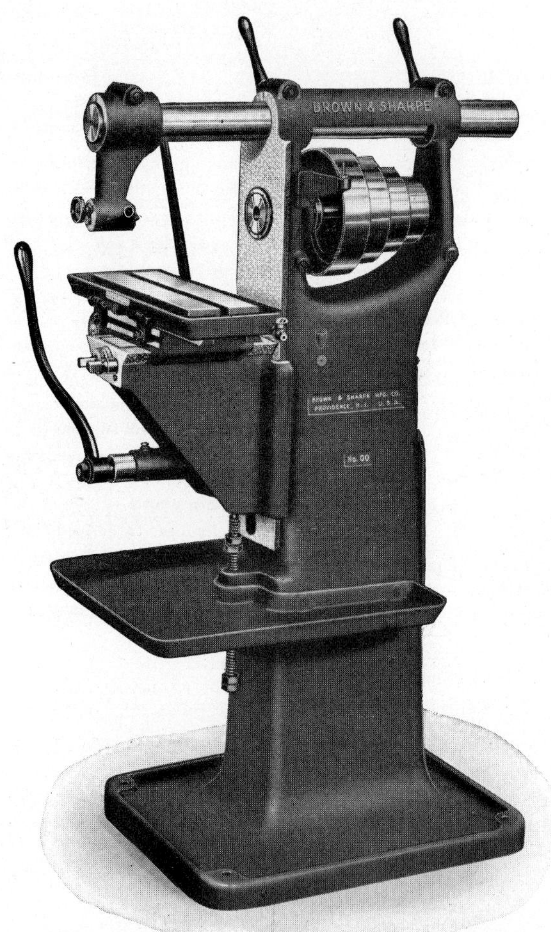

Hand Milling Machine

CHAPTER IV

Spiral Head — Indexing and Cutting Spirals

The mechanism known as the spiral head constituted one of the fundamental parts of the original universal milling machine. Its primary purpose was that of indexing and rotating work in conjunction with the movement of the table for cutting flutes in twist drills. The great possibilities it offered in cutting a large range of spirals, and for doing many other jobs, were soon recognized and developed, until it is now used for an endless variety of operations. With it, ordinary indexing to obtain even spacing on the periphery of pieces, as in cutting teeth in cutters, ratchets, clutch gears, gear wheels and flutes in reamers, taps, drills, etc., can be quickly accomplished. Spiral forms of all common leads can be accurately reproduced by its use.

Spiral Head

The spiral head and foot-stock are furnished as a part of all universal milling machines and can be applied, with few exceptions, to plain and vertical spindle machines. Used in connection with a vertical spindle milling attachment, on a plain machine, much the same variety of work can be done as on the universal machine.

In construction, spiral heads of today embody the same principles as the one on the original universal milling machine, but improvements have made them more solid and convenient to operate. Likewise, improvements have been made in the design and construction of the foot-stock.

Since our spiral head is typical of these mechanisms, a description of its various points may aid in understanding the methods of indexing and cutting spirals. The head itself consists of a hollow, semi-circular casting in which is mounted a spindle that is connected to an index crank through a worm and wheel. Fig. 4 shows the construction of this part. The head casting has dove-tailed bearings at each side that fit the contour of a base plate, which can be clamped to the surface of the table. The alignment of the head with the table longitudinally is provided by means of a tongue on the under side of the base plate that fits a T slot in the table.

The spiral head spindle passes through the head, and is held in place by means of a nut at the small end. The front end is threaded and has a taper hole corresponding to that of the machine spindle.

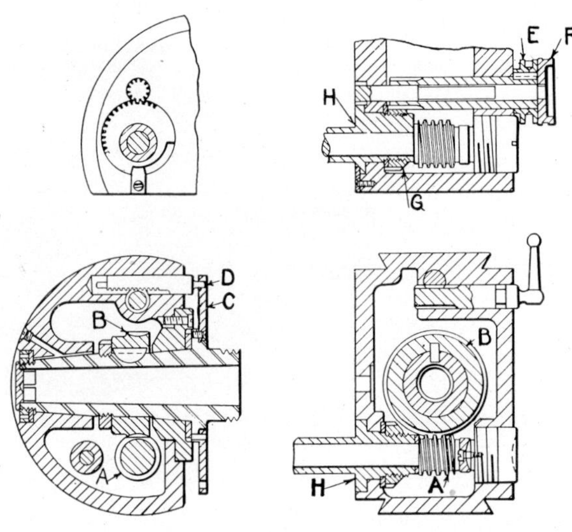

Fig. 4

It is rotated by means of the worm wheel *B*, which is driven by the hardened worm *A* that is located on the shaft to which the index crank is fastened. In order to insure accuracy the worm threads are ground after hardening. Through gearing, the index plate and worm *A* can be driven together from the table feed screw when the index pin is in position in any hole of a plate. When worm *A* is turned by means of the index crank, indexing may be accomplished, and when it is geared to the table feed screw, spiral milling, in addition to indexing, is made possible. The cutting of the spiral is due to the turning of the table feed screw, which through the interposition of change gears between this screw and the gears that drive the shaft carrying worm *A*, causes the spindle of the spiral head to rotate as the table advances, so that the cutter produces a spiral cut in the work. For rapid indexing, when cutting flutes in taps, reamers, etc., the worm *A* is disengaged and the spindle turned by hand, the divisions being made by means of the index plate *C*, which is fastened to the nose of the spindle, and may be locked by the pin *D*.

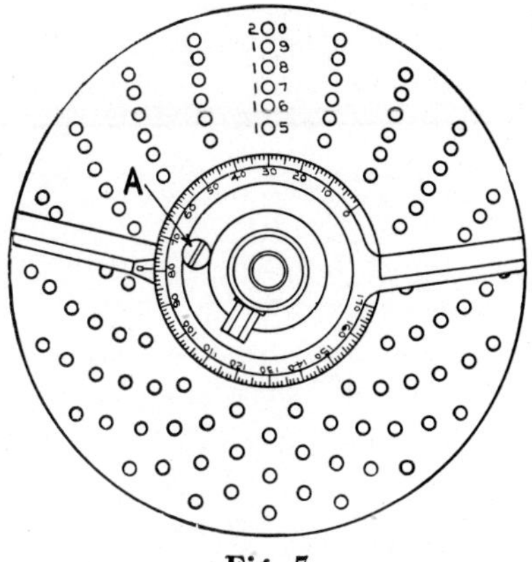

Fig. 5

The spindle may be revolved continuously as when cutting spirals, or may be securely locked after being revolved a desired amount, as in indexing for cutters, the teeth of gears, clutches, ratchets, etc.

It is possible to swing the head in its bearings so that the front end of the spindle can be set to any desired angle from 10° below the horizontal to 5° beyond the perpendicular without throwing the driving members out of mesh. Graduations on the front edge of the head indicate the angle of elevation to half degrees.

The design of the head is such that it permits unusually long and wide bearings. Furthermore, it sets very low and can be so firmly clamped to the base that the whole mechanism practically becomes one solid casting. Hence, it provides a particularly rigid support for the work, which is a factor of much importance in the class of work that is done upon this mechanism.

Index Plates and Change Gears. Three index plates are furnished with the spiral head, and contain circles with the following numbers of holes: —

Plate 1 — 15, 16, 17, 18, 19, 20.
Plate 2 — 21, 23, 27, 29, 31, 33.
Plate 3 — 37, 39, 41, 43, 47, 49.

The change gears that are furnished have the following numbers of teeth: 24 (2 gears), 28, 32, 40, 44, 48, 56, 64, 72, 86 and 100.

Graduated Index Sector. Without the graduated index sector, much care must be exercised in counting the holes in an index plate when indexing to obtain any given number of divisions. Such a sector enables the correct number of holes to be obtained at each indexing with little chance for error. It is shown in Fig. 5 and consists of two arms which may be spread apart when the screw *A*, is loosened slightly. The correct number of holes may be counted and the sector arms set to include them; or better, the graduations on the dial may be used in connection with the tables given on pages 210 to 218. To set the sector arms by this last method, follow down the column headed "Graduation" in the tables referred to, until opposite the number of divisions that is desired. Take the number that is found here and set the arms by bringing the left one against the index pin, which should be inserted in any convenient hole in the required circle, and moving the right one until the graduation corresponding to the number obtained from the table coincides with the zero on the left arm. The correct number of holes will then be contained between the two arms, and counting is unnecessary.

When setting the arms by counting the holes, the left arm should be brought against the index pin as directed above, and then the required number of holes foı each division should be counted from the hole that the pin is in, considering this hole as zero.

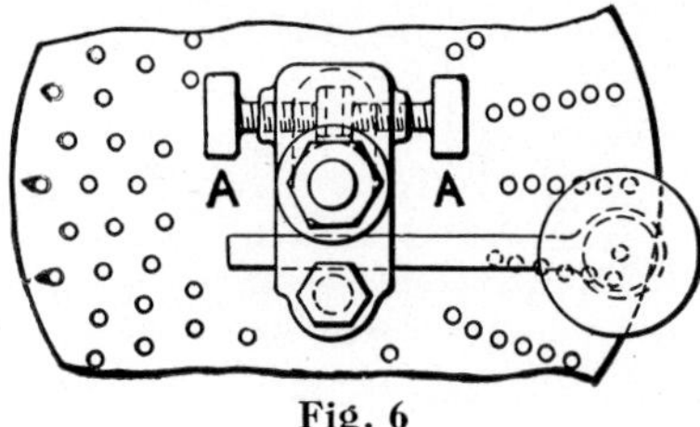

Fig. 6

Adjustable Index Crank. The index crank of the spiral head is adjustable circumferentially. This is shown in Fig. 6. Many times it is desired to make a delicate adjustment of the work, or to bring the index pin to the nearest hole without disturbing the setting of the work. To adjust the index crank after the work has been placed in position, turn thumb screws *A-A*, Fig. 6, until the pin enters the nearest hole in the index plate. To rotate the work relative to the index plate, both the stop pin at the back of the plate and the index crank pin should be engaged, the adjustment being made by means of the thumb screws as before.

Throwing Worm Out of Mesh. When it is desired to turn the spindle by hand and index work by means of the plate on the front end of the spindle, it is necessary to disengage the driving worm *A*, Fig. 4. To do this, turn the knob *E*, by means of a pin wrench furnished, about one-quarter of a revolution in the reverse direction to that indicated by an arrow stamped on the knob. This will loosen nut *G*, that clamps eccentric bushing *H*; then with the fingers turn both knobs *E* and *F*, at the same time, and the bushing *H*, will revolve, disengaging the worm from the wheel. To re-engage the worm, reverse the above operation.

Effect of Change in Angle of Elevation on Spindle. If the angle of the spiral head spindle is changed during operation, the spindle must be rotated slightly to bring the work back to the proper position, for when the spindle is elevated or depressed, the worm wheel is rotated about the worm, and the effect is the same as if the worm were turned.

Foot-stock. The foot-stock shown in Fig 7 is for supporting pieces of work that are milled on centres or the outer ends of arbors, and pieces that are clamped in a chuck. The centre is adjustable longitudinally, and can be elevated or depressed by means of a rack *V*, and pinion actuated by hex *U*. It can also be set at an angle out of parallel with the base when it is desired to mill drills, taper reamers, etc., so that it can be kept in perfect alignment with the spiral head

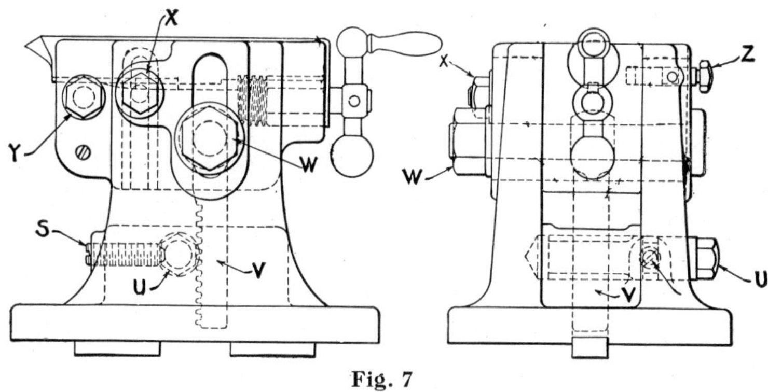

Fig. 7

centre. The advantage of this is readily appreciated from the fact that by the use of centres that cannot be adjusted, work is apt to become cramped at certain positions during its revolution, and, as a result, even spacing cannot be obtained.

When set in any position, the centre is firmly held by means of the nuts *W*, *X* and *Y*. Set screw *S* prevents endwise movement of the elevating pinion.

Two taper pins, one of which is shown at *Z*, are used to quickly and accurately locate the foot-stock centre in line with the spiral head centre, when the centres are parallel to the top of the table. They may be loosened by twisting a little with a wrench.

Fig. 8 shows a gauge that is very handy to use for quickly adjusting the foot-stock centre in line with the spiral head centre when setting for taper work. It consists of a bushing that fits over the centre in the spiral head and a blade, the bottom edge of which is the same distance above the centre as the top of the foot-stock centre.

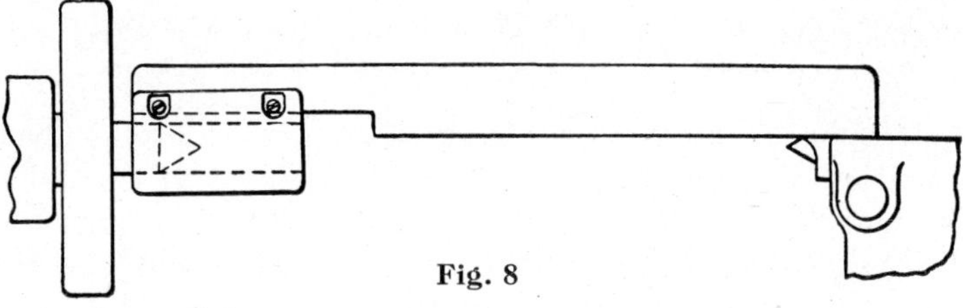

Fig. 8

INDEXING

The first office of the spiral head is to index or divide the periphery of a piece of work into a number of definite or given parts. This is accomplished by means of the index crank and the index plates furnished with the head; or, in the case of some of the more common coarse divisions, by means of the rapid index plate fastened to the nose of the spindle.

There are two practical and accurate methods of indexing, known as Plain and Differential. A third method, known as the Compound, was used extensively in the past, and is still employed by some shops having machines that are not fitted for Differential indexing. The chances for errors in making the complicated indexing moves, and the fact that even when the moves are made correctly, exact results cannot be obtained, causes the Compound method to be of little practical value where accurate spacing is required. It has, as a result, been largely superseded by the Differential method, by which the same numbers can be indexed accurately, and with little liability of errors in making the indexing moves.

Most spiral heads that are not fitted for Differential indexing can be at a nominal cost, and the unusual simplicity and convenience of this method in themselves are sufficient to warrant doing this.

By the Plain method of indexing, which includes rapid indexing, using the plate on the spindle nose, all divisions up to 50, even numbers up to 100, except 96, and many numbers that are multiples of 5 up to 380, besides many others, can be indexed with the three index plates furnished. With the addition of the change gears furnished, divisions obtained by Plain indexing, together with those that cannot be obtained by that method, from 1 to 382, and many others beyond, can be indexed by the Differential method.

Plain and Direct Indexing. Plain indexing on the spiral head is very similar to indexing with ordinary index centres. It depends entirely upon how many times the index crank must be turned to cause the work to make one revolution. When this ratio is known, it is an easy matter to calculate the number of turns or fractions of a turn of the index crank to produce a given number of spaces on the periphery of the work.

The worm wheel on the spindle contains 40 teeth and the worm is single threaded, hence for every turn of the index crank, the worm wheel is advanced one tooth, or the spindle makes 1/40 part of a revolution. This should be remembered, for it is used in all indexing calculations on the spiral head. If the crank is turned 40 times, the spindle and work will make one complete revolution. To find how many turns of the crank are necessary for a certain division of the work, 40 is divided by the number of the divisions which are desired. The quotient will be the number of turns, or the part of a turn of the crank, which will give each desired division. Applying this rule, 40 divisions would be made by turning the crank completely around once for each division, or 20 divisions would be obtained by turning around twice. When the quotient contains a fraction, or is a fraction, it will be necessary to give the crank a part revolution in indexing. The numerator of the fraction represents the number of holes that should be indexed for each division. If the fraction is so small that none of the plates contains the number of holes represented by the denominator, both numerator and denominator should be multiplied by a common multiplier that will give a fraction, the denominator of which represents a number of holes that is available. On the other hand, if the fraction is of large terms, it should be reduced so that its denominator will represent a number of holes that is available. For example, seven divisions are desired. 40 divided by 7, equals 5 5/7 turns of the index crank to each division. There is no plate containing so few holes as 7, so this should be raised. Multiplying by the common multiplier 3, we have $5/7 \times 3/3 = 15/21$. Hence, for one division of the work, the index crank pin is placed in the 21-hole circle, and the crank is given 5 complete revolutions and then is moved ahead 15 additional holes. 35 holes in the 49-hole circle might also be used in place of 15 in the 21-hole circle, as 35/49 is a multiple of the original fraction 5/7.

The tables on pages 210–218 give the correct circles of holes and numbers to index for each division of all numbers that are obtainable by plain indexing, as well as those obtainable by the differential method, and when these are used figuring, such as that above, is unnecessary.

Indexing in Degrees and Parts of Degrees. When it is desired to divide the circumference of a piece in this manner, it can often be done by plain indexing. One complete turn of the index crank produces 1/40 of a turn of the work, or $\frac{360°}{40} = 9$ degrees. Following this method:

2 holes in the 18-hole circle = 1 degree.
2 holes in the 27-hole circle = 2/3 degree.
1 hole in the 18-hole circle = 1/2 degree.
1 hole in the 27-hole circle = 1/3 degree.

Other odd fractional parts of a degree can be easily found by dividing the number of holes in any given circle into 9 degrees. It will be noticed that 1/4 degree spacing cannot be obtained in this way; but with differential indexing, as explained on page 57, it is easy to get 1/4 degree and other fractional spacings.

Differential Indexing. Differential indexing enables a wide range of divisions to be indexed, which cannot be obtained by plain indexing. With the change gears and three index plates furnished with the spiral head, it is possible to index all numbers, not obtainable by plain indexing, from 1 to 382; in addition, many other divisions beyond 382 can be indexed.

Spiral Head Geared for Differential Indexing

By this method, the index crank is moved in the same circle of holes, and the operation is like that of plain indexing. The spiral head spindle and index plate are connected by a train of gearing, as shown above, and the stop pin at the back of the plate is thrown out. As the index crank is turned, the spindle is rotated through the worm and wheel, and the plate moves either in the same or opposite direction to that of the crank. The total movement of the crank at every indexing is, therefore, equal to its movement relative to the plate, plus the movement of the plate, when the plate revolves in the same direction as the crank, or minus the movement of the plate, when the plate revolves in the opposite direction to the crank. The spiral head cannot be used for cutting spirals, when it is geared for differential indexing, for when cutting spirals the head is geared to the table feed screw.

To obviate the necessity of figuring out the change gears every time a certain number of divisions is required, tables on pages 210 to 225 have been compiled. By use of these tables, all numbers obtainable by differential indexing, together with those that can be had by the plain method, can be easily indexed. The tables also give the correct circle and number of holes to be indexed, graduations for setting of the index sector, and the proper change gears to use.

In order to select the proper change gears, it is first necessary to find the ratio of the required gearing between the spindle and plate. After this has been done, the correct gears can be found. The following formulae show the manner in which this gearing is calculated.

N = number of divisions required.
H = number of holes in index plate.
n = number of holes taken at each indexing.
V = ratio of gearing between index crank and spindle.
x = ratio of the train of gearing between the spindle and the index plate.
S = gear on spindle. } Drivers.
G_1 = first gear on stud. } Drivers.
G_2 = second gear on stud. } Driven.
W = gear on worm. } Driven.

$$x = \frac{HV-Nn}{H} \text{ if } HV \text{ is greater than } Nn.$$

$$x = \frac{Nn-HV}{H} \text{ if } HV \text{ is less than } Nn.$$

$$x = \frac{S}{W} \text{ (for simple gearing).}$$

$$x = \frac{S\,G_1}{G_2\,W} \text{ (for compound gearing).}$$

V is equal to 40 on the B. & S. spiral head, and the index plates furnished have the following numbers of holes: 15, 16, 17, 18, 19, 20, 21, 23, 27, 29, 31, 33, 37, 39, 41, 43, 47, 49.

The gears furnished have the following numbers of teeth: 24 (2 gears), 28, 32, 40, 44, 48, 56, 64, 72, 86, 100.

In selecting the index circle to be used, it is best to select one with a number having factors that are contained in the change gears on hand, for if H contains a factor not found in the gears, x cannot usually be obtained, unless the factor is canceled by the difference between HV and Nn, or unless N contains the factor.

When HV is greater than Nn and gearing is simple, use 1 idler.
When HV is greater than Nn and gearing is compound, use no idlers.
When HV is less than Nn and gearing is simple, use 2 idlers.
When HV is less than Nn and gearing is compound, use 1 idler.

Select "n" so that the ratio of gearing will not exceed 6 : 1 on account of the excessive stress upon the gears.

A few examples are given herewith to illustrate the application of the above formulae:

Example 1: $N = 59$. Required H, n and x.
Assume $H = 33$, $n = 22$.

$$\text{Then } x = \frac{(33 \times 40) - (59 \times 22)}{33} = \tfrac{22}{33} = \tfrac{2}{3}.$$

We now select gears giving this ratio, as 32 and 48, the 32 being the gear on spindle and the 48 the gear on worm. HV is greater than Nn, and the gearing is simple, requiring 1 idler.

Example 2: $N = 319$. Required H, n and x.
Assume $H = 29$, $n = 4$.

$$\text{Then } x = \frac{(319 \times 4) - (29 \times 40)}{29} = \tfrac{116}{29} = \tfrac{4}{1}.$$

When the ratio is not obtainable with simple gearing, try compound gearing.

4/1 can be expressed as follows:

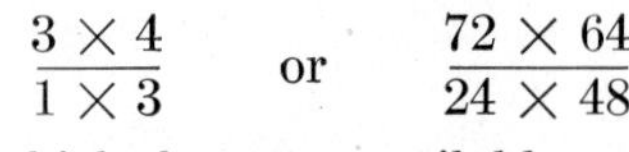

$$\frac{3 \times 4}{1 \times 3} \quad \text{or} \quad \frac{72 \times 64}{24 \times 48}$$

for which there are available gears. HV is less than Nn and the gearing compound, requiring 1 idler.

Fig. 9

Head geared for 271 divisions

Fig. 9 shows the spiral head geared, simple gearing, for 271 divisions. Referring to the table on page 216, the gears called for are: C, 56 teeth, and

E, 72 teeth, with one idler D. The idler D serves to rotate the index plate in the same direction as the crank, thus in making 280 turns of the crank, nine divisions are lost, giving the correct number of divisions, 271. The sector should be set to indicate 1/7 turns, or 3 holes in the 21 hole circle, and the head is ready for 271 divisions, the indexing being made the same as for plain indexing.

Fig. 10

Head Geared for 319 Divisions

Fig. 10 shows the spiral head geared, compound gearing, for 319 divisions. Referring to the table on page 217, the gears called for are: C, 48 teeth; F, 64 teeth; G, 24 teeth; E, 72 teeth and one idler D, 24 teeth. The sector should be set to 4/29 turns, or 4 holes in the 29 circle; the head is then ready for 319 divisions.

Spacing for Quarter Degrees.

Example 3:

Required H, n and x for spacing 1/4 degrees, or 1440 divisions.

Assume $H = 33$, $n = 1$.

$$\text{Then } \frac{(1440 \times 1) - (33 \times 40)}{33} = \frac{120}{33} \quad \text{or} \quad \frac{64 \times 100}{40 \times 44}$$

One idler is required.

The following table gives data required for spacing 1/4° and 1/6°. For fractional parts of degrees obtainable by plain indexing see page 54.

Divisions	Index Circle	No. of Turns of Index	Graduation	Gear on Worm	No. 1 Hole: 1st Gear on Stud	No. 1 Hole: 2d Gear on Stud	Gear on Spindle	Idlers: No. 1 Hole	Idlers: No. 2 Hole
$\frac{1}{6}°$	49	$\frac{1}{49}$		28	64	56	100		24
$\frac{1}{4}°$	33	$\frac{1}{33}$		44	64	40	100		24

Aliquant or Fractional Spacing.

Example 4:

Required: A Vernier to read to 1/12 degree or five minutes, the scale being divided to degrees.

Each Vernier space can equal 11/12 degree.

$$\frac{11 \times 1}{12 \times 360} = \frac{11}{4320} \quad \text{or} \quad \frac{4320}{11} \text{ spaces in whole circle} = 392\tfrac{8}{11} \text{ spaces.}$$

Assume $H = 18$, $n = 2$.

$$\text{Then } \frac{(392\tfrac{8}{11} \times 2) - (18 \times 40)}{18} = \frac{720/11}{18} = \frac{720}{11} \times \frac{1}{18} = \frac{40}{11} = \frac{64 \times 100}{40 \times 44}$$

One idler is required.

CUTTING SPIRALS

Spirals that are most commonly cut on milling machines embrace spiral gears, spiral mills, counterbores, and twist drills. Worms are also cut with the aid of a vertical spindle or universal milling attachment. Examples of some of these classes of work are shown in this chapter, and in operations in Chapters VIII and IX.

The method of producing the spiral movement of the work has been described before, and the manner in which the head is geared is shown in Figs. 11 and 12. The four change gears are known as: *gear on screw; first gear on stud (as it is the first to be put on); second gear on stud; and gear on worm.* The screw gear and first gear on stud are the drivers, and the others are the driven gears. By using different combinations of the change gears furnished, the ratio of the longitudinal movement of the table to the rotary movement of the work can be varied; in other words, the leads of the spirals it is possible to cut are governed directly by these gears. Usually they are of such ratio that the work is advanced more than an inch while making one turn, and thus the spirals cut on milling machines are designated in terms of inches to one turn, rather than turns, or threads per inch; for instance, a spiral is said to be of 8 inches lead, not that its pitch is 1/8 turn per inch.

The feed screw of the table has four threads to the inch, and forty turns of the worm make one turn of the spiral head spindle; accordingly, if change gears of equal diameter are used, the work will make a complete turn while it is moved lengthwise 10 inches; that is, the spiral will have a lead of 10 inches. This is the lead of the machine, and it is the resultant of the action of the parts of the machine that are always employed in this work, and is so regarded in making the calculations used in cutting spirals.

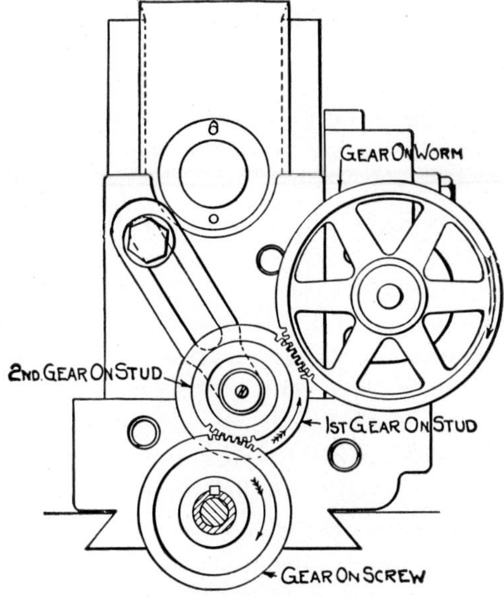

Fig. 11

Showing Gearing When No Idler is Required

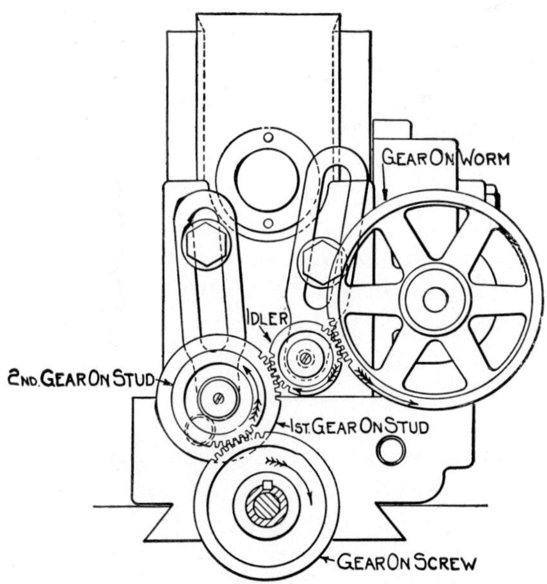

Fig. 12

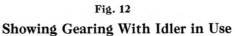

Showing Gearing With Idler in Use

Principle same as for Change Gears of a Lathe. In principle, these calculations are the same as for change gears of a screw cutting lathe. The compound ratio of the driven to the driving gears equals, in all cases, the ratio of the lead of the required spiral to the lead of the machine. This can be readily demonstrated by changing the diameters of the gears.

Gears of the same diameter produce, as explained above, a spiral with a lead of 10 inches, which is the same lead as the lead of the machine. Three gears of equal diameter and a driven gear double this diameter, produce a spiral with a lead of 20 inches, or twice the lead of the machine; and with both driven gears, twice the diameters of the drivers, the ratio being compound, a spiral is produced with a lead of 40 inches, or four times the machine's lead. Conversely, driving gears twice the diameter of the driven produce a spiral with a lead equal to 1/4 the lead of the machine, or 2 1/2 inches.

Expressing the ratios as fractions, the

$$\frac{\text{Driven Gears}}{\text{Driving Gears}} = \frac{\text{Lead of Required Spiral}}{\text{Lead of Machine}}$$

or, as the product of each class of gears determines the ratio, the head being compound geared, and as the lead of the machine is ten inches, the $\frac{\text{Product of Driven Gears}}{\text{Product of Driving Gears}} = \frac{\text{Lead of Required Spiral}}{10}$. That is, the compound ratio of the driven to the driving gears may always be represented by a fraction whose numerator is the lead to be cut and whose denominator is 10. In other words, the ratio is as the required lead is to 10; for example, if the required lead is 20, the ratio is 20 : 10. To express this in units instead of tens, the ratio is always the same as one-tenth of the required lead is to 1. And frequently this is a very convenient way to think of the ratio; for example, if the lead is 40, the ratio of the gears is 4 : 1. If the lead is 25, the gears are 2.5 : 1, etc.

To illustrate the usual calculations, assume that a spiral of 12 inch lead is to be cut. The compound ratio of the driven to the driving gears equals the desired lead divided by 10, or it may be represented by the fraction 12/10. Resolving this into two factors to represent the two pairs of change gears, 12/10 = 3/2 × 4/5. Both terms of the first factor are multiplied by such a number (24 in this instance) that the resulting numerator and denominator will correspond with the number of teeth of two of the change gears furnished with the machine (such multiplications not affecting the value of a fraction) 3/2 × 24/24 = 72/48. The second factor is similarly treated: 4/5 ×

8/8 = 32/40, and the gears with 72, 32, 48 and 40 teeth are selected.
$\frac{12}{10} = \left(\frac{72 \times 32}{48 \times 40}\right)$

The first two are the driven, and the last two the drivers, the numerators of the fractions representing the driven gears. The 72 is the worm gear, 40 the first on stud, 32 the second on stud and 48 the screw gear. The two driving gears might be transposed, and the two driven gears might also be transposed without changing the spiral. That is, the 72 could be used as the second on stud and the 32 as the worm gear, if such an arrangement were more convenient. The following rules express in abridged form the methods of figuring change gears to cut given spirals, and of ascertaining what spirals can be cut with change gears.

Rules for Obtaining Ratio of the Gears Necessary to Cut a Given Spiral. Note the ratio of the required lead to 10. This ratio is the compound ratio of the driven to the driving gears. Example: If the lead of required spiral is 12 inches, 12 to 10 will be the ratio of the gears.

Or, divide the required lead by 10 and note the ratio between the quotient and 1. This ratio is usually the most simple form of the compound ratio of the driven to the driving gears. Example: If the required lead is 40 inches, the quotient is 40 ÷ 10 and the ratio 4 to 1.

Rule for Determining Number of Teeth of Gears Required to Cut a Given Spiral. Having obtained the ratio between the required lead and 10 by one of the preceding rules, express the ratio in the form of a fraction; resolve this fraction into two factors, raise these factors to higher terms that correspond with the teeth of gears that can be conveniently used. The numerators will represent the driven and the denominators the driving gears that produce the required spiral. For example: What gears shall be used to cut a lead of 27 inches?

$$\tfrac{27}{10} = \tfrac{3}{2} \times \tfrac{9}{5} = (\tfrac{3}{2} \times \tfrac{16}{16}) \times (\tfrac{9}{5} \times \tfrac{8}{8}) = \frac{48 \times 72}{32 \times 40}$$

From the fact that the product of the driven gears divided by the product of the drivers equals the lead divided by 10, or one-tenth of the lead, it is evident that ten times the product of the driven gears divided by the product of the drivers, will equal the lead of the spiral. Hence the rule:

Rule for Ascertaining what Spiral May be Cut by Any Given Change Gears. Divide ten times the product of the driven gears by the product of the drivers, and the quotient is the lead of the resulting spiral in inches to one turn. For example: What spiral will be cut by gears, with 48, 72, 32 and 40 teeth, the first two being used as driven gears? Spiral to be cut equals $\frac{10 \times 48 \times 72}{32 \times 40} = 27$ inches to one turn.

This rule is often of service in determining what spirals may be cut with the gears the workman chances to have at hand.

The tables on pages 226 to 228 give the leads and approximate angles of some spirals produced by the gears furnished with our machines, and the combination of gears given in each case is such that they will properly mesh with one another. The tables on pages 229 to 247 contain all the leads that can be obtained with any possible combination of the change gears furnished, even though some of the leads are not available for use on account of the gears interfering or not reaching. Combinations of gears that are too small in diameter to reach for right-hand spirals can generally be used for left-hand spirals, as the reverse gear is then required and will enable the gears to reach.

As we have already mentioned, the two driving gears or the two driven gears of any combination can be transposed, but a driver must not be substituted for a driven or vice versa. Four different arrangements of the gears of any combination are thus possible, without changing the ratio, and when one arrangement interferes, or will not reach, the others should be tried. Thus, the gears to give a lead of 3.60″ are: drivers, 100 teeth and 32 teeth; driven, 24 teeth and 48 teeth. By transposing the gears, the following four arrangements may be obtained.

	1st	2nd	3rd	4th
Drivers				
Gear on Screw	100	32	100	32
1st Gear on Stud	32	100	32	100
Driven				
2nd Gear on Stud	24	24	48	48
Gear on Worm	48	48	24	24

The first arrangement, however, is found by actual test to be the only one available, owing to the interference of the gears in the other combinations preventing their meshing properly.

When very short leads are required, it is preferable to disengage the worm wheel and connect the gearing directly to the spiral head spindle (using the differential indexing centre). This method gives leads one-fortieth of the leads given in the table for the same combinations of gears. Thus, for a lead of 6.160″, the table calls for gear on worm,

56 teeth; 1st gear on stud, 40 teeth; 2nd gear on stud, 44 teeth; and gear on screw, 100 teeth. Putting the 56 tooth gear on the spindle instead of on the worm, gives a lead of $\frac{6.160}{40} = .154''$.

By this method, very short leads may be obtained without excessively straining the mechanism, but the regular means of indexing the work cannot be employed. A method that can be used for indexing when using the differential centre is to have the number of teeth in the gear on the spindle some multiple of the number required to

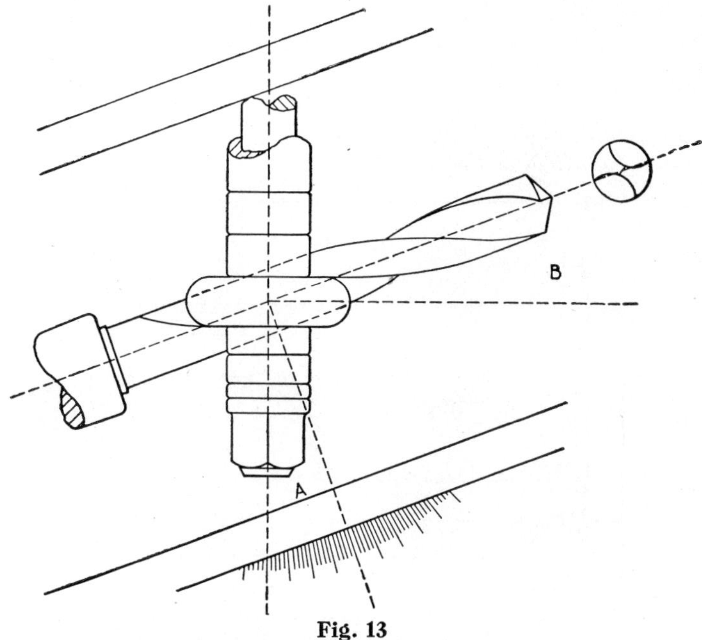

Fig. 13

be indexed. Swing the gears out of mesh and advance the gear on spindle the number of teeth required to index the work one division at each indexing. Thus, if 9 divisions are required with a lead of .261″, we select a lead from the table equal to about $.261'' \times 40 =$ 10.440″, when the gear on worm (which will now be the gear on spindle) is some multiple of 9, as 72. The nearest lead is 10.467″, which gives $\frac{10.467}{10} = .2617''$ lead, giving an error of .0007″. To index the work, the gear on spindle is advanced $72/9 = 8$ teeth at each indexing.

The short lead attachment described in the next chapter can also be used to cut short leads, an index plate being provided for use in cutting multiple threads.

Position of the Table in Cutting Spirals. The change gears having been selected, the next step in cutting spirals is to determine the position at which the table must be placed to bring the spiral in line with the cutter as the work is being milled.

The correct position of the table is indicated by the angle shown at *A*, Fig 13, and this angle, as may be noticed from that figure, has the same number of degrees as the angle *B*, which is termed the angle of the spiral, and is formed by the intersection of the spiral and a line parallel with the axis of the piece being milled. The reason the angles *A* and *B* are alike is that their corresponding sides are perpendicular to each other.

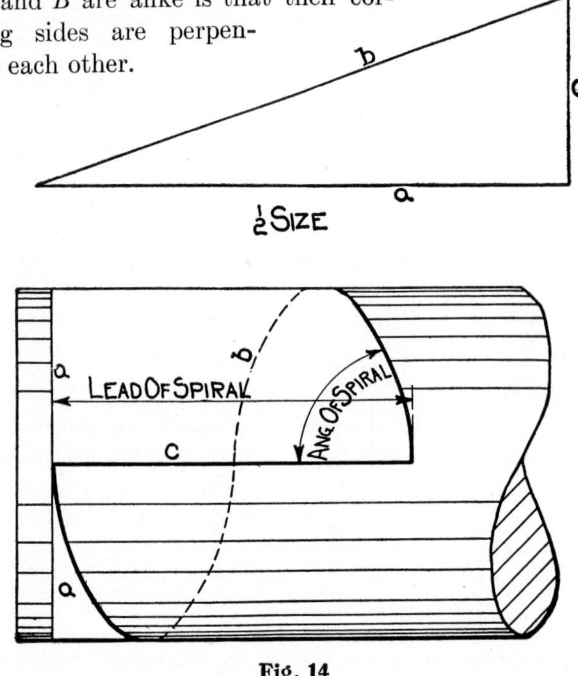

Fig. 14

The angle of the spiral depends upon the lead of the spiral and the diameter of the piece to be milled. The greater the lead of a spiral of any given diameter, the smaller the angle, and the greater the diameter of any spiral with a given lead, the greater the spiral angle.

If the angle wanted is not found in the tables on pages 226 to 228, it can be ascertained in two ways, graphically or more conveniently, by a simple calculation and reference to the tables on pages 311 to 319. In determining it graphically, a right-angle triangle is drawn to scale.

One of the sides which forms the right angle represents the circumference of the piece in inches, and the hypothenuse represents the line of the spiral. The angle between the lines representing the path of the spiral and the lead of the spiral is the angle of the spiral. This angle can be transferred from the drawing to the work by a bevel protractor, or even by cutting a paper templet and winding it about the work as shown in Fig. 14. The machine is then set so that the spiral or groove as it touches the cutter will be in line with the cutter. Or the angle may be measured and the saddle set to a corresponding number of degrees by the graduations on the base.

The natural tangent of the angle of the spiral is the quotient of the circumference of the piece, divided by the lead of the spiral. Accordingly, the second method of obtaining the angle of the spiral is to divide the circumference of the piece by the lead, and note the number of degrees opposite the figures that correspond with the quotients in the tables of natural tangents, pages 311 to 319. The angle having been thus obtained, the saddle is set by the graduations on the base.

Fig. 15

This second method is more satisfactory, as it is more accurate, and there is less liability of error than with the first. The saddle can be set to the proper angle, but before cutting into the blank, it is well to let the mill just touch the work, then run the work along by hand and make a slight spiral mark, and by this mark see whether the change gears give the right lead.

Special care should be taken in cutting spirals that the work does not slip, and when a cut is made it is well to drop the work away from the mill while coming back for another cut, or the mill may be stopped and turned to such a position that the teeth will not touch the work while the table is brought back preparatory to another cut.

Setting Cutter Central. In making such cuts as are alike on both sides, for instance, the threads of worms or the teeth of spiral gears, care must be taken to set the work centrally perpendicular with the centre line of the cutter before swinging the saddle to the angle of the spiral.

Cuts that have one face radial, especially those that are spiral, are best made with an angular cutter of the form shown in Fig. 15, as cutters of this form readily clear the radial face of the cut, keep sharp for some time and produce a smooth surface.

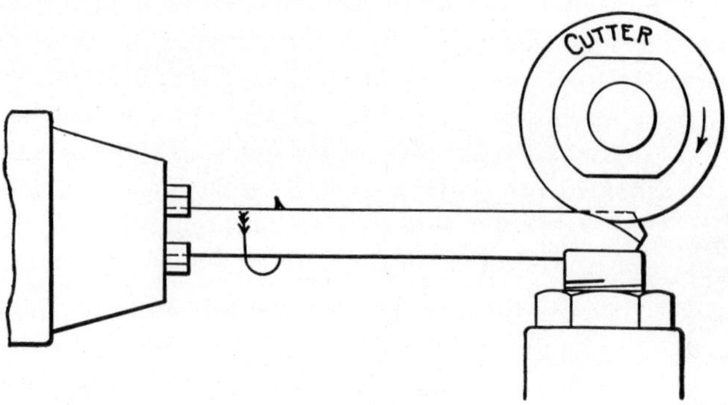

Fig. 16

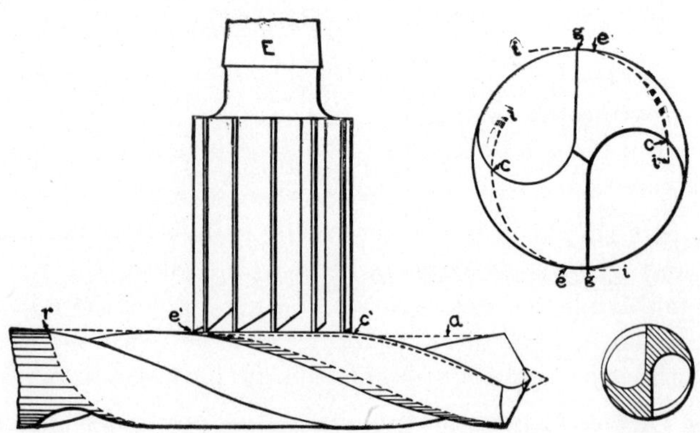

Fig. 17

Twist Drills. The operation of milling a twist drill is shown in Fig. 16. The drill is held in a collet, or chuck, and, if very long, is allowed to pass through the spindle of the spiral head. The cutter is brought directly over the centre of the drill, and the table is set at the angle of spiral.

The depth of groove in a twist drill diminishes as it approaches the shank, in order to obtain increased strength at the place where the drill generally breaks. The variation in depth is conditional, depending mainly on the strength it is desirable to obtain, or the usage the drill is subject to. To secure this variation in the depth of the groove, the spiral head spindle is elevated slightly, depending on the length of the flute and diameter of the drill.

The outer end of the drill is supported by the centre rest, and when quite small, should be pressed down firmly, until the cutter has passed over the end.

The elevating screw of this rest is hollow, and contains a small centre piece with a V groove cut therein to aid in holding the work central. This piece may be made in other shapes to adapt it to special work.

Another and very important operation on the twist drill is that of " backing off " the rear of the lip, so as to give it the necessary clearance, to prevent excessive friction during drilling. In the illustration, Fig. 17, the saddle is turned about one-half degree as for cutting a right-hand spiral, but as the angle depends on several conditions, it will be necessary to determine what the effect will be under different circumstances. A slight study of the figure will be sufficient for this, by assuming the effect of different angles, mills and the pitches of spirals. The object of placing the saddle at an angle is to cause the mill E to cut into the lip at c', and have it just touch the surface at e'. The line r being parallel with the face of the mill, the angular deviation of the saddle is shown at a, in comparison with the side of the drill.

From a little consideration it will be seen that while the drill has a positive traversing and rotative movement, the edge of the mill at e' must always touch the lip at a given distance from the front edge, this being the vanishing point, if such we may call it. The other surface forming the real diameter of the drill is beyond reach of the cutter, and is so left to guide and steady it while in use. The point e, shown in the enlarged section, shows where the cutter commences, and its increase until it reaches a maximum depth at c, where it may be increased or diminished according to the angle employed in the operation, the line of cutter action being represented by *ii*.

Before backing off, the surface of the smaller drills in particular should be colored with a solution of sulphate of copper, water and sulphuric acid. This solution can be applied with a piece of waste, and will give the piece a distinct copper color. The object of this is to clearly show the action of the mill on the lip of the drill, for, when satisfactory, a uniform streak of coppered surface the full length of the lip from the front edge *g* back to *e* is left untouched by the mill.

The above-mentioned coloring solution can be made by the following formula:

Sulphate of copper (saturated solution) .... 4 oz.
Water .... 8 oz.
Sulphuric acid .... 1 oz.

It is sometimes preferred to begin the cut at the shank end. By starting the cut in at this end, the tendency to lift the drill blank from the rest is lessened.

The table given on page 328 is useful for determining the cutters, pitches, gears and angles for twist drills.

Cutting Left-Hand Spirals. When giving directions for cutting spirals in any of the foregoing pages, right-hand spirals are at all times referred to. For the production of left-hand spirals, the only changes necessary are the swinging of the saddle to the opposite side of the centre line, and the introduction of an intermediate gear upon the stud, Fig. 12, to engage with either pair of change gears for changing the direction of rotation of the spiral head spindle.

Cutting Spirals with an End Mill. When spirals cannot be conveniently cut with side or angular milling cutters, as previously described, it is sometimes convenient to use end mills, as for example, when the diameter of the piece is very large, or the spiral is of such a lead that the table cannot be set at the requisite angle, the work is so held that its centre and that of the mill will be in the same plane and the saddle is set at zero.

CHAPTER V

Attachments

A milling machine is, in itself, a most versatile tool, but when equipped with a suitable set of attachments, the range of work that can be done is greatly increased. Also there are often milling operations that can be performed without an attachment, but by using one the jobs can be more easily and quickly done. Attachments are, therefore, most desirable auxiliaries where a machine is not confined to one manufacturing operation, but is used for general milling purposes. And even in manufacturing, where a machine is kept on one operation, an attachment can often be used to good advantage.

Broadly speaking, the variety of attachments for use on milling machines is almost limitless. To fully realize this, one has only to visit several shops producing different kinds of work on milling machines, and observe the methods employed. Devices of every conceivable description will be seen in use in connection with the machines, and, while many of them may be of a more or less special character and adaptable only to a particular operation, they are, strictly speaking, attachments. Some of these devices, however, are so designed that quite a number of different operations can be performed by their use, or the same operation can be repeated on a variety of pieces. It is these mechanisms that we are accustomed to regard more especially as attachments, while those designed for single operations are almost universally known in shops as fixtures. It would be useless to attempt to treat of the latter, as their designs and purposes are as varied as the different lines of mechanical work.

The efficiency of attachments, like machines, depends largely upon their design and construction, and a poorly designed or built mechanism of this type can seriously impair the quality of work and thus defeat its own object.

Many forms of attachments designed for the same purpose will be found, as it is necessary for every manufacturer to adapt attachments to his machine. This is a matter of minor importance, however, and a close examination will reveal that, as a general rule, the principles of the different mechanisms are similar. This chapter is devoted to

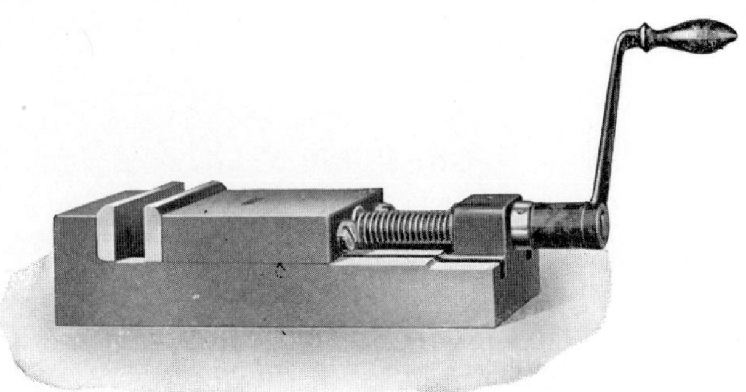

Fig. 18

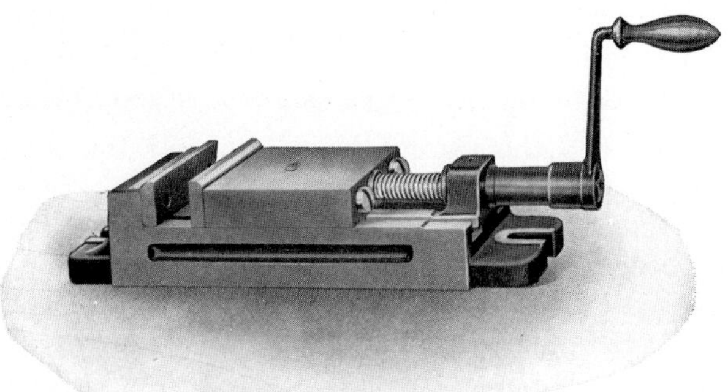

Fig. 19

Fig. 20

our line of attachments, as typical of attachments in general, with brief descriptions of their general designs and functions. From this information it is hoped that the reader will be able to understand the necessity for, and advantages of, these mechanisms.

Vises. While vises are furnished as a part of the regular equipment of most milling machines, and for that reason are not styled as attachments, notwithstanding this, they may be so properly classed.

Vises are useful for holding a large variety of small work while it is being milled or planed. Numerous illustrations of their employment can be found in the examples of operations throughout Chapters VII and IX. It is essential that they be as rigid as possible, and to this end should be built with well-designed, strong, close-fitting parts. It is well to have them set low so as to bring the work close to the table.

There are several styles of vises. Fig. 18 shows a Plain Vise, for lighter operations. The bed and slide are of cast iron, while the jaws are tool steel, hardened and ground. It is fastened to the surface of the table by means of a screw that passes through the bed and threads into a nut inserted in a table T slot. The head of the clamping screw fits a counterbore in the vise bed, and is flush with the top of the casting, so that it does not interfere with the movement of the sliding jaw.

The vise shown in Fig. 19 is known as a Flanged Vise, and differs little from the Plain Vise except in the method of clamping to the table. A slotted flange is provided at each end for this purpose, and regular T slot bolts with nuts and washers are employed. Also a pair of straps are furnished for clamping the vise at the sides when this is necessary.

It is sometimes desired to mill angular or tapering work. A vise provided with a swivel, and known by that name, is shown in Fig. 20, and by its use this work can be readily done. The vise proper is of the same design as the plain vise, but the bottom of the bed fits into a split ring in a base. This ring is tapered on the inside to draw the bed to its seat, and holds it rigidly without disturbing the alignment. The split ring is closed by either one of the two clamping bolts at the side, two being provided for convenience in setting. The entire circumference of the base is graduated to degrees, and the vise can be readily swung to any angle to the table ways. The base is provided with flanges for fastening it to the surface of the table.

Fig. 21 shows a Tool Makers' Universal Vise, designed to meet the requirements of tool makers and machine shops where a great variety of work is encountered. It is found of advantage for holding irregular or angular pieces and forms, also in determining and forming the edges for model parts of machines and work of a similar class. Often this vise will take the place of an expensive fixture. It can be set at any angle and the work placed in position or removed without disturbing the setting. It can also be easily removed from one machine to another and several operations performed without removing the piece of work. The base is double, and is fastened to the table by bolts that fit into the table T slots. It has two sets of bolt slots to allow for moving the vise back when set in a vertical plane. The upper part is a hinged knee, that swivels on the lower part of the base, and it can be set at any angle in a horizontal plane, graduations to degrees indicating the position. The top section of the knee is hinged to the lower part in such a manner that it can be set at any angle to 90° in a vertical plane, and clamped rigidly in position by the nut on the end of the bolt forming the hinge and by the bolt at the joint in the bracing levers. Graduations on a steel dial at the side of the vise indicate the elevation of the knee. A swiveling movement is also provided for the vise proper on the upper part of the hinged knee, and it can be set and clamped at any angle to the axis of the bolt forming the hinge.

Fig. 21

Index Centres. These mechanisms are employed for obtaining exact spacing of more common numbers of divisions upon the periphery of pieces of work, such as in cutting the teeth of small gears, ratchets and cutters, fluting taps and reamers, milling the sides of nuts and heads of bolts, and various other purposes. They are used principally upon machines not fitted with a spiral head, for their functions in most instances can be equally well performed by the latter, which also offers many additional advantages.

Like other attachments, their efficiency is largely dependent upon their design, and it is important that they be exceedingly stiff, in order that the work may be rigidly supported. They should also be convenient to operate, so that indexing may be quickly accomplished.

One of the simplest forms of index centres, known as Single Dial Index Centres, is shown in Fig. 22. It consists of a head-stock and foot-stock of solid construction. The spindle of the head-stock is turned by means of the hand-wheel, and the divisions are indicated on the periphery of an index plate fastened to the spindle near the hand-wheel. There are holes in the back of the index plate corresponding to the divisions on its periphery, and a hardened steel taper pin is provided that is forced into the bushings of these holes by a

Fig. 22

spring, efficiently locking the spindle at any one of the divisions. The small lever near the top of the head-stock withdraws the taper pin when it is desired to index the work.

This style of index centres is found convenient whenever rapid indexing is to be done, as in cutting teeth in sprocket wheels and mills, or in milling grooves in taps, reamers and work of a similar kind. They are built in two sizes, one to accommodate work up to 8 inches diameter, and the other for work up to 12 inches diameter. The index plates or dials furnished have 24 divisions, or holes, but special plates having, for 8 inch centres, any number of holes up to 32, and, for 12 inch centres, any number up to 32, are sometimes made to order.

A common style of index centres, known as Plain Index Centres, is shown in Fig. 23. The spindle of the head-stock is revolved by means of a worm and wheel. The handle of the crank fastened to the worm shaft constitutes an index pin, and indexing is accomplished by means of a plate drilled with circles of different numbers of holes into which the spring pin of the crank fits. Thus it will be seen that the principle of indexing with these centres is the same as with the spiral head. For rapid indexing of the coarser divisions, the worm can be thrown out of mesh with the wheel and the spindle turned by hand; a

Fig. 23

circle of holes in the back of the worm wheel rim, and an index pin at the top of the head-stock provide for indexing when this is done.

These centres are built in sizes to accommodate work up to 10 inches and 12 inches diameter respectively. The nose of the spindle is threaded to receive a face plate or chuck. They are fitted with index sectors similar to those of the spiral head, and the index crank is adjustable so that it can be brought to the nearest hole without disturbing the setting. The index plates furnished divide all numbers to 50 and all even numbers to 100, except 96.

Fig. 24 shows a pair of Universal Index Centres. The resemblance between them and the spiral head is marked; in fact, the foot-stock is identical with that furnished with the latter mechanism. All operations upon centres that do not require other than plain indexing and where there is no spiral to be cut, can be performed with these centres equally as well as with a spiral head.

These universal index centres are built in six sizes, to accommodate work up to 6, 10, 12, 12 1/2, 14 and 15 inches diameter. Divisions are indexed by means of the index crank and plates, the

Fig. 24

same as on the spiral head. The two smaller sizes are arranged for rapid indexing of coarser divisions by disengaging the worm, and indexing with the plate fastened directly to the nose of the spindle, as on the spiral head. The index crank is adjustable and index sectors are employed. The index plates furnished with the 6 inch, 10 inch, 12 inch, 14 inch and 15 inch centres divide all numbers to 50, and all even numbers to 100, except 96; those furnished with the 12 1/2 inch centres divide all numbers to 100 and all even numbers to 134.

Index centres designed for manufacturing purposes where economy and rapidity of production are important factors, often have more than one spindle. Fig. 25 shows triple centres of this type. All three spindles of these centres are indexed simultaneously, and one thumb-screw firmly clamps them all, consequently three pieces of work can

Fig. 25

be finished in practically the same time it takes to machine one on single centres.

The spindles are rotated by a ratchet operated by the lever shown at the left of the head-stock. Indexing is accomplished by an index plate which divides all numbers as follows: 2, 3, 4, 5, 6, 7, 8, 10, 12, 14, 20 and 24. The index stop pin is shown at the left of the head-stock.

Using all three spindles, work up to 2 1/2 inches diameter can be taken; when only the two outside spindles are employed, work up to 5 inches diameter will swing.

Triple index centres of the design that has the index plate at the side of the head-stock similar to the spiral head are shown in Fig. 26. Centres of this same general design, but arranged for rapid indexing only, are also built.

The index plates furnished with these centres divide all numbers to 50, even numbers to 100, except 96. When rapid indexing is desired, the worm of the index crank is disengaged and the centres are turned by means of a pinion actuated by the crank at the left of the head-stock; an index plate and stop pin provide for the divisions.

Fig. 26

The centres swing, using three spindles, 4 inches; using the two outside spindles, 8 inches.

The Plain Index Centres or gear cutting attachment shown in Fig. 27 are useful for cutting spur gears of all diameters up to and including 16 inches, and are similar to ordinary index centres, only

Fig. 27

they will swing larger diameters. They are exceptionally rigid in construction and, to further insure steadiness to the gear while being cut, an adjustable rim rest is placed on the head-stock.

The worm and wheel of this attachment are accurately cut, and the wheel is of much larger diameter than that of ordinary index centres; consequently the possibility for error in spacing is materially lessened. The worm and worm wheel can be disengaged and the spindle turned by hand by means of the handle at the back, when setting or testing work.

The index plates furnished divide all numbers to 100, all even numbers to 134, and all numbers divisible by 4 to 200.

In addition to cutting gears, this attachment may be used on jig work where accurate indexing is an essential element. The spindle is threaded for the purpose of holding a chuck or face plate.

Vertical Spindle Milling Attachments. Vertical spindle milling attachments, including the Compound and Universal types, are used for a wide range of light and heavy milling, such as key seating, T slot cutting, spiral milling, face milling and work of a similar class; in fact, almost any operation that can be performed with a vertical spindle machine can be accomplished with a horizontal spindle machine when equipped with one of these attachments.

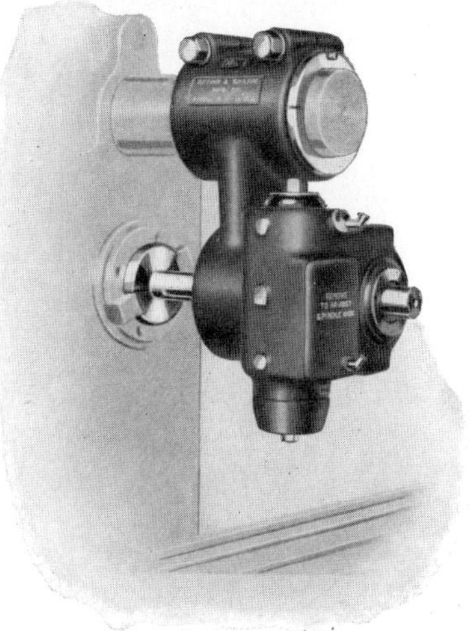

Fig. 28

In die sinking, as well as all kinds of surface milling, the advantage of having the work flat on the table and in plain sight of the operator is readily appreciated. For metal patterns and similar work, these attachments are especially valuable, as a line or template can be followed very closely, thus reducing the hand finishing to a minimum.

It is very essential, in designing attachments of this kind, that ample provision be made for solidly clamping the mechanism to the machine, and unless this can be done, their value is greatly restricted. The method of clamping shown in the accompanying illustrations is such that the attachment becomes practically an integral part of the machine. To be practical, the method of clamping must also be simple, for much of the value of an attachment lies in the convenience with which it can be put on and taken off the machine.

In all cases, the spindles of the attachments illustrated can be set to any angle from a vertical to a horizontal position, the angle being indicated by graduations reading to degrees.

Attachments of this kind are usually driven from the machine spindle through bevel gears, but Fig. 28 shows one that is driven by

For Machines with Single or Double Overarm

Fig. 29

For Machines with Double Overarm

For Machines with Single or Capped Overarm

Fig. 30

means of a worm and wheel, and Fig. 30 illustrates one where spur gears are employed in addition to bevel gears.

Vertical Spindle Milling Attachments as built by us are divided into two classes, light and heavy. With very few exceptions, all of our machines can be fitted with both light and heavy styles.

Fig. 28 shows a light attachment for the smaller sizes of machines, and Fig. 29 a heavy style for the same machines. Fig. 29 is also representative of a light style for the larger sizes of machines, the heavy style for these machines being shown in Fig. 30. The spindle end

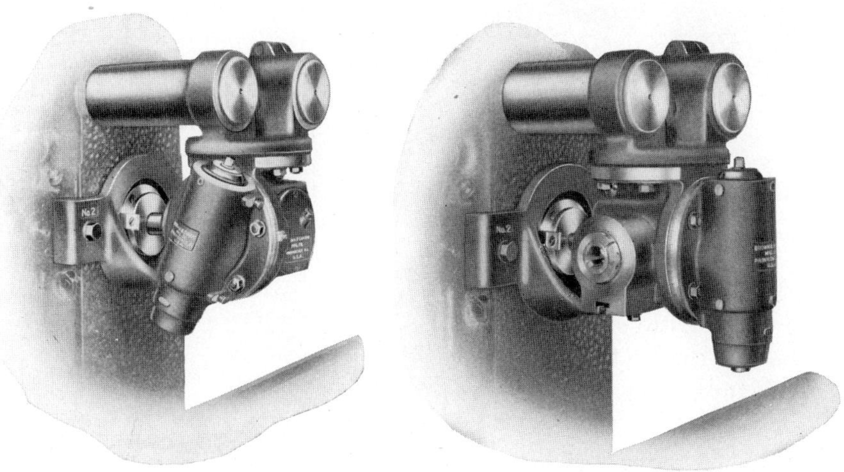

Fig. 31

of these attachments, except that shown in Fig. 28, is the Standardized Spindle End.

Compound Vertical Spindle Milling Attachment. The Compound Vertical Spindle Milling Attachment, shown in Fig. 31, is particularly applicable to a large variety of milling, because it can be set in two planes. (See illustrations.) It is especially advantageous when it is desired to set the spindle at an angle to the table, as in milling angular strips, table ways, etc., for with the spindle in this position, the full length of the table travel is available, and an ordinary end mill, instead of an angular cutter, can be used for milling the angle.

Universal Milling Attachment. Fig. 32 shows the Universal Milling Attachment, and as its name implies, it is fully universal in regard to setting the spindle. In addition to the large amount of work already mentioned in connection with the Vertical and Compound Vertical Attachments, this mechanism can be used for many other operations, because of the fact that the spindle can be set at any angle in both horizontal or vertical planes. It is clamped to the face of the column and the outer end is inserted in the arbor yoke to give additional stability.

Fig. 32

Horizontal Milling Attachment. We have mentioned the advantages to be derived from the use of vertical spindle milling attachments on horizontal spindle milling machines, and it is reasonable to suppose that to a certain extent, similar advantages are to be gained by the employment of a horizontal milling attachment on vertical spindle milling machines. An attachment of this kind is shown in Fig. 33. It is designed for use upon our No. 1 Vertical Spindle Machine, and with it such work as cutting spiral gears, racks, milling keyseats, etc., can be readily done. It is simple in construction and can be quickly attached to the machine.

Fig. 33

Circular Milling Attachments. Circular Milling Attachments provide a means of economically doing such work as milling circles, segments of circles, circular slots, etc., on plain and irregular shaped pieces. With the addition of one of these attachments, a vertical spindle milling machine is fully equipped for all varieties of straight

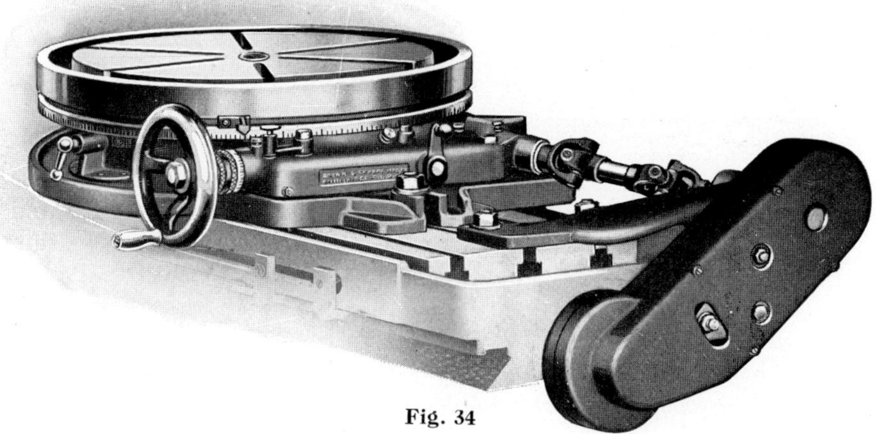

Fig. 34

and circular milling within its capacity. Likewise, one of these attachments used in connection with a vertical spindle attachment offers similar advantages on a horizontal spindle machine. Fig. 34 shows an attachment that can be used on our universal, plain and vertical spindle milling machines. The table is rotated by means of a worm and wheel, and can be fed automatically in either direction by power derived from the table feed screw. It can also be operated by hand when desired. For quick setting, the worm is thrown out of mesh and the table turned to any position. The table remains locked in position when the feed is stopped, but when straight milling or drilling is to be done, an additional clamp, operated by a lever at the side of the attachment, is employed to further insure its stability. The table is heavy and has a wide bearing surface; its circumference is graduated to degrees. The base is provided with an oil rim.

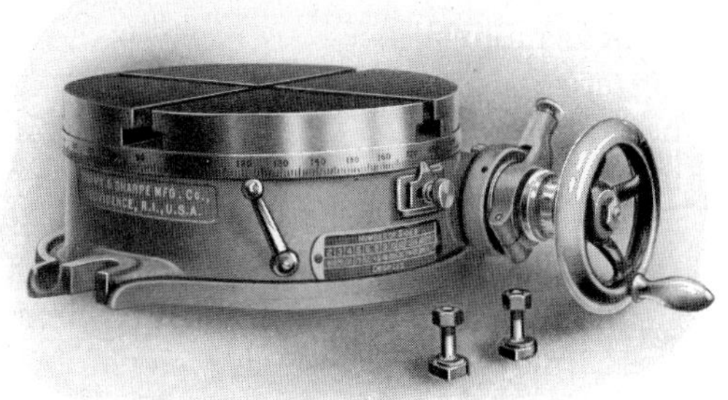

Fig. 35

A Circular Milling and Dividing Attachment is shown in Fig. 35. This attachment is adapted for

Fig. 36

use upon vertical spindle machines, or horizontal spindle machines in connection with the vertical spindle milling and slotting attachments. It has no automatic feed. When used with the vertical spindle milling attachment, the machine is fitted for all varieties of straight, surface and circular milling within its capacity, and with the slotting attachment, for all kinds of slotted work, such as die making, making templates, splining keyways, etc. Its design embodies the same features as the ones just described, and, in addition, the index finger on the front of the attachment is adjustable to allow readings to be taken from any convenient graduation, and an adjustable dial, graduated to read to 5 minutes, is fixed to the worm shaft. An index table mounted on the front of the base gives the degrees required for setting the table to produce work with 2, 3, 4, 5, 6, 8, 9, 10, 12, 15, 16, 18, 20 and 24 sides. This is particularly valuable for use in connection with the slotting attachment.

High Speed Milling Attachment. Sometimes it is necessary in doing such work as milling keyways and slots, die making, etc., to use a small cutter, which should be run more rapidly than the fastest spindle speed available, otherwise it limits the production and is liable to be broken in feeding. In order to obtain correct speeds for these small mills, high speed milling attachments are employed. Fig. 36 shows one of these attachments for use on a vertical spindle milling machine, and Fig. 37 one designed

Fig. 37

for horizontal spindle machines. The construction in each case can be readily understood, as it consists of nothing other than a pair of gears for increasing the speed and an auxiliary spindle that drives the cutter.

Fig. 38

Slotting Attachment. This attachment, shown in Fig. 38, is largely used in tool making, such as in forming box tools for screw machines, making templates, splining keyways, and work of a similar character. The working parts consist of a tool slide that is driven from the machine spindle by an adjustable crank that allows the stroke to be set for different lengths. The attachment can be set at any angle between 0 and 90°, either side of the centre line, the position being indicated by graduations on the circumference of the head. The tool is held in place by a clamp bolt, and a tool stop that swings over the top of tool shank makes it impossible for the tool to be pushed up.

Fig. 39

Attachment for Cutting Short Leads. In cutting spirals with a spiral head, as the lead becomes shorter and a higher ratio of gearing becomes necessary the stress upon the gears and mechanism becomes greater. For this reason, it is impractical to cut very short leads in this way. The attachment shown in Fig. 39 is designed particularly for use when it is desired to cut short leads.

Fig. 40

It consists of a casting clamping over the dovetail of the spiral head carrying a swiveling gear plate and a short shaft which is driven from the rear of the machine spindle by a belt.

The work is rotated from the spindle independently of the feed screw, the latter being disconnected from the power feed mechanism. The regular index change gears are used on the swiveling gear plate to connect with the large index gear to give the work the proper speed of rotation. The lead is obtained as described on pages 58 to 63, allowing the rotation of the work to drive the table feed screw. Eighteen holes in the large index gear allow indexing when cutting multiple threads.

A rack cutting attachment or vertical spindle milling attachment is used to drive the cutter.

Spiral Milling Attachment. This attachment, shown in Fig. 40, is designed for the heavy class of spiral cutting in conjunction with the spiral head. The cutter is placed on the end of cutter spindle, allowing attachments to cover a large variety of work. In addition to cutting spirals, attachments can be used for cutting racks. The spindle can be set at any angle in a horizontal plane.

Rack Cutting Attachment. An attachment for cutting teeth in racks is shown in Fig. 41. It can also be used in connection with the spiral head for cutting worms, on Universal Milling Machines, as shown on page 165, and for other miscellaneous operations.

Fig. 41

The cutter is mounted on the

end of a hardened steel spindle that extends through the attachment case parallel to the table T slots. This spindle is powerfully and smoothly driven from the machine spindle by a train of hardened steel bevel and spur gears.

Fig. 42

A vise, the construction of which can be plainly seen in the cut, is furnished as a part of the attachment.

When cutting racks, some convenient means of indexing to quickly and accurately space the teeth is necessary. Fig. 42 shows an indexing attachment designed for this purpose. It consists of a bracket that is fastened in the table T slot at the left-hand end. The bracket carries a locking disk, together with change gears for gearing to the feed screw. To index any required spacing, change gears are selected that will produce one or more whole turns of the locking disk. For each division the locking pin is withdrawn and the table advanced by the crank on the feed screw until the pin drops into the slot again, and locks the disk. This method of indexing is therefore much easier than relying upon a dial such as ordinarily used for the purpose.

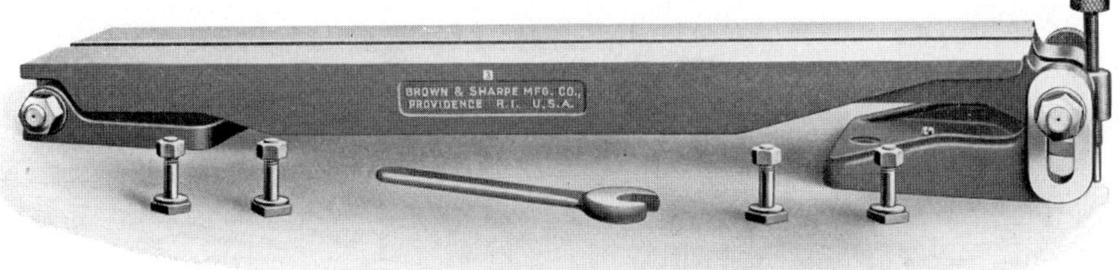

Fig. 43

Tilting Table. A handy attachment, known as a Tilting Table, is shown in Fig. 43. It is designed primarily for use in connection with index centres when fluting taper reamers, taps, etc. In addition to this work, many other kinds of taper pieces can be accurately reproduced. Its general characteristics, the manner in which it is fastened to the table, and the way that it is elevated, are all clearly shown in the cut.

Cam Cutting Attachment. The Cam Cutting Attachment, shown in Fig. 44, is used for cutting either Face, Peripheral or Cylindrical Cams from a flat former. The former is made from a disk about 1/2 inch thick, on which the required outline is laid out. The disk is machined or filed to the required shape.

Fig. 44

The table of the machine remains clamped in one position during cutting, and the necessary rotative and longitudinal movements are contained in the mechanism itself. The rotative movement is obtained by a worm driving a wheel fixed to the spindle of the attachment. The former is secured to the face of the worm wheel, and as the wheel revolves, the former depresses a sliding rack that in turn drives a pinion geared to another rack in the sliding bed of the attachment, thus giving the necessary longitudinal movement. In the cut the former is shown in position on the face of the worm wheel.

The attachment is sometimes driven automatically by means of a round belt leading from a small jack-shaft to a three-step cone pulley fastened on the end of the worm shaft. The pulley is clutched to the worm so that either hand or automatic feed may be used by the simple movement of a lever. Illustrations of the use of this attachment are to be found in Chapter IX.

Scales and Verniers for Milling Machines. Scales and verniers are useful on such work as boring jigs, fixtures, or wherever extreme accuracy is required and it is necessary to make fine adjustments

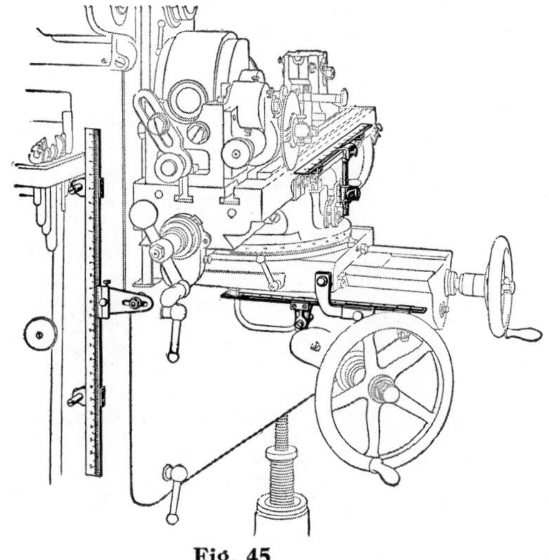

Fig. 45

of the table. The scales are graduated to 40ths of an inch, and the verniers read to thousandths of an inch. A machine with all of the table adjustments fitted with scales and verniers is shown in Fig. 45.

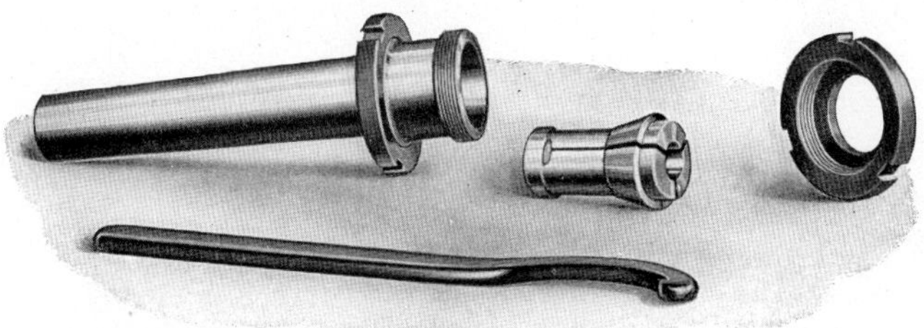

Fig. 46

Spring Chucks. Fig. 46 shows an unassembled spring chuck. This chuck is convenient for holding wire, small rods, straight shank drills, mills, etc. The collet holder is of steel, ground to fit the standard taper hole of the machine spindle, and has a hole its entire length. The front end is fitted to receive a spring collet, which is held in place by a cap nut that forces it against the taper seat and closes the chuck centrally. A nut is provided for withdrawing the collet holder from the spindle.

Heavy Manufacturing Milling Machine

In addition to the attachments already mentioned in this chapter, there are many minor fixtures frequently used in milling operations. These are spoken of in connection with general notes on milling in Chapter VII.

CHAPTER VI

Cutters

The development of the manufacture of milling cutters, and a better understanding of their care and use, have resulted in a rapid growth in the number and variety of milling operations, and a corresponding increase in the sizes and varieties of cutters. It is evident, therefore, that the selection, care and use of milling cutters are points of utmost importance in attaining success in the process of milling. The failure to obtain commercial results may often be attributed to the fact that the wrong cutter has been used on a certain job, or even if the right cutter has been chosen, the work has not been done under the most favorable conditions.

Either the operator or the person in charge of the job should be proficient in the selection and care of cutters, and capable of determining the correct speeds and feeds at which to operate them. No theoretical knowledge of the design and manufacture of cutters is necessary to aid in this work, although a general understanding of these points is of material help. While we are able to give in the following pages such information as applies in common to the running of milling cutters, the most valuable experience will come only through actual work at the milling machine.

Carbon and High Speed Steel. Milling cutters are made from either of two varieties of steel, known as Carbon Steel and High Speed Steel. Those made from High Speed Steel can be subjected to more severe service than those made from Carbon Steel, and they are especially desirable where large amounts of metal must be removed rapidly, as in roughing out pieces of work. Cutter manufacturers can usually furnish all styles and sizes in either steel. No fixed rules can be given for their choice. The requirements of each job and experience in the use of cutters must determine which steel is more economical and will give the most satisfactory results.

Plain Milling Cutter. This is a common type of cutter found in every shop, and may be described as a cylinder having teeth on the periphery only and producing a flat surface parallel to its axis. It is manufactured in a large variety of diameters and widths to meet

Coarse Tooth Plain Milling Cutter with Spiral Teeth

Helical Milling Cutter

Plain Milling Cutter

Coarse Tooth Side Milling Cutter

Spiral Shell End Mill

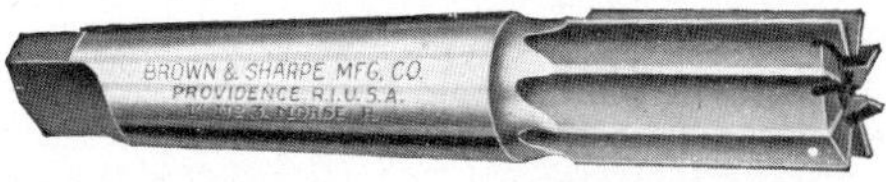

End Mill with Straight Teeth

End Mill with Spiral Teeth

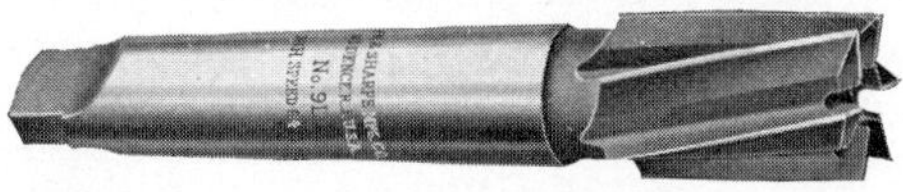

Coarse Tooth End Mill with Spiral Teeth

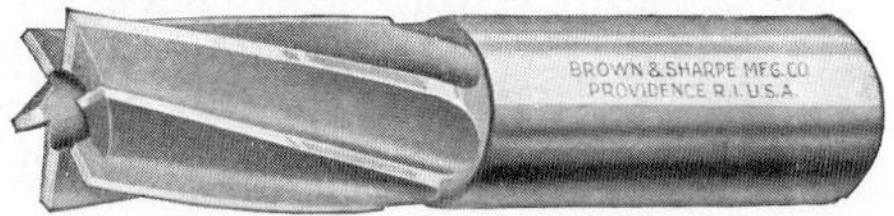

Straight-Shank End Mill

Two-Lipped Slotting End Mill

T Slot Cutter

Inserted Tooth Face Milling Cutter

Cutter for Grooving Taps and Fluting Reamers

Gear Cutter

Metal Slitting Saw

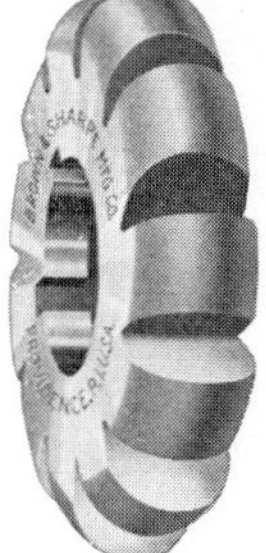

Convex and Concave Cutters with Teeth that can be sharpened without changing Form

Angular Cutters

Convex and Concave Cutters with Plain Milling Cutter Type of Teeth

Formed Cutter. Teeth can be sharpened without changing Contour

different requirements in slab milling, cutting keyways in shafts, etc. Saws for slitting metal and slotting screws are essentially plain milling cutters, although rarely regarded as such on account of their extreme thinness.

Plain milling cutters 3/4″ or less in width are usually made with straight teeth, while those above that width have teeth of a spiral form. The object of the spiral is to give a shearing cut, reducing the stress upon the teeth, and preventing a distinct shock when each tooth engages the work as is the case with straight teeth. Consequently, a spiral tooth cutter on wide surfaces produces much smoother results than a straight tooth cutter. It requires less power to operate and, in relieving the cutter of strain, the tendency to vibrate or chatter is reduced.

Fig. 47

Helical Milling Cutter. This rugged cutter has three or four teeth and has a much steeper spiral than the plain milling cutter. It is especially proficient in taking slabbing cuts, producing a fine finish without chatter. It can be used to particular advantage in removing an uneven amount of stock without gouging.

Side Milling Cutter. This type of cutter is like a plain milling cutter with the addition of teeth on both sides.

Side milling cutters are employed on a large variety of work, being used often in pairs with a space between, as shown in Fig. 47. When so used, they are known as "straddle mills." In work that has to be milled on two parallel sides at once, as milling the heads of bolts, nuts, tongues, etc., straddle mills can be used most advantageously.

A type of side milling cutter designed for deep cuts in steel is shown at the left in Fig. 49. It is known as a Staggered Tooth Side Milling Cutter. The Single Side Side Milling Cutter shown at the right in the same figure is used for side cuts where only one side is needed. In both types the shearing cut gives easy cutting action.

Side milling cutters are also made with interlocking side teeth for milling slots to standard width. The teeth interlock, as shown in Fig. 48, and the standard width of the slot is maintained by packing washers between the cutters.

Fig. 48

Face Milling Cutter. This cutter may be likened to a disk with teeth on the periphery and on one face. It is fastened to the end of the machine spindle, and the teeth on the flat face come in full contact with the work, while only a small length of the teeth on the periphery act on the piece. There are cutters of this type made which have no teeth on the periphery.

End Mill. This type of cutter, like the face milling cutter, has teeth on the periphery and at the end.

End mills are used for a large variety of light milling operations, such as milling cuts on the periphery of pieces, cutting slots, and facing narrow surfaces. They are made in three distinct styles, the ordinary solid end mill, with either straight or spiral teeth, the slotting end mill with two lips, and the shell end mill with either straight or spiral teeth.

Fig. 49

The ordinary solid end mill has its teeth cut on the same piece of steel that forms its shank; in reality, the space where the teeth are cut is only a continuation of the shank. The shell end mill has a hole through the centre so it can be mounted on the end of an arbor. This type should be used whenever possible, because it is cheaper to replace when worn out or broken than the solid mill. Slotting end mills with two lips, or cutting edges, are especially adaptable to fast milling of deep slots from the solid where there has been no hole previously drilled for starting the cut. In fact, these mills embody both the principles of a drill and end mill. A depth of cut equal to one-half the diameter of the mill can usually be taken from solid stock. The best results are obtained by maintaining a high surface speed.

End mills with right-hand teeth usually have a left-hand spiral, and those with left-hand teeth have a right-hand spiral. By having the direction of spiral opposite to the faces of the teeth the thrust of the spiral tends to force the shank of the mill solidly into the spindle, although there is little danger of pulling out the mill when the teeth and spiral are of the same hand.

T Slot Cutter. The T slot cutter has teeth upon its periphery, and alternating teeth on the sides. The teeth are cut in the same piece of steel that forms the shank, as in the case of solid end mills. In making a T slot, an ordinary side milling cutter, or a two-lipped end mill, is first used, and then the wide groove at the bottom is formed with the T slot cutter.

Angular Cutters. Angular Cutters differ from the cutters described above in that the teeth are neither parallel nor perpendicular to the axis of the cutter, but are at some oblique angle. The cutter may have more than one angle.

These cutters can be employed on a variety of work, as cutting the edge of a piece to a required angle and milling teeth of cutters and reamers. Where the nature of the work is such, as in dovetailing a piece, that the cutter cannot be fastened to the arbor with a nut, the cutters are furnished with threaded holes, or made solid on a taper shank.

Formed Cutters. Formed Cutters constitute an important group, their cutting edge usually being an irregular outline. These cutters have teeth that are relieved so that they may be resharpened repeatedly or until the teeth are too slender to permit further grinding, without changing the original form as long as the teeth are ground radially on their faces. Illustrations of this type are shown on page 91, and Figs. 50 and 51 show the extent to which they can be ground without changing the form of the teeth. Formed cutters with teeth relieved so that they may be ground on the faces without changing the contour, should be employed wherever the requirements of work demand that the original form of the cutter be maintained, as in manufacturing duplicate irregular pieces.

With this style of cutter, exact duplicate pieces of irregular outline can be produced far more cheaply than by any other method. In fact, no invention has so revolutionized the manufacturing of small parts of machinery and tools.

Concave and convex cutters, cutters for grooving taps, corner rounding cutters, gear cutters, etc., are made with teeth relieved so that they may be sharpened repeatedly without changing the contour.

Spiral formed cutters take a smooth shearing cut while having the feature of maintaining their form. The undercut is constant irrespective of the cutter width. Angular gash cutters also take a shearing cut and, as the sharpening face is a plane surface at an angle with the cutter axis, they are easier to sharpen. However, the undercut varies with the cutter width, making this type only suitable for cutters of narrow width.

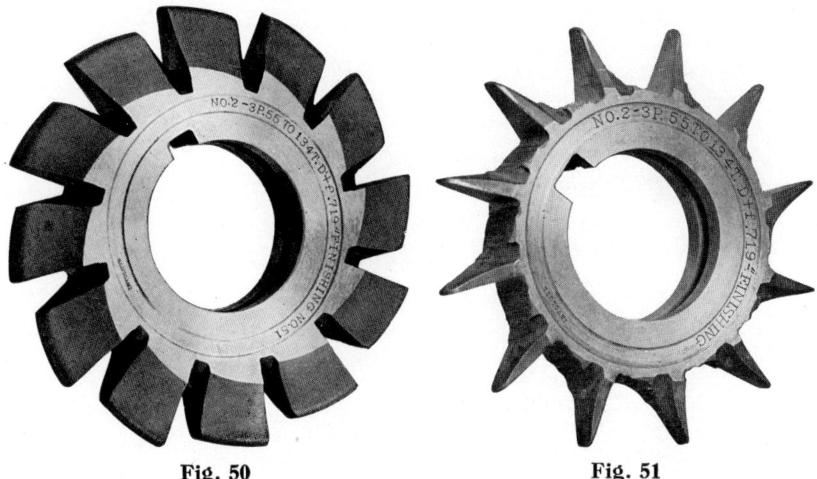

Fig. 50 Fig. 51

Cutters for producing irregular outlines are also made with plain milling cutter type of teeth, but it is necessary to have special grinding machines for them, and the concave cutters have to be made interlocking to preserve the size of circle. Cutters of this type are shown on page 91 and are known as " form cutters."

Fly Cutter. The most simple cutter for producing a form is the fly cutter, shown in Fig. 52. This cutter is very similar to a planer tool but is held in an arbor and rotated instead of being clamped in a tool head. It can hardly be classed with the cutters previously mentioned,

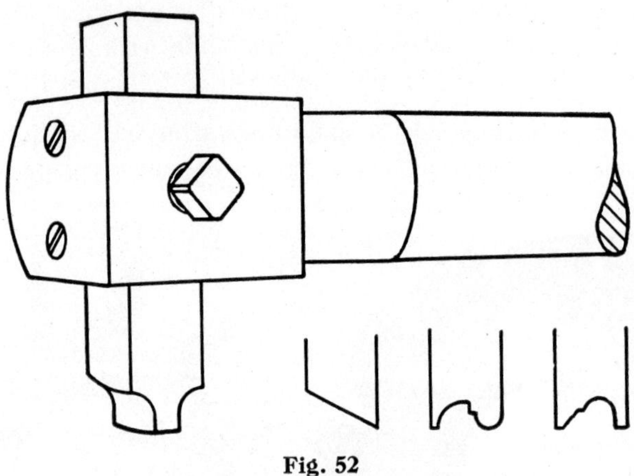

Fig. 52

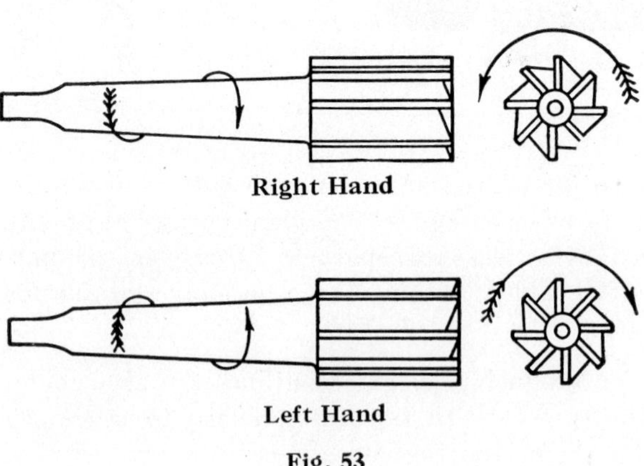

Right Hand

Left Hand

Fig. 53

for it is rarely used outside of the tool room or in experimental shops, but there it fills an important place. As it has only one cutting edge, it mills accurately to its own shape, but it does not cut so fast or wear as long as cutters with a number of teeth. It can be formed very exactly to any desired shape at a comparatively small expense, and thus may be used for many operations that otherwise would not bear the cost of special cutters, as, for example, when one or two teeth of special form are wanted in experimental work. The outlines of several possible shapes are shown in connection with the figure.

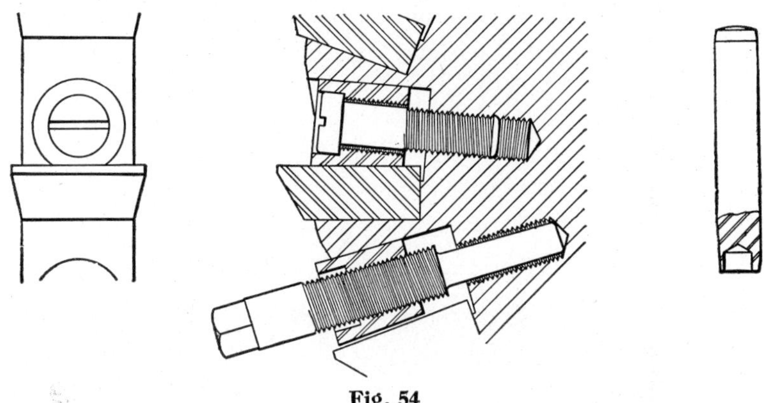

Fig. 54

Right- and Left-Hand Cutters. Cutters or end mills with taper shanks and those which have end teeth, may be either right- or left-hand, according to the direction in which the cutting edges of the teeth point. Taking an end mill for example, a right-hand mill is one which, held in the hand with the teeth away from you, presents the cutting edges of the teeth when revolved to the right or clock-wise. A left-hand mill is one that, similarly held, presents the cutting edges of its teeth when revolved to the left. Milling cutters having straight holes can be used either right- or left-hand as desired.

Inserted Teeth. Plain milling cutters above 8 inches diameter, side milling cutters above 6 inches diameter, and face milling cutters, are usually made with inserted teeth. The body of the cutter is of steel, the teeth being held securely in place by various means. We employ a bushing and screw for this purpose, as shown in Fig. 54.

The introduction of cutters of this style has done more for heavy milling than any other improvement in the cutter line, for with them the heaviest and fastest cuts can be taken, and should any of the teeth become broken, it is not a question of a new cutter, but simply that of replacing the broken teeth. The economy of this is of considerable importance to a shop.

If, for any reason, it becomes necessary to replace the full set of blades, or teeth, the new ones are clamped securely in position, and afterwards sharpened to correct any slight difference in height.

Teeth are released by removing the screw and inserting an extractor that threads into the bushing, and has a long end that reaches to the bottom of the hole in the cutter body. This extractor is shown in position in Fig. 54. As the extractor is turned by means of a wrench, the bushing is forced out and the tooth can then be removed.

Cutters for Special Purposes. In manufacturing something of a special nature, it is often of great advantage to use cutters especially designed for the particular job.

While nearly every milling operation can be performed with one of several different styles of cutters, there is usually only one style which is the most economical.

Fig. 55

Special cutters often have a tooth outline formed to the shape of the part being produced. Many times, however, they are similar to stock cutters, except for length, diameter, number of teeth, or some other particular quality necessary to overcome certain difficulties of the job.

Methods of Holding Face Milling Cutters. The latest type milling machines are equipped with the Standardized Spindle End which was adopted by the milling machine manufacturers of the National Machine Tool Builders' Association. Face milling cutters are centered on the outside diameter of the spindle and secured in place by four holding screws. They are positively driven by keys on the end of the spindle as shown in the left cut in Fig. 55. Face milling cutters are drawn directly onto the taper nose of taper nose spindle milling machines by a cutter driver and draw-in bolt. The cutter driver fits into a slot in the face of the cutter and a recess in end of spindle. The shank of the cutter driver is threaded in the end to receive draw-in bolt by which the cutter is drawn onto the spindle.

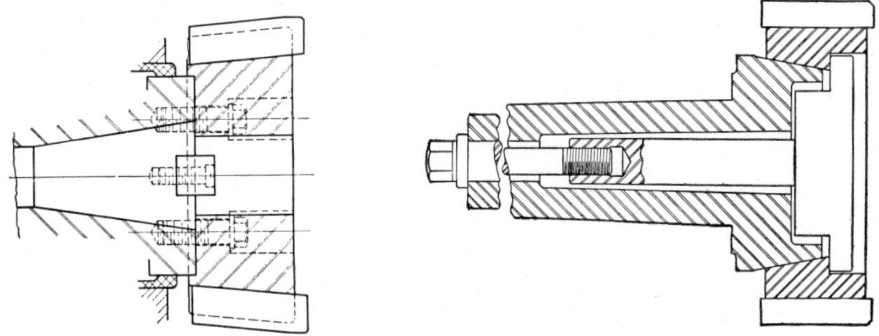

Fig. 55

Section through spindle and cutter, right view Fig. 55, shows cutter driver in place. Face milling cutters used on taper nose spindle machines can be used on Standardized Spindle End machines by means of an adapter which bolts securely to the spindle end.

An advantage is found in the face milling cutter in the increased available working space. There is no long hub, as the cutter is held close to the spindle. The body of each cutter is made of steel, and the blades of high speed steel.

On earlier machines, the spindle nose was threaded and a different style of face milling cutter was used. Face milling cutters designed for use on taper-nose spindles can be used on threaded-nose spindles by the use of an Adapter Outfit. This outfit consists of taper sleeve with threaded hole, cutter driver and draw-in bolt.

The taper sleeve fits over threaded nose of spindle and, being of the same taper as hole in face milling cutter, allows cutter to be drawn onto it by use of the cutter driver and draw-in bolt; cutter driver fitting recess in spindle and slot in cutter.

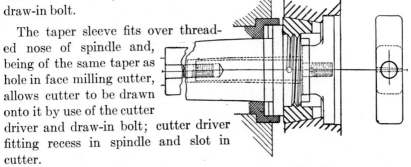

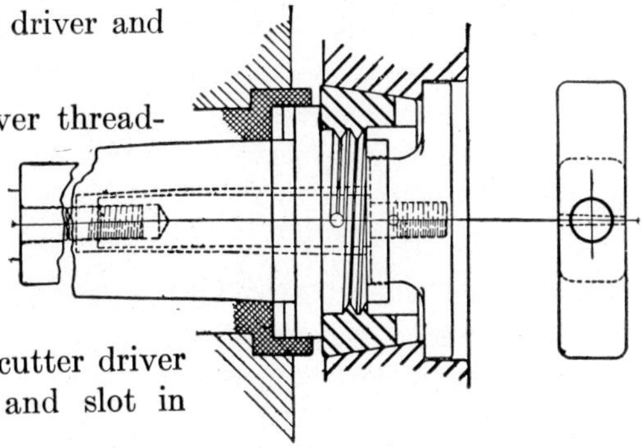

Fig. 56

Diagram, Fig. 56, shows sleeve and cutter driver in place.

Number of Teeth in Cutters. This subject has been discussed at some length by various writers in books and technical papers. Standard cutters have been found satisfactory for the majority of work, and practically indispensable on some work of the lighter class, but cutters having wide spaced teeth have a marked advantage over the standard type in their ability to remove a considerably greater quantity of metal in a given time without distressing the cutter or overloading the machine.

The free cutting action of these coarse tooth cutters is largely due to the fact that less cutting is actually required to remove a given amount of metal, each tooth taking a large, deep chip. This results in a considerable decrease in the tendency to slide over the surface and spring the cutter arbor. The rake and increased spiral of the teeth give a more nearly perfect shearing, rather than a pushing or dragging action. Accordingly there is less friction generated for a given cut, leaving the teeth much cooler and causing them to do considerably more work between grindings.

A marked advantage arising from the free cutting action is the consumption of less power, as might be expected from the fact that there is less friction and heating.

The wide spaces between the teeth allow the cutting edges to be well backed up, which was not always possible with closely spaced teeth. This increase in the strength of the teeth is much greater in proportion than the increase in work done by each tooth in removing the larger chips. Therefore the cutters are well prepared to handle deep and rapid cuts without danger of failing.

In developing the line of Brown & Sharpe Coarse Tooth Milling Cutters, particular attention has been given to the angle of rake and the lead of the spiral of the teeth. After a long series of practical experiments we have adopted a type with steep spiral and considerable angle of rake as the most economical and practical form, this type also being adapted to a large range of work which is not of the heavier class.

Angle of Tooth Face. Single point tools such as those used on the lathe and planer are usually given a slight rake; that is, the face of the tool is undercut a few degrees from a radial line. A similar practice is followed in setting the teeth in the body of large inserted tooth cutters so that they have a certain amount of rake. A smoother cut is gained and less power is consumed than would be with radial teeth. For other cutters, however, it will be found that satisfactory results as to finish are gained with cutters whose tooth faces are perfectly radial. Practically all ordinary stock cutters with the above noted exception have radial teeth.

The clearance or angle of the teeth back of the cutting edge is also of considerable importance, and it will be taken up later in connection with sharpening cutters.

Diameter of Cutters. It is well to use cutters as small in diameter as the strength will admit. The reason is shown by Fig. 57. Suppose the piece *I D C J E* is to be cut from *I J* to *D E*. If the large mill *A* is used, it will strike the piece first at *I* when its centre is at *K*, and will finish its cut when the centre is at *M*. The line *G* shows how far the work must travel to cut off the stock *I J D E*. If the small mill *B* is used, however, it will strike the piece when its centre is at *L* and the work travels only the length of the line *H*.

Small mills are also preferable because they can do more and better work than larger ones, as there is less possibility of their chattering. Furthermore, they require less power and are not as expensive as large mills. The advantage of small mills has been illustrated in our own works, where a difference of 1/2 an inch in the mills has made a difference of 10 per cent in the cost of the work.

Temper of Cutters. A cutter is not necessarily too soft because it can be scratched with a file. On the other hand, care should be taken that cutters are not too hard or brittle, for trouble will quickly arise from the teeth breaking. If there is any question as to the temper of a cutter, it is better policy to consult with the cutter manufacturers than to attempt to correct it by drawing the temper, or re-tempering.

Gang Milling. Gang Milling receives its name from the fact that two or more cutters are placed together on an arbor and used at one time. Sometimes plain milling cutters are so combined in order to cover a wider space than the longest stock cutter. Again, formed cutters are used either with or without plain or side milling cutters. The use of formed cutters and plain milling cutters together should be avoided whenever possible, on account of the difficulty of maintaining relative diameters in sharpening the gang.

The value of gang milling is found in the fact that it reduces the cost of production and insures accurate duplication of parts, in that several operations can be performed simultaneously, and with one setting.

It should be kept in mind that in this kind of milling, cutters of the largest diameter, or those that take the heaviest cuts, should, if possible, be used nearest the nose of the spindle, thereby reducing the strain on the arbor. If several of the cutters are plain milling cutters, it is well to use both right-hand and left-hand spirals in order to equalize the end thrust of the arbor. When, in gang milling, the cutters vary considerably in diameter, the inequality of the peripheral speeds may be overcome by having the cutters of large diameter made of high speed steel, and those of small diameter made of the ordinary carbon steel.

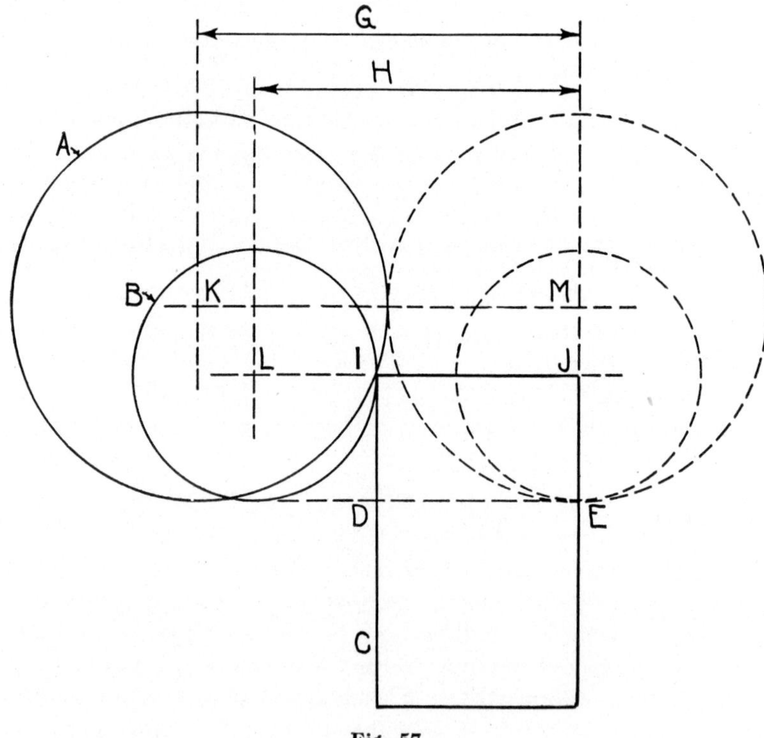

Fig. 57

Speeds and Feeds. Speeds and feeds are of extreme importance when considered in connection with the life and efficiency of a cutter and volume of output. Little can be said, however, in the matter of general rules to follow in determining correct speeds and feeds, owing to the different conditions that exist in different shops, and, in fact, in the same shop, where one set of rules will not always hold on like jobs. The amount of power and rigidity in different machines, kind of material, width and depth of cut, quality of finish required, and many other factors, all enter into the question, and prevent the establishing of any definite rules. Sometimes the speed must be reduced, yet the feed not changed, and vice versa; again both speed and feed must be reduced or increased, as the case may be. Often the rate of feed depends almost wholly upon the degree of accuracy and quality of finish required. In general, work of a delicate character, requiring an accurate finish, demands light cuts and fine feeds, and work of a heavy character, where the principal object is to remove metal rapidly, requires deep cuts and coarse feeds. On work that permits of heavy roughing cuts, the finishing cuts should usually be light. The feed, inasmuch as it governs the output of work, is of greater importance than the speed of a cutter, and it is generally a safe rule to follow, that the speed should be as fast as the cutter will stand, and the feed as coarse as is consistent with good work. Much must be left to the judgment of the operator as to the correct speed and feed to use for the work in hand, and many cases will require repeated experiments before the best results are obtained. When any difficulty is encountered in obtaining the right combination of speed and feed, it is well to seek the advice of the foreman in charge of the job, or that of a widely experienced milling machine operator.

The following surface speeds will serve to give an idea, or basis, to work from. They may be varied slightly to suit the requirements of the work in hand. Using carbon steel cutters: For brass, 80 feet to 100 feet per minute; for cast iron, 40 feet to 60 feet per minute; for machinery steel, 30 feet to 40 feet per minute; and for annealed tool steel, 20 feet to 30 feet per minute, have been found satisfactory. With high speed steel cutters for the same materials, the following speeds are advocated: For brass, 150 feet to 200 feet per minute; for cast iron, 80 feet to 100 feet per minute; for machinery steel, 80 feet to 100 feet per minute; and for annealed tool steel, 60 feet to 80 feet per minute.

Useful tables for determining the number of revolutions per minute to obtain the more common surface speeds of cutters of different diameters will be found on pages 329 and 330.

Sharpening Cutters. The importance of keeping all kinds of milling cutters well sharpened must not be overlooked. It might be supposed upon first thought that better economy in cutter wear would be gained by regrinding no oftener than positively necessary. This is not the case, however, as experience has shown that a dull cutter wears more rapidly than a sharp one, and consequently one that is kept in good condition by frequent regrinding will invariably outlast one that is not so cared for. Besides, a dull cutter not only consumes more power, but cannot be operated as rapidly or take as heavy cuts as a sharp one, and the quality of the work is never as good. Too frequently in shops today, the efficiency of milling machines is impaired by the use of dull cutters, for no other reason than carelessness and negligence on the part of the operator. Milling is never a complete success where such conditions exist, and with the improved grinding machines and convenient means of removing and replacing cutters, there is no reason for limiting the capabilities of a machine by using dull cutters. Grinding a cutter takes only a short time, and the good results that are obtained, together with the economy assured, more than compensate for the time expended in grinding. Whenever possible, it is a good plan to have two sets of cutters, so that one set can be reground while the other is in use; the milling machine then need only be stopped long enough to change the cutters.

Plain milling cutters, side milling cutters, end mills, etc., are sharpened upon the tops of the teeth, while formed cutters of all kinds are sharpened upon the faces of the teeth. Modern cutter grinding machines are necessary where many cutters are employed, and are advantageous, even where there are only a few cutters used, for it is nearly impossible to properly resharpen cutters, except with a machine especially designed for that purpose. We illustrate at the back of the book the cutter grinding machines we build that are very suitable for use in connection with milling machines.

It is impossible to treat in detail the many points about resharpening cutters without going to great length, but we issue a book and booklet* devoted exclusively to the subject, one of which is furnished with each of the machines mentioned above.

* "Construction and Use of No. 13 Universal and Tool Grinding Machine," and "Construction and Use of No. 2 Cutter Grinding Machine and No. 3 Universal Cutter and Reamer Grinding Machine."

Beveling the Corners of a Coarse Tooth Shell End Mill

Grinding a Formed Cutter on Index Centres

Grinding the Face Teeth of a Spiral End Mill

Grinding the End Teeth of a Coarse Tooth End Mill

Grinding the Teeth of an Angular Cutter

Grinding the Teeth of a Small Saw

Clearance on Cutters. The clearance or relief of milling cutters is the amount of material removed from the top of the teeth back of the cutting edge to permit the teeth to clear the stock and not scrape over it after the cutting edge has done its work. On formed cutters, the clearance does not have to be considered in resharpening. This is because the teeth are so formed that when ground on the faces, the clearance remains the same.

The angle of clearance depends upon the diameter of the cutters, and must be greater for small cutters than for larger ones. The clearance on the teeth of plain milling cutters should be 4° for cutters over 3 inches in diameter, and 6° for those under 3 inches diameter. The clearance of the end teeth of end mills should be about 2°, and it is well to have the teeth a little hollowing, making them .001 or .002 inch lower near the centre than at the outside, so that the inner ends of the teeth will not drag on the work. This can be done by setting the swivel on the cutter grinding machine slightly away from 90°.

Vibration of Cutters. If the clearance of a cutter is too great, vibrations are likely to occur in operation, and this should be corrected by regrinding the teeth. " Chattering " is a serious drawback to successful milling, as it impairs the quality of the work, limits the capacity and injures a machine, and reduces the life and efficiency of a cutter. While it is impossible in many cases to eliminate it, every precaution should be taken to reduce it to a minimum.

CHAPTER VII

General Notes on Milling, together with Typical Milling Operations

Milling, as we have already explained, is a process that cannot be governed by any fixed set of rules, but there are a few general instructions which, if carefully followed, will enable the machine to be more efficiently operated and largely influence the success that is attained. These we have collected in this chapter, and, in addition, show illustrations of a number of common milling operations to give an idea of how various and widely different jobs can be set up.

GENERAL NOTES ON MILLING

Pickling Castings and Forgings. Due to the rapid cooling or chilling of the outside of castings and forgings, a tough, hard skin, or scale, forms that is very destructive to the cutting edges of the teeth of milling cutters. There is also considerable of the moulding sand left on castings, and this is likewise harmful to the cutting edges. The sand can be removed and scale softened to some degree by the process of pickling, and it is essential that this be done preparatory to milling. Castings are usually pickled in the foundry, but it is well to make sure that this has been done before attempting to mill them. It is also an advantage in some cases to have castings rattled after being pickled. Where they are small, and are to be finished rapidly, they should be annealed.

For pickling castings, a solution of oil of vitriol, or sulphuric acid, reduced with water to a specific gravity of 25° (Baumé hydrometer) is recommended. The castings should be stacked on a bench over a vat containing the solution, and the solution poured over them.

Castings should never be immersed in the pickling bath if they are to be painted, because the iron is more or less porous, and the acid that is absorbed in pickling will work out after the pieces are finished, causing the paint to flake off. Furthermore, the pickle works better when it is poured over the castings and then allowed to dry off before another application of the solution.

The time required for the process is usually about a day, and the solution should be poured over the castings from four to five times.

Forgings may be pickled by immersing in a solution of sulphuric acid and water of 30° specific gravity (Baumé hydrometer) for a period of from 3 to 12 hours, according to hardness of scale.

When either castings or forgings are pickled, they should be thoroughly washed off with hot water, as this will wash out sand and remove the acid better than cold water. The water may be conveniently heated for this purpose by injecting steam into the cold water pipe.

Cutter Close to End of Spindle. In all milling operations, especially the heavier ones, care should be taken to have milling cutters as near the nose of the spindle as practicable. This will reduce to a minimum any possible vibration and spring of the arbor. It also brings the table close to the face of the column and ensures additional rigidity. Other valuable points about cutters have been taken up in Chapter VI, and it may be well to review these previous to starting to operate a machine.

Fastening Cutter on Arbor. See that the ends of the collars and washers are clean, for particles of dirt or chips between them will cause the arbor to be sprung when the nut is tightened. Small cutters can be held securely by the mere clamping effect of the collars on each side when the nut is tightened, but medium and large cutters should always be keyed to the arbor to prevent slipping.

Manner of Driving and Supporting Arbors. Milling machine arbors are driven in several different ways, some of which are shown in Fig. 58. In *A*, the arbor has a tenon at the small end of the taper that fits a slot at the end of the taper hole in spindle, thus giving a positive drive. The method of driving arbors *B* and *C* is similar to that of driving face milling cutters, described on page 98. The arbor is positively driven by keys on end of spindle, and has a threaded hole in end of shank. The arbor is drawn into place and held securely by the draw-in bolt (see Fig. 58). The method of driving collets is the same as that of arbors.

The method of driving arbors on machines with taper nose spindle is the same as above except that a driving clutch is used instead of the spindle keys.

All milling machines are equipped with some support for the outer end of the cutter arbor. The adjustable centre shown at *A* is one form that is used for lighter classes, or work where an arbor with a flat tenon is employed. The centre serves to support the outer end of the arbor and helps to keep the flat tenon in place in the slot in the spindle. Another form of support is shown at *B*. This support is a bronze bushing mounted in the arm that extends down from the overhanging arm, and is used where an arbor with clutch drive is employed. An example of the use of arm braces that extend from the knee to the outer arbor yoke carrying the bronze bushing for the outer end of the arbor is shown at *C*. These braces firmly tie the knee and overhanging arm together, and give a stiff support for the arbor. They should be used whenever the character of the work is heavy. This illustration also shows the use of an arbor yoke for stiffening the arbor between the cutters. This yoke should be used to bring a bearing either between or as near to the cutters as possible.

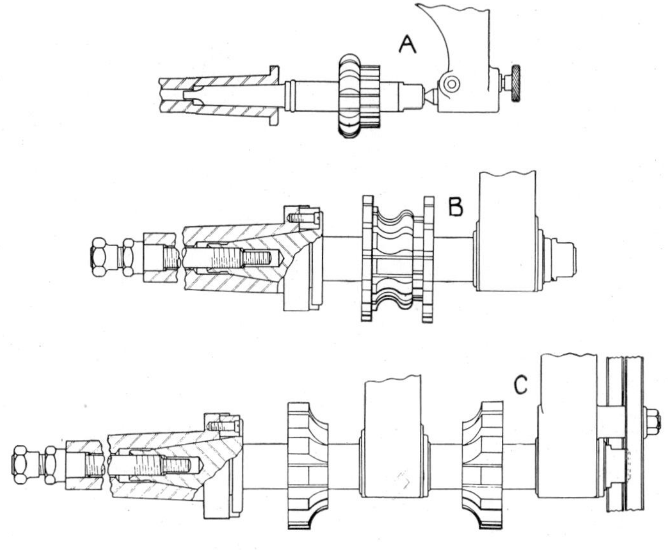

Fig. 58

Before tightening or loosening the arbor nut, when putting on or removing cutters, be sure the arbor support is in position, so that a bearing is provided near the nut, otherwise the arbor is liable to spring.

Clamping Work. An operator should pay particular attention to clamping work on a milling machine, for the success of milling is more dependent on this than one would realize at first thought. It is an easy matter to place clamps on some work in such positions that the piece is sprung, consequently when the clamps are loosened and the piece resumes its natural shape, the milled surface is found inaccurate. Again, faulty clamping results in work becoming loosened during operation, and not only impairs the accuracy of the piece, but many

times damages the cutters and machine. It is very essential, therefore, that work be clamped solidly, but in such a manner that it is not sprung.

An assortment of clamps or straps, together with jacks, a shim, step block and clamping bolt, are shown on the opposite page. These accessories form an important part of the equipment of a milling machine, and are needed where a variety of work is done. Several sets of each style of strap, and different sizes of step blocks and clamping bolts should always be at hand for use on work of varied shapes.

Whenever clamping a piece to the table, the straps should be placed squarely across, so as to have a full bearing at each end and, if possible, at points where the work extends down to the table beneath the strap. If it is necessary to place a strap over an overhanging part, such as on the piece of work shown on the next page, some support should be put between the overhanging part and the table, otherwise this part is liable to be sprung or broken off.

Another point in connection with clamping such work is the position of the clamping bolt. It should always be placed as near the work as the slot in the strap or other conditions will permit, for in this position it will exert the greatest pressure on the work and will not require setting up so tightly.

When milling work held in a jig or fixture, it is advisable to have the thrust of the cutter taken against the solid support, not against the removable member, for in this case there is more tendency toward vibrations that might loosen the clamping nuts.

When duplicate pieces are milled, using a fixture, care should be taken to clean the bearing points each time before putting a new

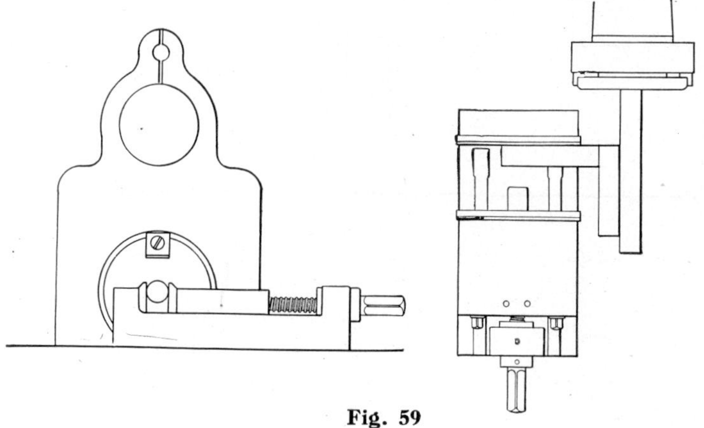

Fig. 59

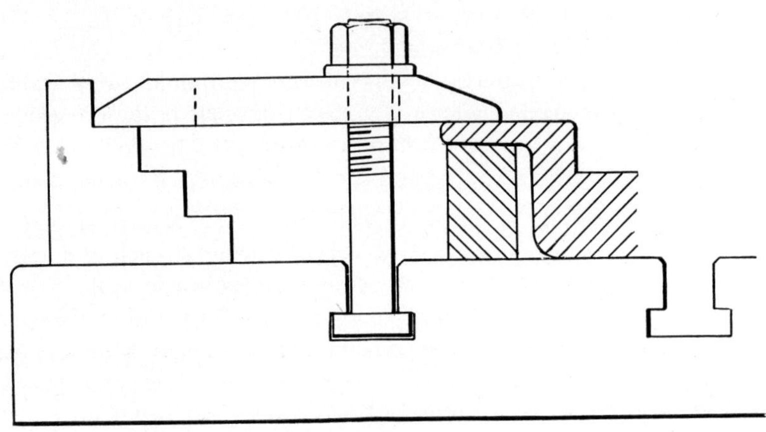

Right

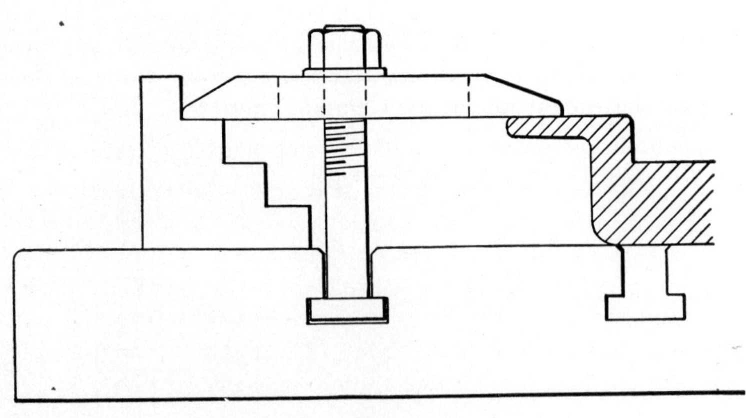

Wrong

piece of work in place. A narrow, stiff hair-bristle brush is good for this purpose when milling cast iron, but one with wire bristles is better for cleaning out steel or wrought iron chips. It is well to clamp a piece lightly, then tamp it down at all bearing points with a hammer, after which it can be solidly fastened.

Aside from these few general instructions on placing and clamping work, little can be said, because the shape of a piece of work alone determines how it may be best fastened. But a study of the methods of clamping shown in the examples of work in this and succeeding chapters will be of great value to the reader.

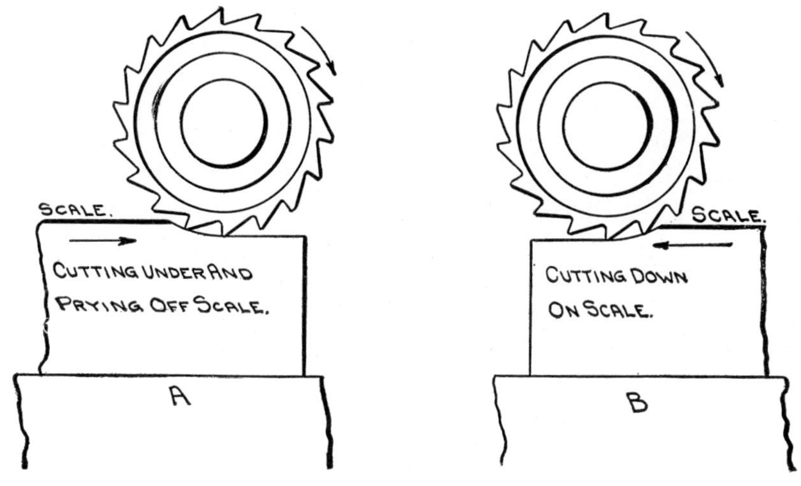

Fig. 60

Setting Vise. Light work is usually held in a vise, as it is more convenient than any other method of fastening it to the table. To set a vise with plain base so that its jaws are parallel to the spindle, place an arbor in the spindle and then bring the vise jaws up to the arbor. (See Fig. 59.) It can be set at right angles with the spindle by a square placed against the arbor and the jaws. The front of the table of the machine can also be used in setting the vise.

Swivel vises can be set by aid of the graduations on their base.

Direction to Move Work Under Cutter. Whenever possible, it is advantageous to feed the work in the opposite direction from that in which the cutter runs. (See *A*, Fig. 60.) Then the cutter cannot draw the work in as it is liable to do when the table moves in the direction indicated at *B*. Moreover, when the piece moves as shown at

A, the cutter teeth are first brought into contact with the softer metal, and as the scale on the surface is reached, it is pried or broken off.

On the other hand, in milling deep slots, or in cutting off stock with a thin cutter, or saw, it is sometimes better to move the work with the cutter, as the cutter is then less likely to crowd sidewise and make a crooked slot.

When the work is moving with the cutter, the table gib screws must be set up rather hard, for the teeth of the cutter tend to draw the work in, and if there is any lost motion in the table, the teeth may catch and injure the cutter or work. A counter-weight to hold back the table is excellent in such milling.

With vertical spindle milling machines, when a cutter is working on a flat surface, it does not matter which way the table is fed, but if the cutter is milling a side of a casting, as well as a flat surface, the table should be fed in the opposite direction to that in which the cutter revolves, for the reasons already mentioned.

Limits in Milling to Size. The limit for error in size to which work should be milled depends entirely upon the character of the job. With some work, a limit of one-hundredth of an inch is plenty good enough, while many other pieces must be finished to within one-thousandth of an inch of being exactly parallel or straight, as the case may be.

In milling to a given thickness or size, the most accurate results are ordinarily obtained by straddle mills or side milling cutters; for when only one side is milled at a time, and the piece has to be changed from one side to the other, it is hardly practicable to work to a smaller limit than two-thousandths of an inch. Side milling frequently requires more attention to keep the work smooth than ordinary surface milling.

Very accurate milling may be done and excellent surfaces obtained by small end mills running at high speeds.

In all cases where roughing and finishing cuts are to be taken on work, and precision is required, it is best to first remove most of the stock with a coarse feed, leaving enough for a light finishing cut. At a second operation, finish at a higher speed with a feed that will give the required surface.

Some light work will spring when the scale and a thickness of the metal are removed by the roughing cut. It is, therefore, advisable to loosen the holding clamps and permit the piece to assume a natural form before taking the finishing cut; otherwise, whatever inaccuracy might result from the foregoing cause would be present in the finished work.

Remove Backlash or Lost Motion from Feed Screws. Backlash or lost motion is apt to be present in the feed screws and nuts of any machine, especially in those that have been in use some time. To obviate errors in making fine adjustments, the operator should be very careful to eliminate all backlash before setting to the graduations on the feed screw dials. This may be done by turning the hand-wheel a quarter or half turn in the opposite direction to that in which the adjustment is to be made, and then bringing the wheel back to the point from which adjustment is to be made.

Use of Oil or Other Lubricant. Lubricant is used in milling to obtain smoother work, to keep the cutters cool so that the teeth will retain their cutting edges longer, and, where the nature of the work requires, to wash the chips from the work or from the teeth of the cutters. Oil is generally used in milling steel, wrought iron, malleable iron or tough bronze, where a smooth finish is desired. A soda water mixture can also be used to good advantage on these materials.

For very light cuts, oil should be applied to the cutter with a brush; for heavier cuts, it should be allowed to drip freely upon the cutter from a can, and on the heaviest cuts, a large supply of lubricant should be supplied by means of a pump, which can be affixed to the machine.

A good quality of lard oil is generally used, but any animal or fish oils may be employed. An excellent soda water lubricant that is less expensive and cleaner to use than oil can be made by mixing together and boiling for one-half hour, 1/4 lb. sal soda (sodium carbonate), 1/2 pint lard oil, 1/2 pint soft soap and water enough to make ten quarts.

Cutting Cast Iron. In cutting cast iron, lubricant is seldom used, as cutters do not usually heat very much, and the chips are so fine that the use of a lubricant results in a sticky mass that clogs the teeth of the cutter, and is difficult to clean from the work and machine.

Compressed air can be used to some advantage on cast iron, and will serve to keep the cutters cool and free from chips. In using compressed air care should be exercised not to have too much pressure, as it will scatter the dust and chips, which will fill bearings and cause trouble.

Collars and Washers for Arbors. Collars sent with milling arbors are not always the right thickness to bring cutters into the desired position. In these cases, washers should be employed. The following thicknesses are convenient: .001″, .002″, .004″, .008″, .016″, and .032″, as these give all steps from .001″ to .032″.

The collars should be of uniform thickness, otherwise they are likely to spring an arbor when they are clamped up.

Lead or Brass Hammer, and Brass Bar. Lead or brass hammers are useful to drive arbors or collets into the spindle, and seat work in a jig or vise. A steel hammer should not be used for these purposes, as it will mar pieces. Short lengths of gas piping with a cap on the protruding end make good handles for lead hammers.

A bar of brass or copper, 3/4 inch in diameter and five or six inches long, will also be found useful to place against end mills, or the end of small collets after the mills are in place. In this way the driving is often more conveniently done, and any hammer may be used.

TYPICAL MILLING OPERATIONS

In the illustrations of milling operations given upon the following pages, it should be understood that we have not attempted in every case to show how a job should be rigged up for commercial manufacturing, as special fixtures designed solely for certain operations are then employed. Our object is simply to show the novice how any number of jobs he is likely to meet with daily can be best set up. If it is a question of performing the same operation continuously, special fixtures, by use of which the work can be more conveniently and quickly handled, can be designed.

Milling a Slot in a Cylindrical Part

In the illustration above, the work is a cylindrical piece of steel in which a tangent slot is to be milled. The work is held in a standard vise which has specially shaped jaws. These jaws are quickly and economically made for the particular job and hold the piece very firmly. A staggered tooth milling cutter is used which gives a good finish and at the same time permits using coarse feeds.

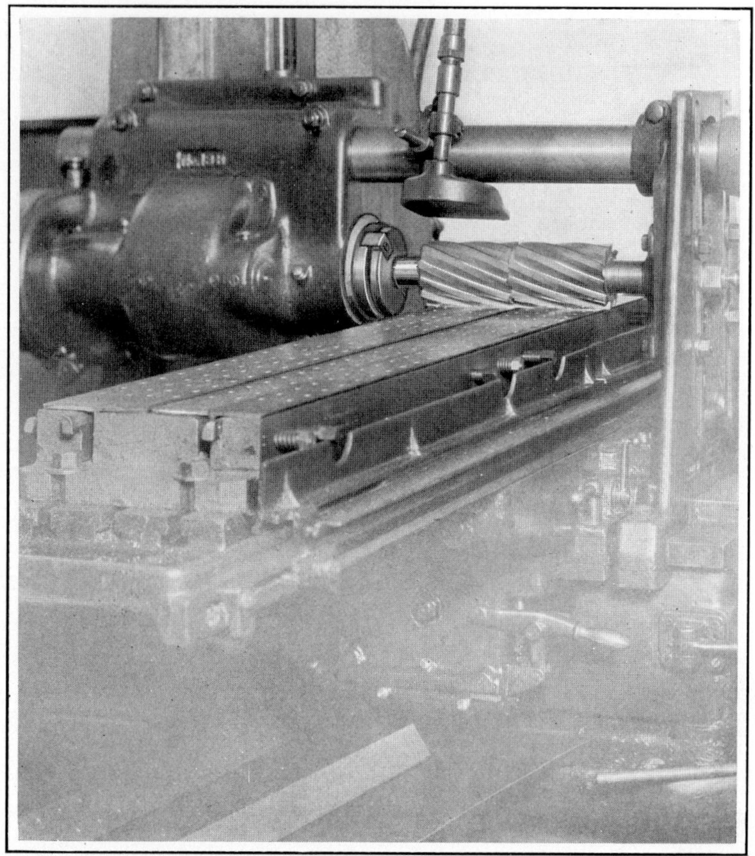

Slab Milling

This type of job is one of the most often met with in milling work. Often the piece can be clamped directly to the table, or as in this case simple fixtures are used to hold it rigidly. In milling the angle irons shown above, it was necessary to support them to prevent springing under the cut. The fixture used is a simple cast iron block with two slots through the center and provided with suitable clamping screws. Four pieces can be milled at one pass of the cutters.

Because of the width of cut, two Spiral Milling Cutters are mounted on the arbor as near as possible to the spindle nose.

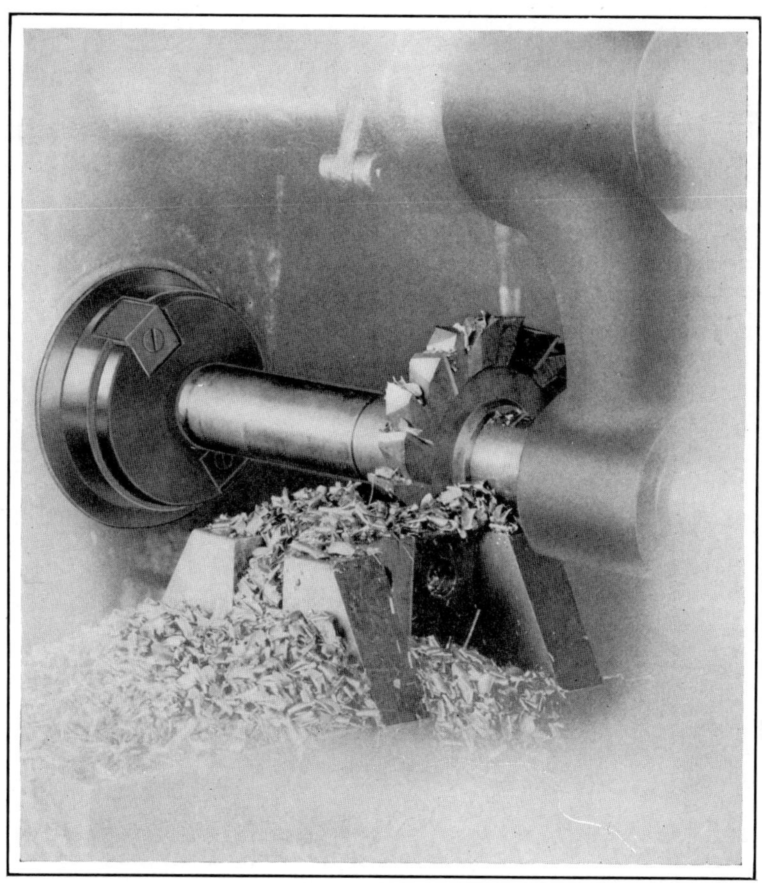

Making a Deep Slot

The piece shown above is a block of steel with a turned and threaded shank. This is to be milled out to form a yoke. The work is placed in a standard vise having special jaws to securely clamp and support the work.

A staggered tooth side milling cutter is used and it takes a cut $1\frac{1}{8}''$ wide and $2''$ deep. This type of cutter is remarkably efficient on work of this kind.

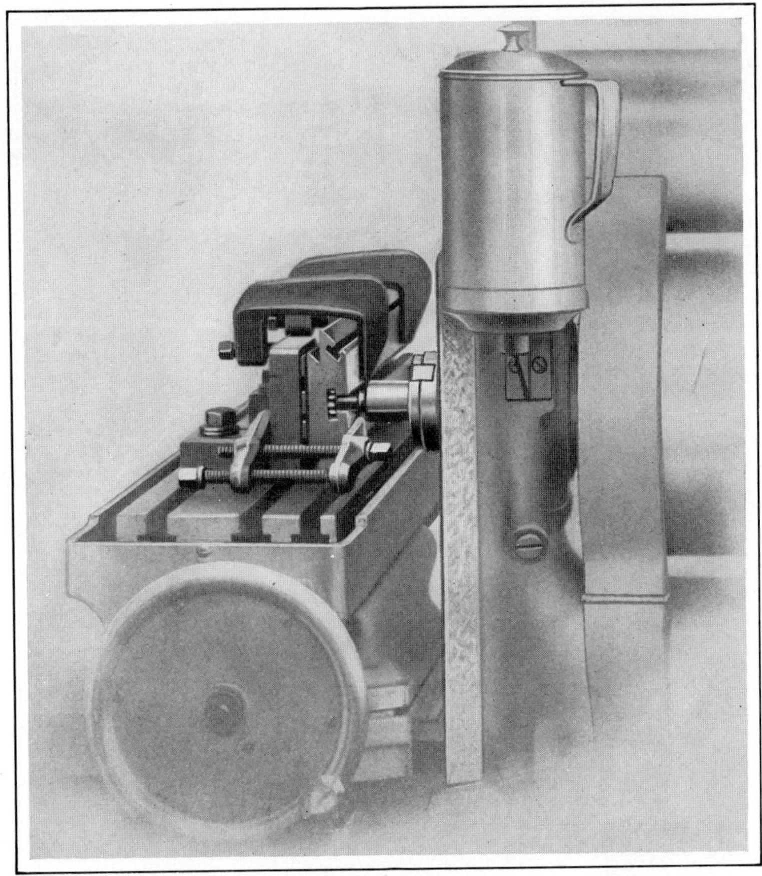

Milling T Slot in a Table

Milling a T slot consists, as we have already explained in Chapter VI, of two separate operations. A straight slot is first milled to the full depth with a plain milling cutter, which is 1/2″ wide in this case. The work is then turned on edge and clamped to knees so that it is square with the spindle. It is leveled by means of a surface gauge or height gauge, measuring from the straight slot to the top of the table.

A standard 1/2″ T slot cutter is used, and the table is fed longitudinally in the path of the straight slot.

This job can be done to good advantage on a vertical spindle machine, or with a vertical spindle attachment, using a two-lipped end mill and T slot cutter.

Milling Steel Block for Parallel Sides

This operation is, apparently, simple enough, but care must be exercised if accuracy is required. The piece is supported on parallels and clamped in a vise. In fastening it one must be careful to be sure that there are no particles of dirt or chips between the parallels and bottom of piece, and that it is tamped down so that it seats properly when the vise is firmly clamped.

A helical cutter is used as this is better where considerable stock is to be taken off. A plain milling cutter with spiral teeth would be used where a finished surface is desired.

The table is fed longitudinally, and it should be noted the arbor should be supported as ruggedly as possible.

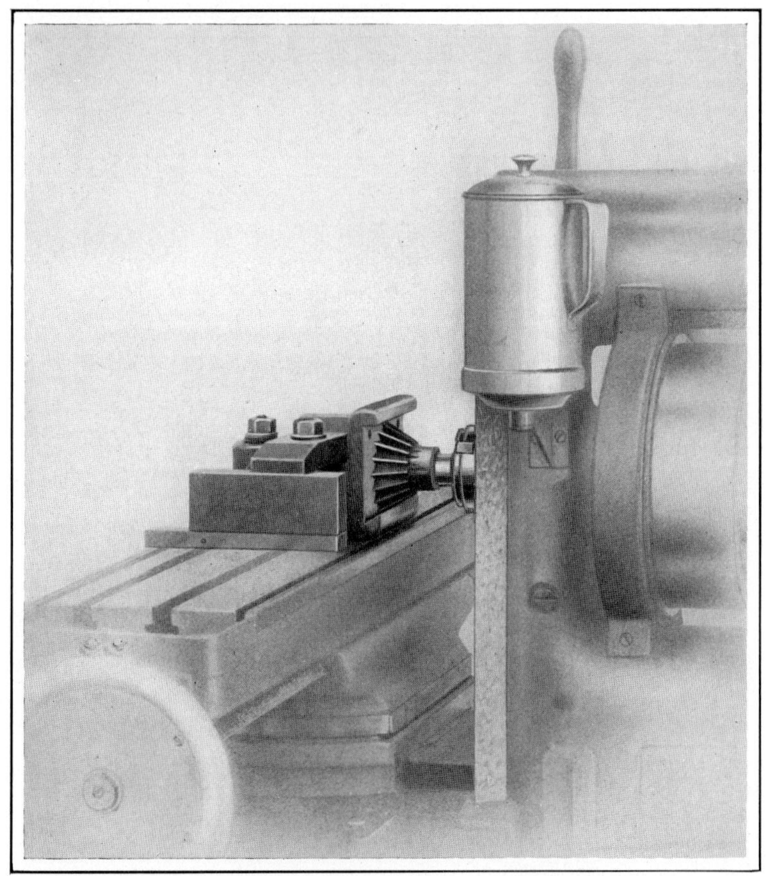

Milling Seat on Bottom of Bracket

The flat surface and V on a bracket can be milled in the manner shown in this cut. The bracket illustrated is of cast iron, and is clamped to the table by a bolt passing through a hole at the outer end of the casting, and a strap and bolt near the middle of the piece.

A 60° angular cutter is used and the table is fed longitudinally. A smaller cutter of the same angle can be used, but it will require several cuts to finish the piece.

This job, and others of a similar character, can also be done to good advantage on a vertical spindle milling machine or a horizontal machine fitted with a vertical spindle attachment.

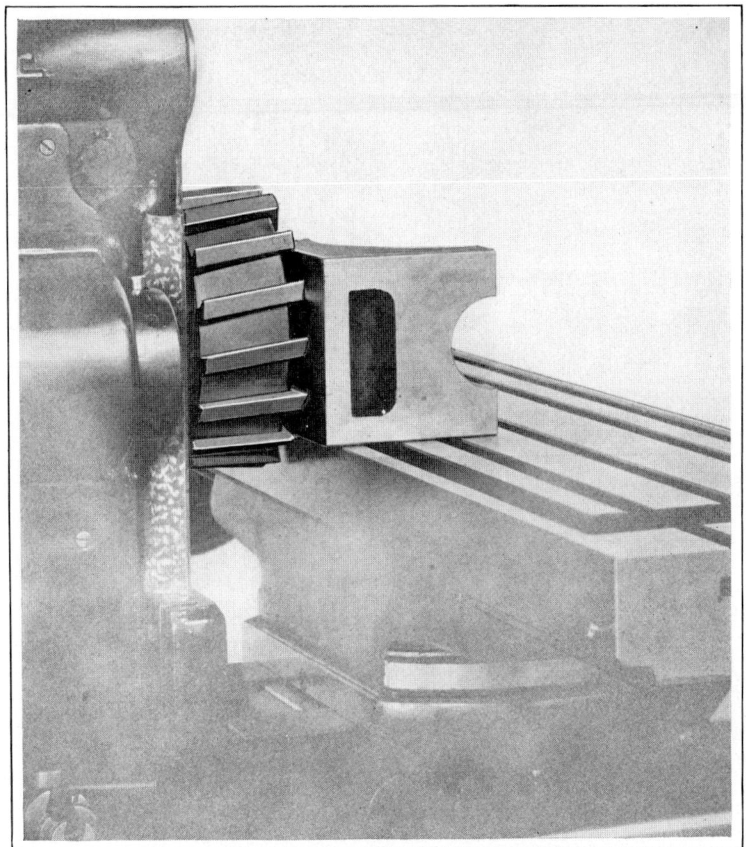

Face Milling Surface of Casting

This operation illustrates the use of a face milling cutter with inserted teeth for surfacing a piece of work.

The piece, which is of cast iron, is clamped to a knee to keep it square with the spindle. A strap in front prevents it being pushed away from the cutter, toward which there is a strong tendency.

The cutter is mounted directly on the nose of the spindle, and, in feeding, the work is moved longitudinally from right to left, or so as to force the work down against the table, rather than raise it. Only one cut is taken over the surface.

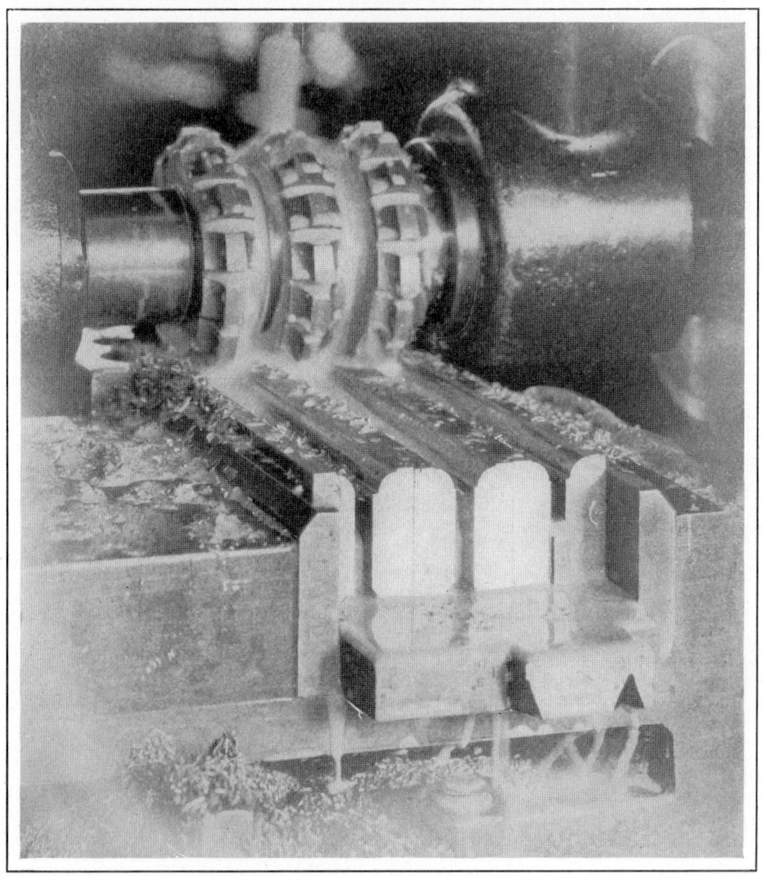

Form Milling Operation

When it is desired to mill the outline of work of this type, several pieces may often be completed at once. Six plates are placed in an ordinary vise with suitable spacing plates and the corner of each piece is removed. After one side has been milled the plates may be turned over and the opposite corner removed. As shown in the illustration plenty of cutter lubricant should be used on cuts in steel.

Outlines of quite elaborate shape can be cut by this method when special cutters made to the desired outline are used.

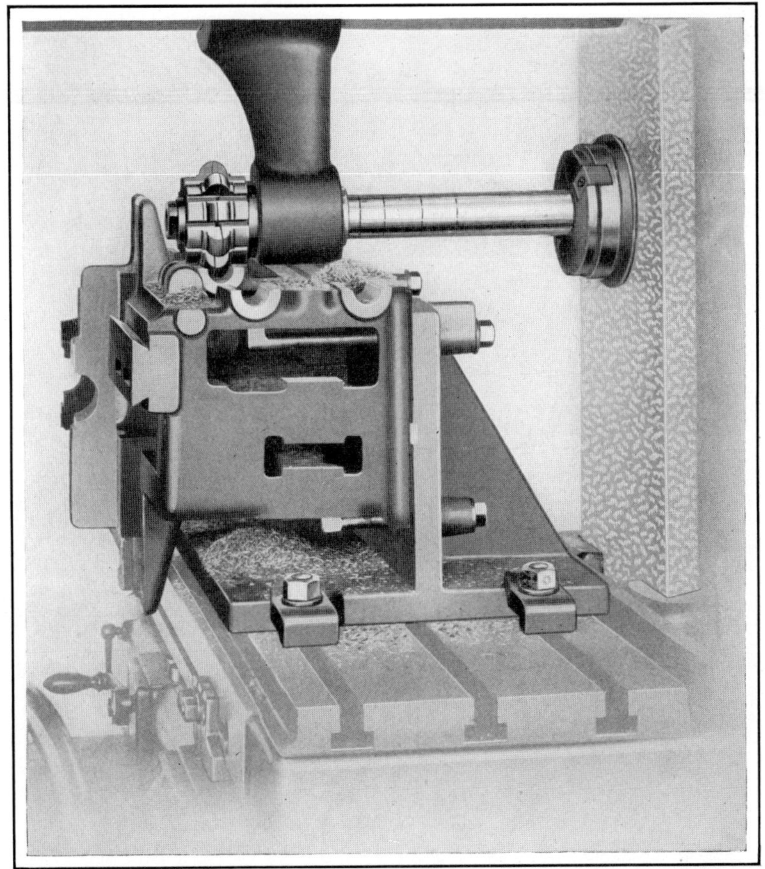

Milling Bearings

It is the usual practice to put the caps on bearings, and bore them out, but this operation shows how bearings can be milled to good advantage. The caps can be milled at another operation so accurately that it is only necessary to pass a reamer through the bearings after the caps are put on to line them up exactly.

The cutter is made in two parts that are interlocking, and thin washers may be packed between to maintain the correct diameter.

It should also be noted that the cutter has to be located at the end of the arbor because of the high projection on the casting.

Surfacing Top and Sides of a Steel Block

The possibility of milling the deep sides of a piece and at the same time surfacing the top is illustrated in the above cut. A special clamp is used to hold the piece while the thrust is taken by a block bolted to the table T slots. The special clamp is provided with a spring to hold the clamp up out of the way after loosening the clamping nut when a piece is completed.

Only one piece can be milled at a time owing to the distance it takes for the large cutters to clear the work at the beginning and end of the cut.

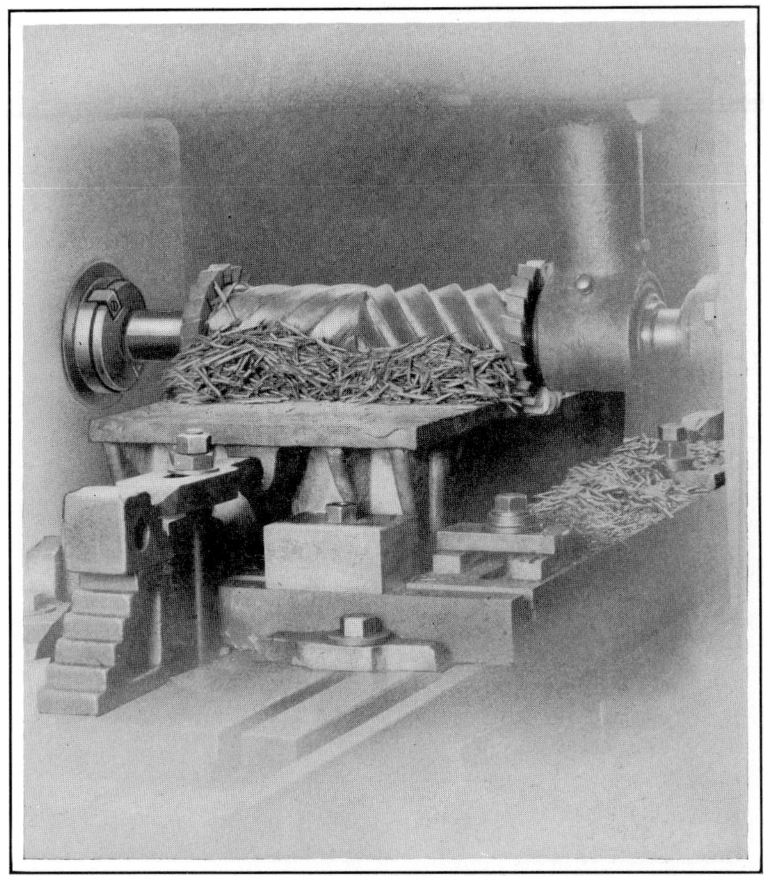

Surfacing the Bottom and Sides of a Heavy Casting

The possibility of simultaneously milling three surfaces of a casting is shown in the illustration. The casting is securely clamped to the milling machine table and blocks are bolted to the T slots so there is no danger of the work creeping under the exceedingly heavy cut.

Two opposed helical milling cutters and two single-side side milling cutters are used with a table feed of 16″ per minute and take a cut averaging 1/8″ in depth.

As may be noted the cutter arbor should be supported as near the cutters as is possible.

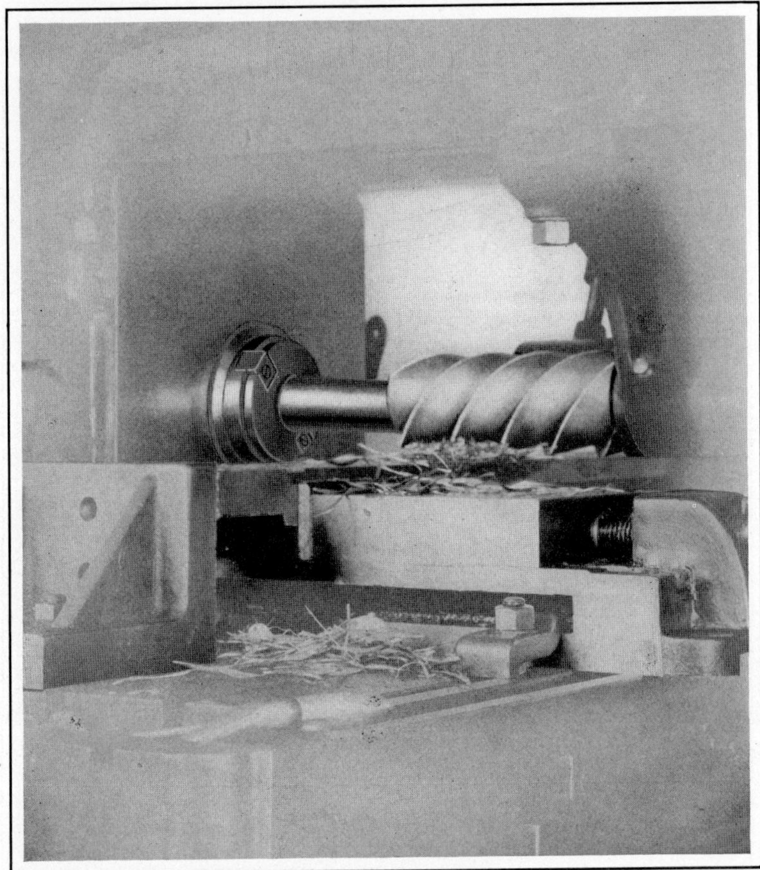

Slab Milling on a Heavy Steel Part

On this operation, a large steel gib had to be finished accurately. A standard vise was used, placed at right angles to the table and securely bolted to it. The right-hand end of the piece is similarly supported in a vise although this is not shown in the illustration. As the thrust of the cutters cannot be taken by the vises alone, a cast iron knee is securely fastened to the table at the end of the piece. The helical milling cutter is placed as near the spindle as possible and by using plenty of cutter lubricant, this heavy plain slabbing cut can be taken with a good finish.

Cutting Slots in Circular Milling Attachment Table

Three parallel slots are cut in the top of this table by spacing three cutters on the arbor by means of collars.

Considerable power is required for the operation, as the slots are cut from solid stock to the depth of 7/8 of an inch, and 9/16 of an inch wide.

Specially shaped straps are necessary to fasten the work to the table, in order to make use of cutters of small diameter.

The cutters employed are regular stocking cutters 6″ in diameter, and are rigidly supported on the arbor.

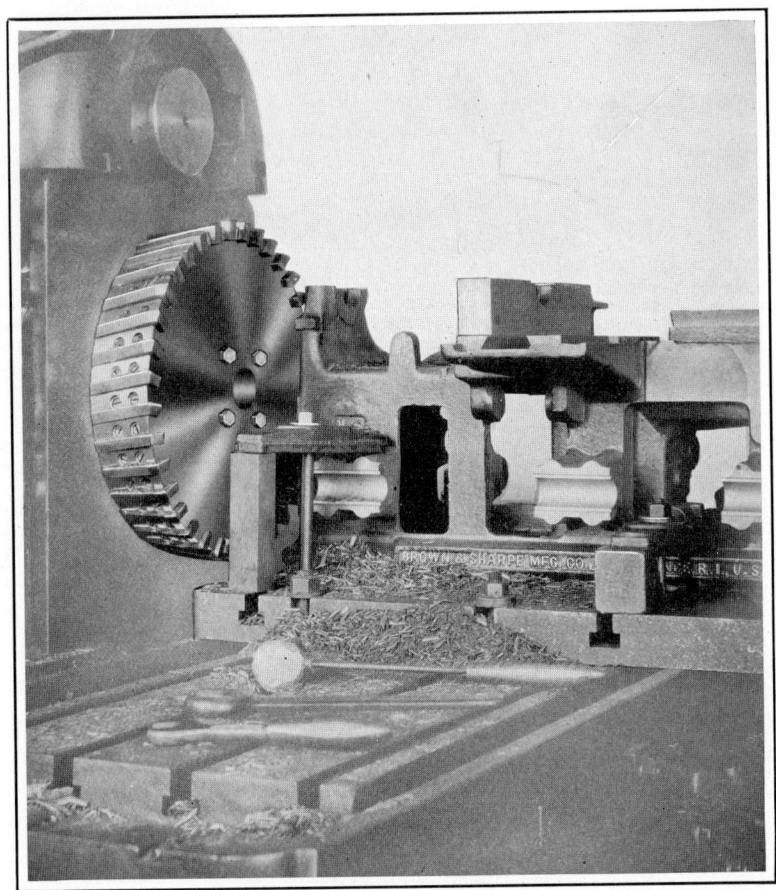

Large Face Milling Operation

Jobs similar to this are done on the planer in many shops, but by setting up the work as shown it is often possible to get a greater production on a milling machine. As this is a production job the casting is placed in a frame constructed for the particular piece and securely clamped. A frame of this type assures accurate duplication of the work and on long runs will pay for itself in time-saving. This piece could be milled by clamping to the table directly. In that case, straps would be used on either side to hold the piece on the table and stops would be placed in the table T slots to prevent slipping of the casting.

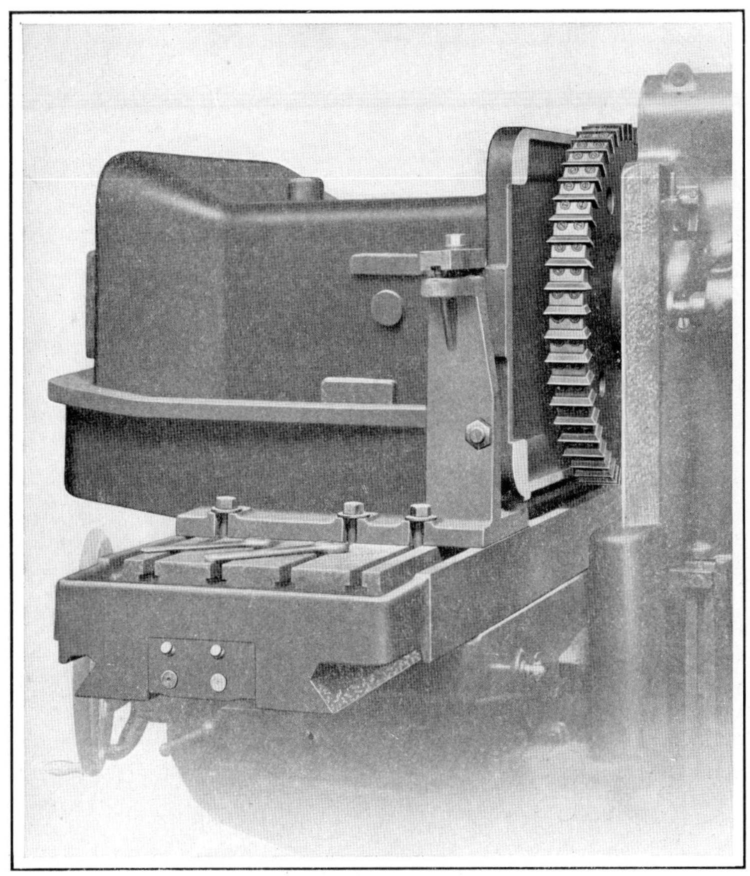

Surfacing Bottom of Screw Machine Bed

This illustration shows the possibilities of the milling machine for doing work that might be termed in many shops as suitable for the planer only.

The extreme weight, large size and powerful leverage due to the large overhang of the piece, are all factors that serve to make this an unusual milling job that requires a rigid machine.

The work and fixture together weigh over 1000 pounds, and the piece as it is fastened to the table is 25″ high, and extends 35″ out from the cutter.

Another unusual point is the size of the inserted tooth face milling cutter, which is 26″ in diameter.

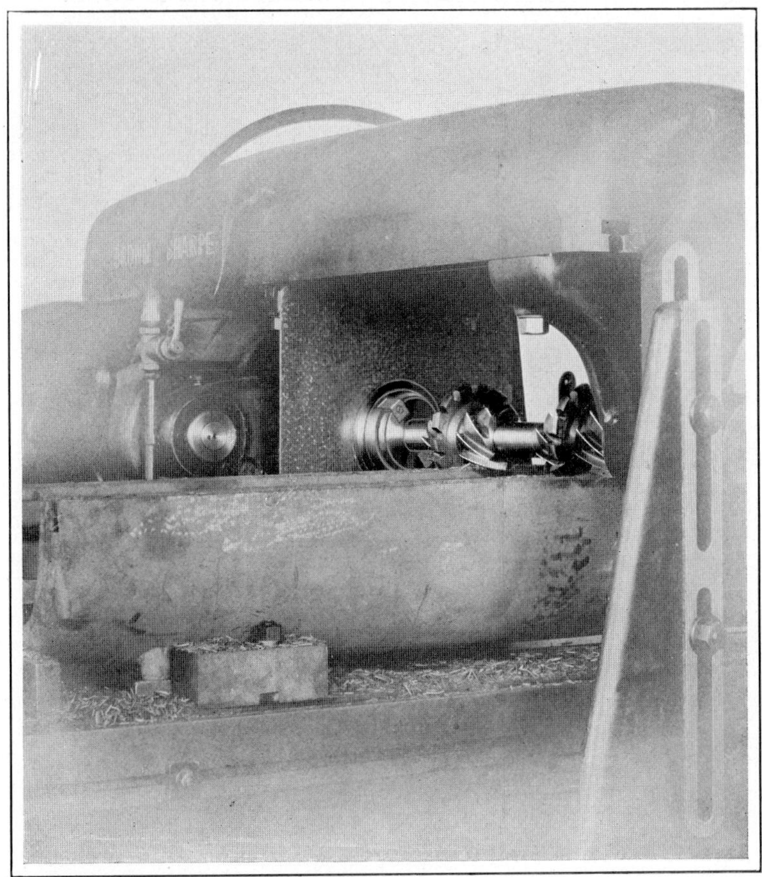

Gang Milling

On production work and where interchangeability is necessary, parts can be advantageously milled by using stock or special cutters in the manner shown above. In this particular case a fairly deep slot is cut in either side of the casting and the two pairs of smaller cutters finish the surface on either side of the slots. It is interesting to note the method of holding the work. Formed blocks are clamped to the table and two bosses are cast on the piece for leveling on the machine table. These are afterward cut off.

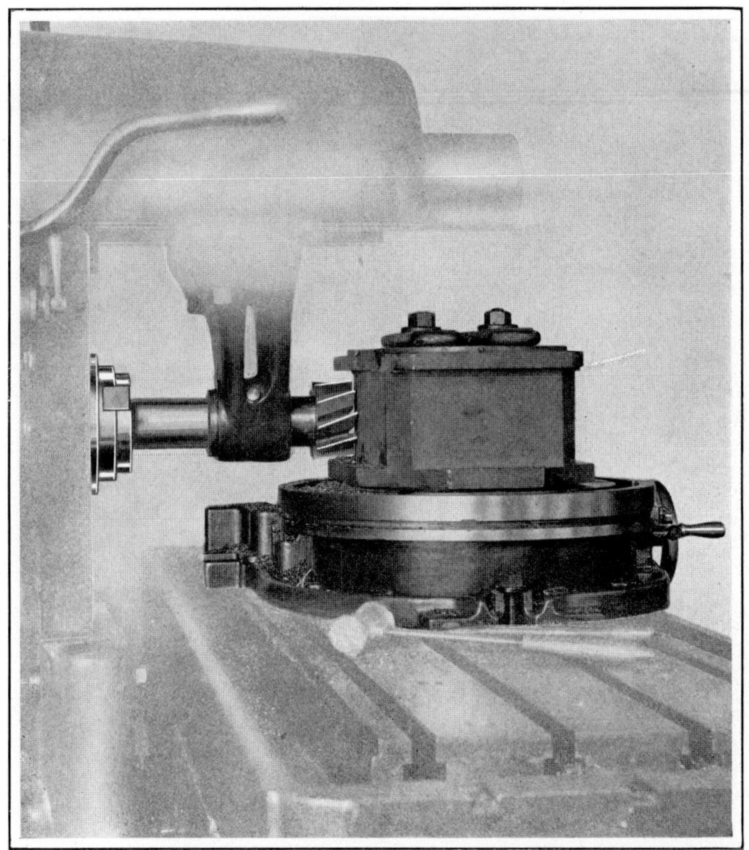

Surfacing Four Sides of a Casting

This casting has to be finished on four sides all exactly at right angles to each other. The lips on each side of the finished surface also have to be accurately milled. These operations are done without removing the piece from its original position by the use of a circular milling attachment and a shell end mill which is rigidly held on an arbor.

One cut is taken to mill part of the vertical surface and the lower lip. The machine table is dropped the correct amount and the upper part of the vertical surface and the upper lip is finished. The table of the circular milling attachment is then rotated 90° and these operations are repeated.

This method saves much labor in setting up and the finished piece is very accurate.

Cutting Two Grooves in Six Steel Cores at One Traverse

This illustration shows an unusually heavy milling operation, consisting of cutting two grooves, each 1.17″ wide and 5/16″ deep, in six steel forgings at one traverse of the table.

Three sets of index centres of a special design are employed, and two steel cores are mounted on the arbor on each pair of centres.

The cutters are of a special form to cut two grooves and the top of the intervening space between the grooves.

For such a cut as this, a large arbor is required, and it must be very rigidly supported; intermediate arbor yokes are, therefore, placed between the cutters.

Lard oil is used as a cutting lubricant.

Milling a Dovetail in Milling Machine Saddle

The casting is held on a special fixture which has a slide corresponding to the slide on the top of the knee of the milling machine. The piece can be removed by simply loosening the gib.

The top plate of the fixture also swivels, so that one side of the ways can be milled on an angle for a taper gib. Both operations are, therefore, completed at one setting of the fixture, thus insuring the surfaces being milled in relation to each other. A 50° angular cutter is used for this operation.

Milling the Back of the Teeth on an Inserted Tooth Cutter

The special inserted tooth milling cutter shown above has teeth shaped in the segment of a circle. The operation is to mill off the back corners of the teeth so as to give relief.

An angular cutter is placed on an arbor in the spindle of a vertical spindle milling machine. The work is placed on the spiral head which in turn is mounted on a circular milling attachment. The work is fed to the cutter by merely rotating the circular milling attachment.

The whole secret in this job is to have the distance between the centres of the machine spindle and circular milling attachment exactly the same as the radius of the cutter tooth. The spiral head is used to index the work from one tooth to the next.

Cutting a Circular T Slot in Universal Milling Machine Saddle

The operation shown above illustrates another excellent example of the use of the circular milling attachment in connection with a vertical spindle milling machine, for cutting the circular T slot in the saddle of a universal milling machine.

The piece of work is centred by placing it over a stud and bushing inserted in the hole in the centre of the circular attachment table. It is prevented from swinging by four bolts with washers, two of which are shown, and a strap from a stepped block across to the casting on each side fastens it to the table.

The first, or plain, slot is cut out on a boring mill or can be milled at the same setting shown above, using a two-lipped end mill, which is then replaced by the T slot cutter.

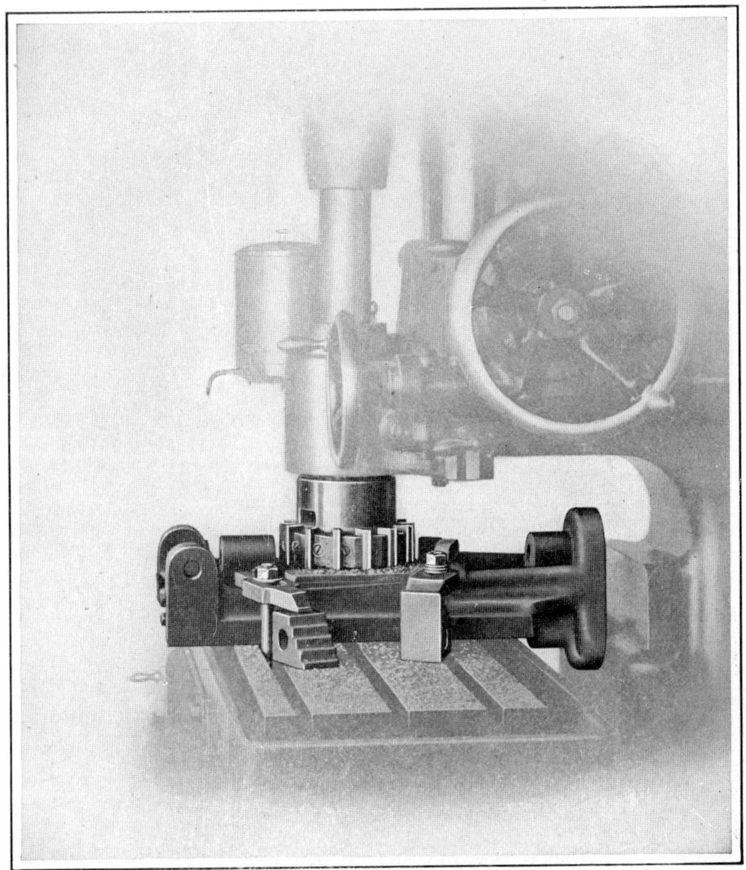

Milling a Plain Surface

It is advisable in milling castings, such as that shown, to do the work on a vertical spindle machine, as it is much more convenient. If a horizontal spindle machine is employed, and the work is clamped to the table, plain cutters of unusually large diameter are required, and when a face milling cutter is used, the work must be clamped to a knee. This, too, is unhandy when the casting is somewhat unwieldy.

The piece of work illustrated is of cast iron, and it is fastened directly to the surface of the table by means of straps extending from step blocks to the casting and secured in place by bolts set in the table T slots.

The face mill employed has inserted teeth. The table may be fed longitudinally in either direction.

Milling Grooves in Rim of Pulley

Here a vertical spindle machine equipped with a circular milling attachment is shown milling belt grooves in the rim of a three step pulley.

The pulley is easily fastened in place and a continuous cut is taken around the rim, using the automatic feed of the attachment. The knee is then lowered to bring the cutter at the right height for the next smaller step and the table is moved longitudinally to get the correct depth of cut. This operation is repeated for the smallest step and the piece is finished.

This operation can also be done on a horizontal milling machine when equipped with both vertical spindle and circular milling attachments.

Face Milling with a Vertical Spindle Attachment on a Horizontal Spindle Milling Machine

It will be seen from the above cut that in shops where the volume of work does not warrant installing a vertical spindle milling machine the operations that would generally be done on that machine can be done on a horizontal machine equipped with a vertical spindle attachment.

The operation shown is milling cast iron pieces rigidly held in vises having special jaws. Ordinarily, only one vise would be used to hold the work but in this case the machine is a small automatic and the operator can load one piece while the other is being milled.

CHAPTER VIII

Milling Operations — Gear Cutting

We do not propose in this chapter to go deeply into the subject of gearing, for it would be impossible to properly treat it in so limited a space. Neither do we intend to describe the manner in which gears are cut on automatic gear cutting machines designed especially for that purpose. Our object is rather to give a few practical points applying to the cutting of different kinds of gears on a milling machine, and to show illustrations of how various gear cutting jobs and work of a kindred nature can be set up. Anyone desirous of making a detailed study of gears is referred to the many books now published that are devoted exclusively to the subject, among which are our "Practical Treatise on Gearing," and "Formulas in Gearing."

Cutting Spur Gears. The first things that are necessary to know in order to cut a spur gear are the pitch, either diametral or circular, and number of teeth required. These must be had in order to select the correct cutter to use.

We make eight cutters for each pitch, as follows:

No. 1	cutter will	cut wheels from	135	teeth to	a rack
No. 2	"	"	55	"	134 teeth
No. 3	"	"	35	"	54 "
No. 4	"	"	26	"	34 "
No. 5	"	"	21	"	25 "
No. 6	"	"	17	"	20 "
No. 7	"	"	14	"	16 "
No. 8	"	" with	12	" and	13 "

For those who require a finer division of the number of teeth to be cut with each cutter than can be cut with the regular numbers listed above, we can furnish half numbers in cutters from 2 to 8 pitch inclusive, as follows:

No. 1½	cutter will	cut wheels	from 80	teeth to	134	teeth
No. 2½	"	"	" 42	"	54	"
No. 3½	"	"	" 30	"	34	"
No. 4½	"	"	" 23	"	25	"
No. 5½	"	"	with 19	" and	20	"
No. 6½	"	"	" 15	"	" 16	"
No. 7½	"	"	" 13	"		

Care should be exercised that the teeth of a cutter selected are ground radially and equidistant, for the teeth are so formed that unless ground in this manner, the correct shape is not produced in the work.

If a universal milling machine is employed, the table should be set at exact right angles to the arbor by the graduations on the saddle. This precaution does not have to be taken on plain machines, as the table is fixed at right angles to the spindle or arbor.

Set Cutter Central. It is essential that the cutter be exactly central with the axis of the gear blank, especially when the gear is to be run fast, otherwise the gear will be cut " off centre," and will run more noisily in one direction than in the other. It may be set centrally as follows: Set the table or the cutter on the arbor as nearly as possible in position; fasten the gear blank, or preferably an odd blank of about the size of the gear to be cut, on an arbor and lock it in position on the centres. Take a single cut, then remove the blank from the arbor, turn it end for end and put it back on. Permit the blank to remain loose on the arbor, and see if the cutter will pass through the groove already cut without taking any stock off on either side. If the cutter is not exactly central, stock will be cut from the upper part of one side of the groove and from the lower part of the opposite side of the groove. If this is found to be the case, the table can be slightly adjusted to compensate for the error and another trial cut taken.

Some of the gear cutters made by us have a line on the tops of the teeth that is central with the form, and for ordinary slow running gears, the cutter may be centred by bringing this line to coincide with the centre in the spiral head- or foot-stock.

Measure Blanks. Measure all gear blanks carefully. It is impossible to cut correct running gears from blanks that are of the wrong diameter unless the error is small. The amount of error allowable in the diameter depends upon the pitch of the gear; the heavier the pitch, the greater the allowable error. It is better to return to the lathe any blanks that are oversize and throw away those that are turned very much undersize. If blanks are only slightly undersize, they can be cut by making allowance for the error in setting for depth of teeth, and the resultant gears will run satisfactorily, though not perfectly.

Secure Blank on Arbor. The next important step is to see that the work arbor runs true and that the blank does not spring it when forced or tightened. A good method of holding blanks is on arbors, such as our milling machine cutter arbors, that have a taper shank to fit the index spindle, the outer end of the arbor being supported by the foot-stock centre. Another way of holding blanks is by means of a shank arbor with expanding bushing, such as our gear cutting machine " work arbors." A nut is located on the arbor at each end of the bushing, one nut forcing the bushing up on the arbor and holding the blank, while the other pushes the bushing off the taper and releases the gear when finished.

If a common arbor and dog are used, care should be taken that the tail of the dog is fastened between the set screws provided on the spiral head, so there will be no backlash between the index spindle and work; also see that the dog does not spring the arbor when it is clamped.

Set Knee for Depth of Cut. The depth of cut is regulated by the height of the knee of the machine. To make this setting, the knee is brought up until the cutter just touches the blank. Then the blank is moved out from under the cutter and the knee is raised the number of thousandths of an inch required for the depth of tooth, which can be ascertained from the tables on pages 323 to 326, or by dividing the constant 2.157 by the diametral pitch.

When raising the knee, use the graduated dial on the vertical hand feed screw for a guide to get the required depth, but be sure to take out any backlash that may exist before making an adjustment.

Testing for Correct Depth. To make certain that the depth of groove cut is correct and the size of teeth accurate, cut two grooves into the face of the blank far enough so that the full form of the tooth is produced, and then measure the resultant tooth at the pitch line for thickness and the depth of the tooth to the pitch line. The correct thicknesses of spur gear teeth of different pitches at the pitch line are given in the tables on pages 323 to 326, or can be found by dividing the constant 1.57 by the diametral pitch.

By cutting only part way across the face of the blank the trial grooves can be quickly made and measured. If, on the other hand, the grooves are cut across the full width of the face, there is liability, under some conditions, of more stock being taken from these grooves when the actual cutting is commenced and the cutter is allowed to pass through the same grooves a second time, thus making these grooves too deep.

Chordal Thickness of Gear Teeth. When accurate measurements of gear teeth are required, it is necessary to work to the chordal

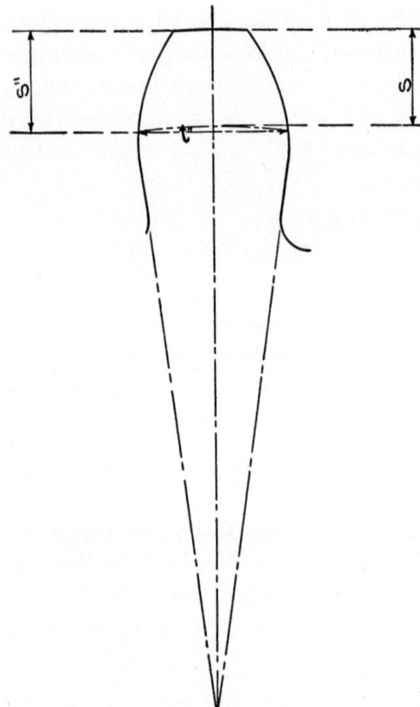

Fig. 61

figures, t'' = thickness of tooth and s'' = distance from chord t'' to top of tooth (see Fig. 61).

These dimensions vary from the standard dimensions of tooth parts shown on pages 323 to 326. The fewer the number of teeth in the gear, the greater the variation.

The Table of Chordal Thickness t'' and Distances from Chord to top of Tooth s'' on page 325 gives these dimensions for gears of 1 diametral pitch. To obtain t'' and s'' for any diametral pitch, divide the figures given in the table opposite the required number of teeth by the required diametral pitch.

Example: Find t'' and s'' for a gear 5 diametral pitch, 23 teeth.

$1.5696 \div 5 = .3139 = t''$.
$1.0268 \div 5 = .2054 = s''$.

To obtain t'' and s'' for any circular pitch, multiply the figures given in the table opposite the required number of teeth, by the addendum s (taking s from the Table of Tooth Parts, pages 323 and 324).

Example: Find t'' and s'' for a 3/4'' circular pitch gear, 15 teeth.

$1.5679 \times .2387 = .3743 = t''$.
$1.0411 \times .2387 = .2485 = s''$.

If number of teeth required is not shown in table, take the nearest number of teeth.

An accurate and convenient tool for taking the measurements of gear teeth is shown in Fig. 62. With this gear tooth vernier, the distance from the top of the teeth to the pitch line, and thickness at the pitch line, can be accurately determined.

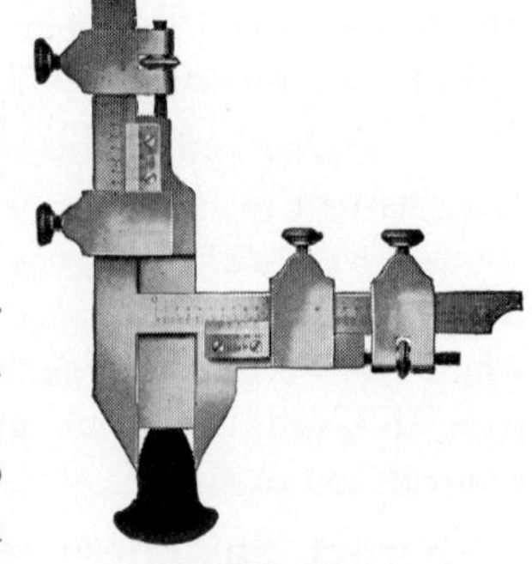
Fig. 62

Another tool, Vernier Caliper, No. 573, by use of which the bottom diameter of the teeth may be accurately measured to determine the depth of grooves, is shown in Fig. 63.

The depth of grooves may be ascertained when there are an even number of teeth by cutting two grooves opposite each other on the circumference of the blank and calipering the diameter from the bottom of the grooves, then computing the depth. When the number of teeth is uneven cut one groove and caliper the diameter from the bottom of the groove to the opposite side of the blank. In this last case be sure that the blank is of the correct diameter and runs true, otherwise the measurement will not be correct, unless allowance is made for these points.

Indexing. Indexing gear blanks is essentially the same as indexing any other work, and the instructions in Chapter IV are complete on

Fig. 63

this subject; therefore it is unnecessary to make any additional remarks here upon this point.

Cutting Two or More Gears Simultaneously. If the holes in the blanks are straight, and the hubs do not project beyond the face, a number of blanks may be fastened together on a gang arbor and several gears cut at a time. Care should be taken, however, if this is done, to see that the sides of the blanks are exactly parallel, otherwise when the arbor nut is clamped, the blanks will spring the arbor, causing it to run out and making it impossible to produce accurate gears.

Cutting Bevel Gears. The teeth of bevel gears constantly change in pitch from their large to small end, and for this reason it is impossible to cut gears whose tooth curves are theoretically correct, with rotary cutters having fixed curves, such as those used for cutting these gears on a milling machine. The cutter employed must be of a curve that will make the correct form at the large end of the tooth, hence it will necessarily leave the curve too straight at the small end. It is, therefore, the practice to cut the teeth as nearly correct as possible, and then finish the gears by hand, filing the small ends of the teeth to get the correct curve.

Pitch of Bevel Gear. The pitch of a bevel gear is always considered as that at the largest end of the teeth.

Data Required to Cut Bevel Gears with Rotary Cutter. Pitch and number of teeth in each gear.

The whole depth of tooth spaces at both large and small ends of teeth.

The thickness of teeth at both ends.

The height of teeth above the pitch line at both ends.

The cutting angle; the angle to set spiral head on milling machine, and the proper cutter or cutters.

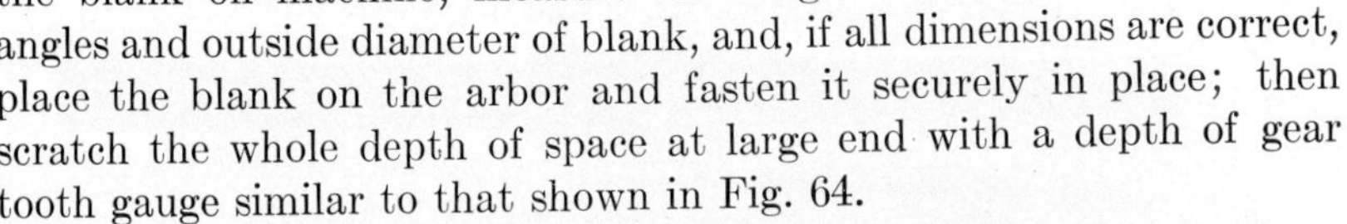

Fig. 64

Scratch Depth Line on Blank. Before placing the blank on machine, measure the length of face, angles and outside diameter of blank, and, if all dimensions are correct, place the blank on the arbor and fasten it securely in place; then scratch the whole depth of space at large end with a depth of gear tooth gauge similar to that shown in Fig. 64.

Selection of Cutter for Bevel Gears. The length of teeth or face on bevel gears is not ordinarily more than one-third the apex distance, *Ab*, Fig. 65, and cutters usually carried in stock are suitable for this face. If the face is longer than one-third the apex distance, special thin cutters must be made.

Rule for Selecting Cutter. Measure the back cone radius *ab* for the gear, or *bc* for the pinion. This is equal to the radius of a spur gear, the number of teeth in which would determine the cutter to use. Hence twice *ab* times the diametral pitch equals the number of teeth for which the cutter should be selected for the gear. Looking in the list given on page 141, the proper number for the cutter can be found.

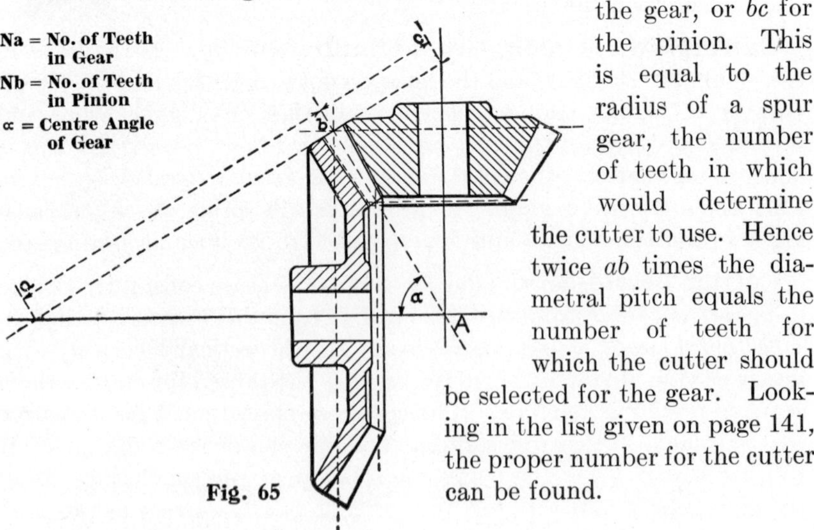

Fig. 65

Thus, let the back cone radius *ab* be 4″ and the diametral pitch be 8. Twice four is 8, and 8 × 8 is 64, from which it can be seen that the cutter must be of Shape No. 2, as 64 is between 55 and 134, the range covered by a No. 2 cutter.

The number of teeth for which the cutter should be selected can also be found by the following formula:

$$\text{Tan } \alpha = \frac{Na}{Nb}$$

$$\text{No. of teeth to select cutter for gear} = \frac{Na}{\text{Cos } \alpha}$$

$$\text{No. of teeth to select cutter for pinion} = \frac{Nb}{\text{Sin } \alpha}$$

If the gears are mitres or are alike, only one cutter is needed; if one gear is larger than the other, two may be needed.

Setting Cutter out of Centre. As the cutter cannot be any thicker than the width of space at small end of teeth, it is necessary to set it out of centre and rotate the blank to make the spaces of the right width at the large end of the teeth.

The amount to set cutter out of centre can be calculated with the table on page 328 and the following formula:

$$\text{Set-over} = \frac{Tc}{2} - \frac{\text{factor from table}}{P}$$

P = diametral pitch of gear to be cut.

Tc = thickness of cutter used, measured at pitch line.

Given as a rule, this would read: Find the factor in the table corresponding to the number of the cutter used and to the ratio of apex distance to width of face; divide this factor by the diametral pitch and subtract the quotient from half of the thickness of the cutter at the pitch line.

As an illustration of the use of this table in obtaining the set-over, take the following example: A bevel gear of 24 teeth, 6 pitch, 30 degrees pitch cone angle and 1 1/4″ face. These dimensions call for a No. 4 cutter and an apex distance of 4 inches.

In order to get the factor from the table, the ratio of apex distance with length of face must be known. This ratio is $\frac{4}{1.25} = \frac{3.2}{1}$, or about $\frac{3\frac{1}{4}}{1}$. The factor in the table for this ratio with a No. 4 cutter is 0.280. Next, measure the cutter at the pitch line. To do this, refer to the regular "Table of Tooth Parts" on pages 325 and 326, and get the depth of space below pitch line $s + f$. This depth of space below pitch line can also be found by dividing 1.157 by the diametral pitch. In the case of 6 pitch $s + f = 0.1928''$. The thickness of the cutter at the pitch line is then found to be 0.1745″. This dimension will vary with different cutters, and will vary in the same cutter as it is ground away, since formed bevel gear cutters are commonly provided with side relief. Substituting these values in the formula, the following result is obtained:

Set-over $= \frac{0.1745}{2} - \frac{0.280}{6} = 0.0406''$, which is the required dimension.

After selecting a cutter and determining how much to set it out of centre, proceed as follows:

Set the cutter central with the spiral head or universal index head spindle, as the machine may be equipped.

Set the head to the proper cutting angle.

Set the index head for the number of teeth to be cut, placing the sector on the straight row of holes that are numbered to start with.

Set the dial on the cross feed screw to the zero line.

Scratch the depth of both the large and small end of the tooth to be cut in the blank.

Index and cut two or three grooves or centre cuts to conform to the lines in depth.

Set the cutter out of centre the trial distance, according to the formula on the previous page, by moving the saddle and noting adjustment on the cross feed screw dial.

Rotate the gear in the opposite direction from that in which the table is moved off centre (Fig. 66), until the side of the cutter nearest the centre line of the gear will cut the entire surfaces of the approaching sides of the teeth.

After making one or more cuts in accordance with this setting, move the table the same distance on the opposite side of the centre and rotate the gear in the opposite direction from that in which the table is moved until the cutter just touches the side of a tooth at the small end and cuts the entire surface of this side the same as the other.

Cut one or more spaces and measure the teeth at both large and small ends, either with a gear tooth vernier or with gauges made from thin pieces of metal and having a slot cut to give the correct depth and width at the pitch line.

If the teeth at the large end are too thick when the small end is correct, the amount to set the table out of centre must be increased.

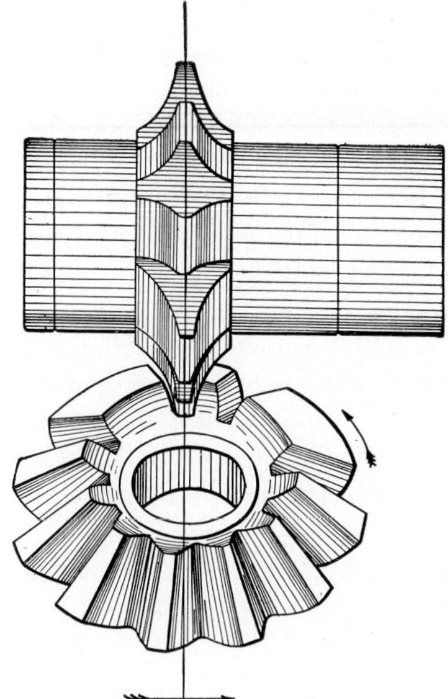

Fig. 66

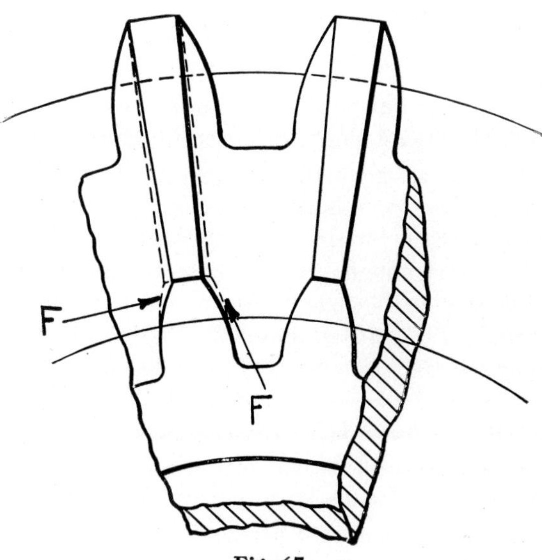

Fig. 67

On the other hand, if the small end is too thick when the large end is correct, the amount the table is set out of centre is too great. In either case, the settings must be changed, and the operations of cutting repeated, remembering that the blank must be rotated and the table moved the same amount each side of centre, otherwise the teeth will not be central. It is well to bear in mind that too much out of centre leaves the small end proportionately too thick, and too little out of centre leaves the small end too thin.

The adjustment of the cutter and the rotating of the blank are shown in Fig. 66, which shows the setting, so that the right side of cutter will trim the left side of tooth and widen the large end of the space. The table has been moved to the right and the blank brought to the position shown, by rotating it in the direction of the arrow; the first out of centre cut was taken when the cutter was set on the other side of the centre.

After determining the proper amount to set cutter out of centre, the teeth can be finished, without making a central cut, by cutting round the blank with the cutter set out of centre, first on one side and then on the other.

To prevent the teeth being too thin at either end, it is important, after cutting once around the blank with cutter out of centre, to give careful attention to the rotative adjustment of the gear blank, when setting the cutter for trimming the opposite sides of the teeth. If by measurement, both ends are a little too thick, but proportionately right, rotate the gear blank and make trial cuts until one tooth is of the correct thickness at both ends. The cutting can then be continued until the gear is finished. Teeth of incorrect thickness may be more objectionable than a slight variation in depth.

The finished spaces, or teeth, as already mentioned, are of the correct form at the larger ends, and the teeth are of the correct thickness their entire length, but the tops of the teeth at the small ends are not rounded over enough. It is, therefore, generally necessary to file the faces of the teeth slightly above the pitch line at the small ends, as indicated by the dotted lines *F F*, Fig. 67. In filing the teeth, they should not be reduced any in thickness at or below the pitch line.

When cutting cast iron gears coarser than five diametral pitch, it is best to make one central cut entirely around the blank before attempting to find the correct setting of the cutter or rotation of the blank for correct thickness of teeth; and it is generally advantageous to take a central cut on nearly all bevel gears of steel.

Cutting Spiral Gears. In Chapter IV, we have gone into the subject of cutting spirals thoroughly, and, inasmuch as spiral gears are essentially cylinders having a succession of spiral grooves evenly spaced on their periphery, many of the points we have treated apply equally well to cutting them.

An important point in cutting these gears is the selection of the proper cutters to use. It is impossible to give in concise form any set of rules for doing this that will be readily understood, and anyone who desires to cut spiral gears should make a far more complete study of the subject of spiral gearing than we can possibly give in this book. It is treated upon in our " Practical Treatise on Gearing," and " Formulas in Gearing," both of which books are extremely useful to the practical workman.

One point that it is well to remember is that in calculating spirals, the angle should be figured as that at the pitch line of the teeth, and not that on the surface or periphery of a gear.

Spirals of any angle to 45° can be cut on all of our universal milling machines with the cutter mounted in the regular way, and the swivel table swung to the proper angle, while those of an angle up to 55° with the axis can be cut in some of our universal machines. If, however, the required angle is greater than that to which the table can be set, a vertical spindle milling attachment is required, and the adjustment for the cutting angle is then done with the attachment.

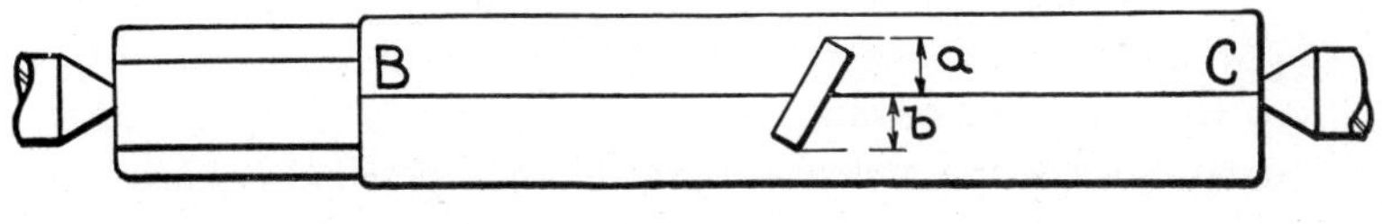

Fig. 68

To Set Cutter Central. It is essential that the cutter be set central with the work centres, and it may be done as follows: First, set the table, or attachment, in case the latter is used, to the correct cutting angle. Take a trial piece, Fig. 68, which is simply a cylindrical piece with centre holes in the ends, and mount it on the work centres, dogging it to the spiral head spindle. Draw or scratch the line *B C* on the side of the arbor at the exact height of the work centres, and then revolve the arbor one-quarter of a turn by means of the index crank; that is, bring the mark *B C* exactly on the top of the piece. Now, start the machine and raise the knee until a gash is cut on the top of the piece. This gash shows the position of the cutter, and if *a* and *b* are equal, the cutter is centred with the trial piece, which will, of course, bring it central with the work.

The same method is employed when using a vertical spindle milling attachment, except the scratched line is left at the side of the piece where it is at the exact height of the centres. The gash is then cut and examined as described above.

Test Settings and Index Gears. Before cutting a blank, it is well to raise the knee until the cutter will just make a slight trace on the work to see if the lead obtained by the change gears is correct. If the material in the gear blank is expensive, it is sometimes advisable to make a cast iron blank to experiment with before cutting into the expensive material.

Fastening Blanks. Spiral gears are more liable to slip in cutting than spur gears. Small blanks may be dogged to the spindle, but the dog must be far enough from the blank so that it will not interfere with the cutter. For blanks that are more than three or four inches in diameter, it is better to use a taper shank arbor held directly in the spindle; and for still heavier work, the arbor may be drawn into the spindle with a threaded rod.

Cutting Teeth. In cutting the teeth, either the cutter should be stopped after cutting each groove and positioned so that the teeth will not scrape the sides and bottom of the groove, the table being returned by hand, or the knee should be dropped so that cutter will clear the groove just cut, and then run the table back to the starting point. Most mechanics prefer to stop the machine, for in dropping the knee, there is more liability of error, as the depth of cut has to be set for each groove, and this also takes more time than it does to stop the machine.

The remaining pages of this chapter are devoted to illustrations and descriptive data of gear cutting and similar operations on milling machines. These operations show how different gear cutting jobs can be set up, and are given simply as suggestions for those not familiar with this class of work.

Cutting a Spur Gear, Using the Spiral Head

Cutting a spur gear on a milling machine is a comparatively simple operation, as can be seen from the illustration. No special rigging whatsoever is required. The blank in this case is fastened on an ordinary lathe arbor mounted on the centres and dogged to the spiral head spindle.

In commercial manufacturing, gears such as that shown would be produced in quantities on automatic gear cutting machines, but where only an occasional gear is wanted, such as in replacing a broken one, it is advantageous to cut it on a milling machine. A new gear for a machine can usually be secured in this manner far quicker than it can be ordered and delivered.

Cutting a Large Spur Gear, Using 16″ Plain Index Centres

This operation shows the use of the Plain Index Centres described in Chapter V. The gear being cut is too large to be accommodated by the spiral head centres without using raising blocks, and then the results are not as satisfactory as can be gained by using this attachment.

The gear is supported similarly to that on the opposite page. The advantage of a rim rest is illustrated, and it should also be noted that a heavy cutter arbor is used to give added stiffness and assure accuracy. The table is fed from left to right, or so that the cut is against the rim rest.

Gashing Teeth in Worm Wheel

Finishing a worm wheel on a milling machine requires two separate operations. First, the operation of gashing the teeth, shown above, is performed; and then the teeth are hobbed, as shown in the illustration on page 156.

In gashing the teeth, the blank is dogged to the spiral head spindle, and the swivel table is swung to the required angle. The vertical feed is used and the teeth are indexed the same as in cutting a spur gear. Most of the stock is removed in gashing, only enough being left to allow the hob to take a light finishing cut.

Hobbing Teeth in Worm Wheel

The work is set up practically the same as in the operation of gashing the teeth, only the dog on the arbor is removed and the swivel table is set at zero. The worm wheel revolves freely on the centres, being rotated by the hob.

The wheel can be hobbed to the right depth by using a steel rule at the back of the knee to measure a distance equal to the centre distance of the worm and wheel from a line marked " Centre," on the vertical slide to the top of the knee. This line on the vertical slide indicates the position of the top of the knee when the index centres are at the same height as the centre of the machine spindle.

Cutting Teeth in Bevel Gear

The illustration on this page shows a milling machine set up for cutting the teeth of a bevel gear.

The gear is held in place by a split bushing that is expanded in the hole. The spiral head is elevated to the proper cutting angle and the table is fed longitudinally from left to right.

In setting off centre to trim the sides of the teeth to the proper thickness, the table is adjusted the required amount on the knee and then the blank is rotated by means of the index crank, as previously explained.

Cutting Teeth in Spiral Gear

The machine is shown, in the illustration above, set in position to cut a left-hand spiral gear.

The gear is mounted in the same manner as in several previous operations, but instead of remaining stationary as the table advances, it is rotated by means of the required change gears to give the correct lead to the teeth. The table is fed longitudinally from left to right.

A right-hand spiral gear of the same angle may be cut in the same manner by setting the table to the other side of zero and leaving out the intermediate or reverse gear.

Cutting Spiral Teeth in Milling Cutter

This operation shows the arrangement for cutting teeth in a right-hand spiral milling cutter.

The work is 6″ long and 4″ in diameter, and an angular cutter 3″ in diameter is employed. The saddle is set to the angle desired and the head is geared to give the necessary lead.

The work is mounted on an arbor that is dogged to the spiral head spindle, and care is taken that there is no lost motion between the spindle and work.

Gashing a Hob

While this is not strictly a gear cutting operation, it is set up and performed in practically the same manner, the principal difference being in the shape of cutter used. Many hobs are gashed spirally, and this is done in a similar way to cutting the teeth in a spiral gear.

In this operation the hob should be supported as firmly as possible as the cut is comparatively deep. A coarse feed can thus be used to do the job more quickly.

The table is fed longitudinally from left to right, the spiral head gearing giving the required rotative movement as the cutter advances through the work. Although not shown in the view above, ample cutter lubricant should be used on steel.

Cutting Teeth in Spiral Gear, Using Compound Vertical Spindle Milling Attachment

This operation shows the use of a compound vertical spindle milling attachment in cutting a spiral gear.

It will be noticed that where this attachment is used, the swivel table is set at zero and the angle of the spiral obtained by swinging the head of the attachment. The cutting is also done on the side, instead of the top of the gear.

In cutting left-hand spirals, the cutter would be at the back of the blank, the head of the attachment swung to the other side of zero, and an intermediate gear would be introduced in the train to reverse the direction of rotation.

Cutting a Short Lead Spiral Gear, Using a Vertical Spindle Milling Attachment

When the table cannot be swung to the required angle, a vertical spindle attachment may be used. The attachment is swung 90° up from zero, and the required angle of the spiral is then obtained by the swivel table.

Where the lead is as short as that above, it is better to employ the special attachment shown in Chapter V, for the ratio of gearing of the spiral head is such that severe stresses are brought to bear upon it in feeding the work. If, however, the job is set up as above, it is necessary to feed the work by hand.

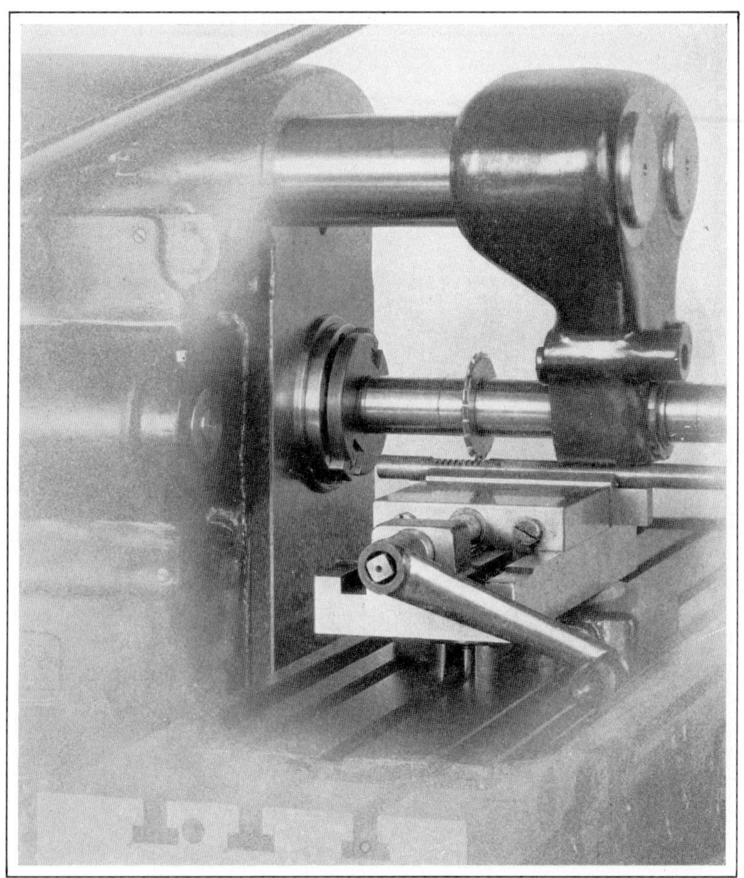

Milling Rack Teeth in Cylindrical Shaft

Sometimes it is required to mill a few rack teeth in a cylindrical shaft or plunger, and where a rack cutting attachment is at hand, this can be readily done. If one is not convenient, however, the work can be done in the manner shown above.

The shaft is supported on a parallel and clamped in a vise, and the teeth are indexed by means of the graduated dial on the cross feed screw.

Before indexing, care should be taken to remove backlash from the screw.

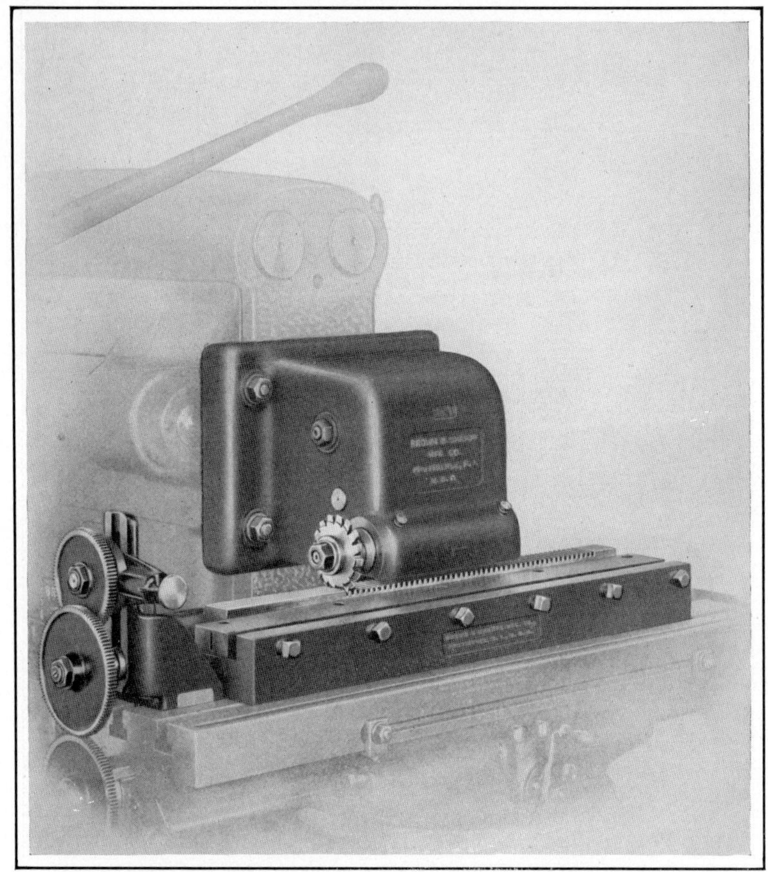

Cutting Teeth in Rack, Using Rack Cutting and Indexing Attachments

The method of cutting a steel rack, using the rack cutting and indexing attachments described in Chapter V, is clearly shown in this illustration.

The rack is fastened in the vise of the attachment, and the teeth are indexed by the indexing attachment.

The automatic transverse table feed is used and the direction of cut is from the back of the rack toward the front, that is, against the direction in which the cutter rotates.

Cutting a Worm Thread, Using Rack Cutting Attachment

Another use of the rack cutting attachment on a universal milling machine is illustrated in this operation. It is especially serviceable for cutting short lead spiral gears, when the angle is such that they cannot be cut on the milling machine in the usual way. An advantage of the rack cutting attachment over the vertical spindle milling attachment for this purpose is that work of smaller diameter can be accommodated, or a smaller cutter can be used.

The cutting is done on the top of the work.

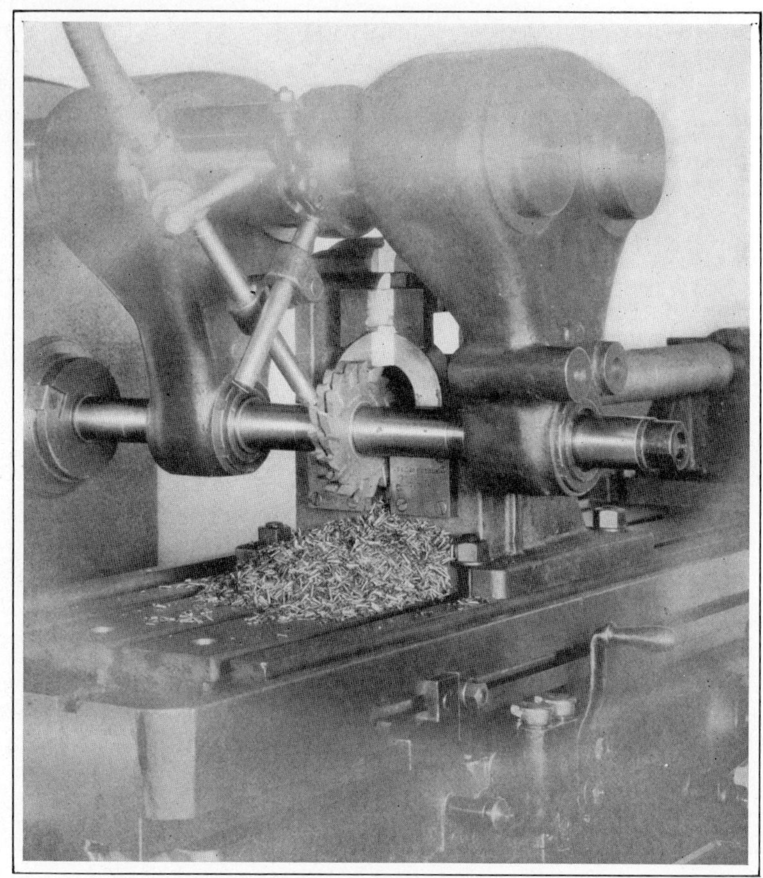

Cutting Slots in the End of a Steel Spindle

This milling machine spindle is firmly held in a simple fixture while the slots in the end are being milled. Due to the length of the work, it is impossible to mount it vertically and take a cut by moving the table longitudinally. Therefore, for this job the table is clamped and the vertical feed is used.

The two arbor yokes rigidly support the arbor on either side of the cutters permitting taking a fast accurate cut.

Sections of Milling Machine Departments in Our Works, Showing Erecting of Machines in Large Lots

Constant Speed Drive Milling Machines fitted with Motor Drive

CHAPTER IX

Milling Operations — Cam Cutting, Graduating and Miscellaneous Operations

Cam Cutting. Face, peripheral and cylindrical cams of all ordinary sizes can be cut upon a milling machine, and a far more satisfactory job can be obtained than is possible by drilling around the outline on a cam blank, breaking it off and then milling or filing to a line.

When it is required to cut several cams of the same outline at frequent intervals, it is an advantage to add the cam cutting attachment, illustrated and described in Chapter V, to the equipment of the machine. The formers that are required to produce the different cams can be preserved, and it is then only a matter of a few minutes' time to set up the machine to cut any number of cams for which a former is at hand.

Another method that is often followed, in cutting peripheral cams, especially those for use on automatic screw machines, is that of using the spiral head and a vertical spindle milling attachment. Illustrations of this are shown on pages 179 and 180. The spiral head is geared to the table feed screw, the same as in cutting ordinary spirals, and the cam blank is fastened to the end of the index spindle. An end mill is used in the vertical spindle milling attachment, which is set in each case to mill the periphery of the cam at right angles to its sides, or, in other words, the axes of the spiral head spindle and attachment spindle must always be parallel to mill cams according to this method. The cutting is done by the teeth on the periphery of the end mill. The principle of this method is as follows: Suppose the spiral head is elevated to 90°, or at exact right angles to the surface of the table (see Fig. 69), and is geared for any given lead. It is then apparent that, as the table advances and the blank is turned, the distance between the axes of the index spindle and attachment spindle becomes less. In other words, the cut becomes deeper and the radius of the cam is shortened, producing a spiral lobe, the lead of which is the same as that for which the machine is geared.

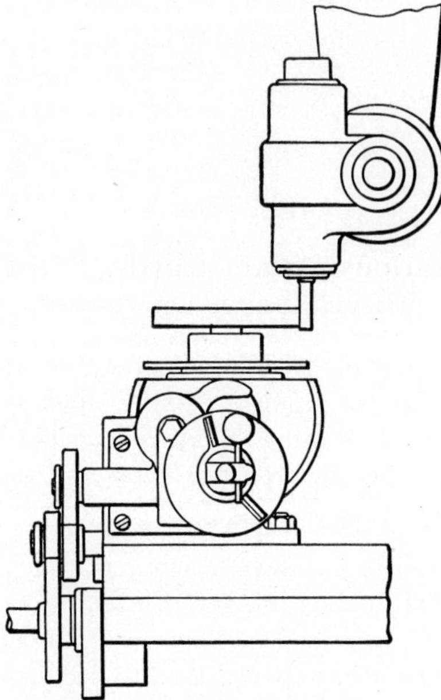

Fig. 69

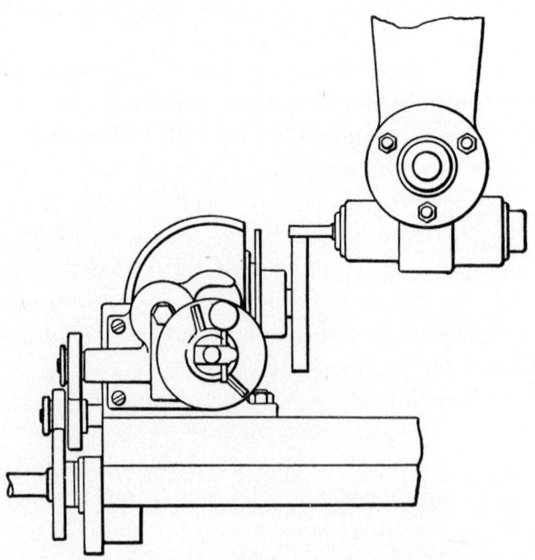

Fig. 70

Now, suppose the same gearing is retained and the spiral head is set at zero, or parallel to the surface of the table (see Fig. 70). It is apparent, also, that the axes of the index spindle and attachment spindle are parallel to one another. Therefore, as the table advances, and the blank is turned, the distance between the axes of the index spindle and attachment spindle remains the same. As a result, the periphery of the blank, if milled, is concentric or the lead is 0.

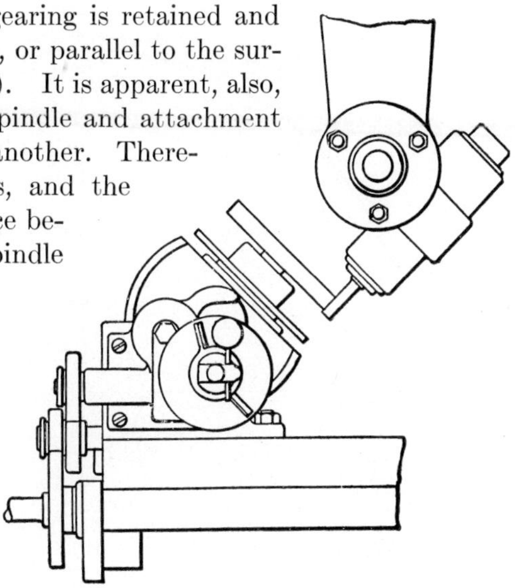

Fig. 71

If, then, the spiral head is elevated to any angle between zero and 90° (see Fig. 71), the amount of lead given to the cam will be between that for which the machine is geared and 0. Hence it is clear that cams with a very large range of different leads can be obtained with one set of change gears, and the problem of milling the lobes of a cam is reduced to a question of finding the angle at which to set the head to obtain any given lead.

In order to illustrate the method of obtaining the correct angle, drawings of two cams to be milled, and data connected with same, are given in Figs. 72 and 73.

It is first necessary to know the lead of the lobes of a cam, that is, the amount of rise of each lobe if continued the full circumference of the cam. This can be obtained from the drawings as follows: For cams where the face is divided into hundredths, as those shown: multiply 100 by the rise of the lobe in inches and divide by the number of hundredths of circumference occupied by the lobe. For cams that are figured in degrees of circumference: multiply 360 by the rise of the lobe in inches and divide by the number of degrees of circumference occupied by the lobe. Taking Fig. 72 for example, we have a cam of one lobe which extends through 91 hundredths of the circumference, and has a rise .178″. Then $\frac{100 \times .178''}{91} = .1956$ lead of lobe, or .196″, which is near enough for all practical purposes.

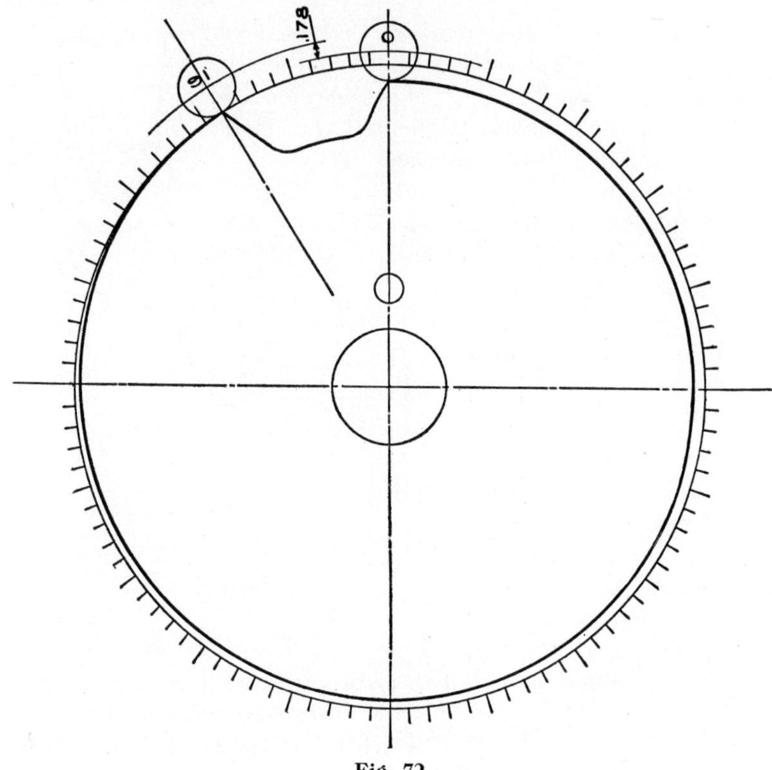

Fig. 72

As a .196″ lead is much less than .67″, which is the shortest lead* regularly obtainable on the milling machine (see Table of Leads, pages 229 to 247), the change gears that will give a lead of .67″ may be used, and then the angle of the head can be adjusted so that a lead of .196″ will be obtained on the cam lobe with these change gears. The rule for this is:

Divide the given lead of the cam lobe by a lead obtainable on the machine, and the result is the sine of the angle at which to set the head.

Continuing the calculation for the lobe of the cam in Fig. 72, we therefore have: $\frac{.196''}{.67} = .29253.$

Hence, .29253 is the sine of the correct angle. Turning to the Table of sines and cosines on pages 302 to 310, we find that .29253 is very

* By the use of the short lead attachment illustrated and described in Chapter V, much shorter leads than .67″ are obtainable.

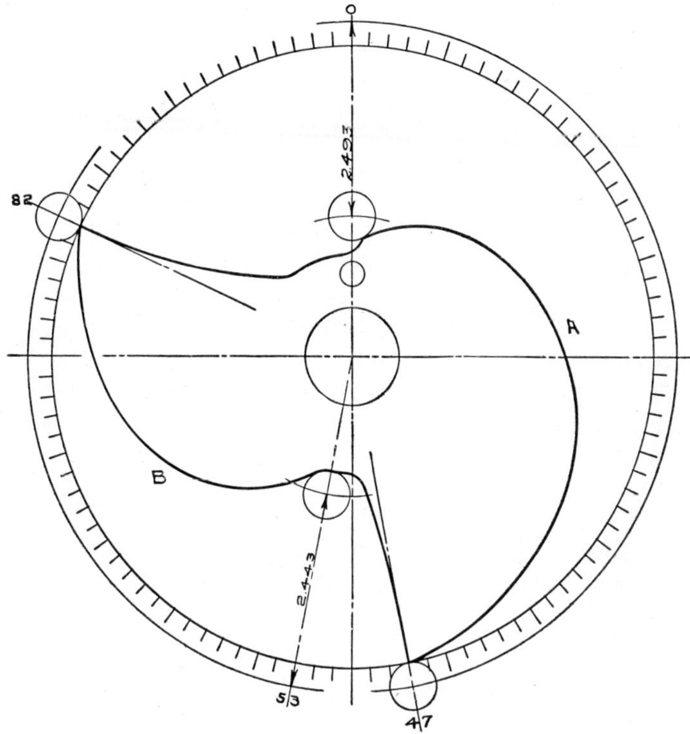

Fig. 73

near .29265, which is the sine of an angle of 17° and 1′. As the spiral head is not graduated closer than quarter degrees, it will be satisfactory to elevate the head just a hair over 17°; then, with the gearing for a lead of .67″, a cam with a lead of .196″ will be obtained.

The minute errors between the actual lead .1956″ and .196″, and in the sines and angles of this calculation can be safely ignored, as it is not possible in practice to work very much closer than we have outlined.

The portion of the periphery of the cam from 91 hundredths to zero represents a clearance of the cutting tool prior to the beginning of the throw. It is usually milled to a line, or drilled, broken out, and filed.

In Fig. 73, we have a cam with two lobes, one, *A*, having a rise of 2.493″ in 47 hundredths, and the other, *B*, having a rise of 2.443″ in 29 hundredths. On cams such as this, where it is necessary to remove considerable stock, it is usually the practice to first outline the approximate shape of the lobes on the blank and drill and break off the surplus stock.

Following the same method of figuring to find the lead of the lobes on this cam, we have: $\frac{100 \times 2.493''}{47} = 5.304''$ lead for lobe A, and $\frac{100 \times 2.443''}{29} = 8.424''$ lead for lobe B.

Where there are two or more lobes on a cam, the machine is geared for a lead slightly longer than the longest one required, which in this case is 8.424″, then the other lobes are milled without changing the gears. Referring to the Table of Leads, we find a lead of 8.437″, which is slightly larger than 8.424″. This gearing is, therefore, accepted, and it is required to find the sine of the angle at which to set the head for lobe B.

$\frac{8.424}{8.437} = .99846$ sine of angle at which to set head. Looking at a table of sines and cosines, .99846 is found to be the sine of an angle of 86° and 49′. The head is, therefore, set at a trifle over 86 3/4°.

When lobe B has been milled, the head is set for lobe A.

$\frac{5.304}{8.437} = .62865$ sine of an angle at which to set head. Referring again to the table of sines and cosines, we find that .62865 is very near to .62864, which is the sine of an angle of 38° and 57′. The head is, therefore, set slightly under 39° for this lobe.

The other portions of the periphery of this cam are formed up either by filing to a line before the blank is put on the milling machine or by milling to the line after the lobes have been formed.

Whenever possible, the job should be set up so that the end mill will cut on the lower side of the blank, as this brings the mill and table nearer together and makes the job more rigid. It also prevents chips from accumulating, and enables the operator to better see any lines that may be laid out on the face of the cam.

When the lead of the machine is over 2″ the automatic feed can be used, but when the lead is less than 2″ the job should be fed by hand, with the index crank, as shown on page 179.

By the use of the calculations just given, we have compiled tables on pages 250 to 301 that give a wide range of leads from 0 to 20″ that can be obtained with the spiral head in the manner described. These tables will be found useful, as they give all data and settings without the necessity of figuring.

Graduating. Another use to which the milling machine may be put is that of graduating flat scales and verniers.* It is possible to obtain very accurate results, and when required, odd fractional divisions can be easily spaced.

This operation requires the use of the spiral head and a single pointed graduating tool which is held stationary in a fly cutter arbor, mounted directly in the spindle, or can be fastened to the spindle of a vertical milling or rack cutting attachment. The scale to be

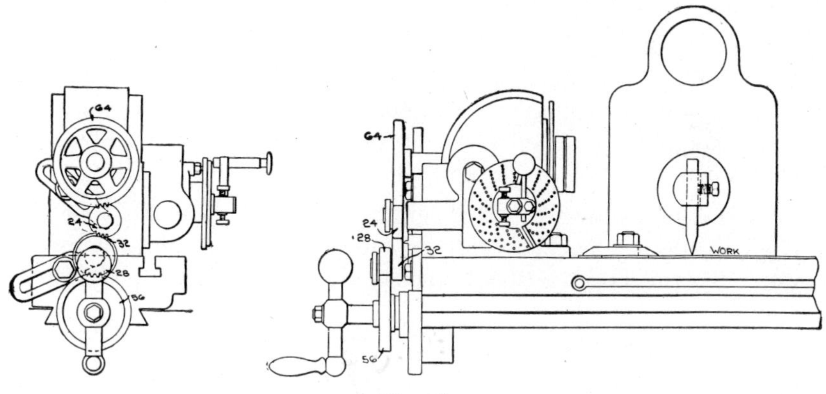

Fig. 74

graduated is clamped to the surface of the table parallel to the table T slots. No power is required for the operation, as the lines are cut by moving the table transversely under the point of the tool, and this can be easily done by hand. The spiral head spindle is equal-geared to the table feed screw as shown in Fig. 74, and indexing for the divisions required is accomplished by means of the index plates, the index crank being turned in the usual manner for each division.

It has already been explained that one turn of the index crank moves the spiral head spindle 1/40 of a revolution, and if equal gearing is employed between this spindle and the table feed screw, the feed screw will likewise make 1/40 of a complete revolution. The lead of the feed screw being .25″, it is apparent that one turn of the index crank will advance the table an amount equal to .25″ × 1/40, or .00625″.

Suppose it is required to graduate a scale with lines .0218″ apart. Now, if one turn of the index crank moves the table a distance of

* A method of obtaining fine divisions on a circular plate is mentioned under Differential Indexing in Chapter IV.

.00625″, it will take more than one turn to move the table a distance of .0218″. Hence,

$$\frac{.02180}{.00625} = 3\frac{.00305}{.00625}.$$

Taking the remainder, .00305″, and referring to the tables on pages 320 to 322, we find that it is very near .0030488, which is the distance the table will be moved by using the 41-hole circle in one of the index plates furnished and indexing 20 holes. The error between the actual remainder and the amount given in the table is so small that it can be safely ignored.

Therefore, to graduate a scale with divisions .0218 of an inch apart, an index plate having a 41-hole circle would be used and the crank would have to make three complete turns and then be advanced 20 holes in the 41-hole circle for each division.

It should be remembered in graduating that care must be exercised to prevent backlash between the index crank and table feed screw. To this end, the crank should always be turned in the same direction.

If required, the ratio of gearing between the spiral head spindle and the table feed screw can be changed, but this complicates the operation somewhat and should be resorted to only when it is impossible to get accurate enough results with the method described. Upon referring to the tables on pages 320 to 322 and noting the extreme fineness in divisions that it is possible to obtain, it is apparent that there is little occasion to change the ratio of gearing.

Accurate graduating can also be done by using scales and verniers such as illustrated and described in Chapter V.

Illustrations of cam cutting, and many miscellaneous milling operations will be found on the following pages, and a careful study of the cuts and descriptions may be of value to the reader.

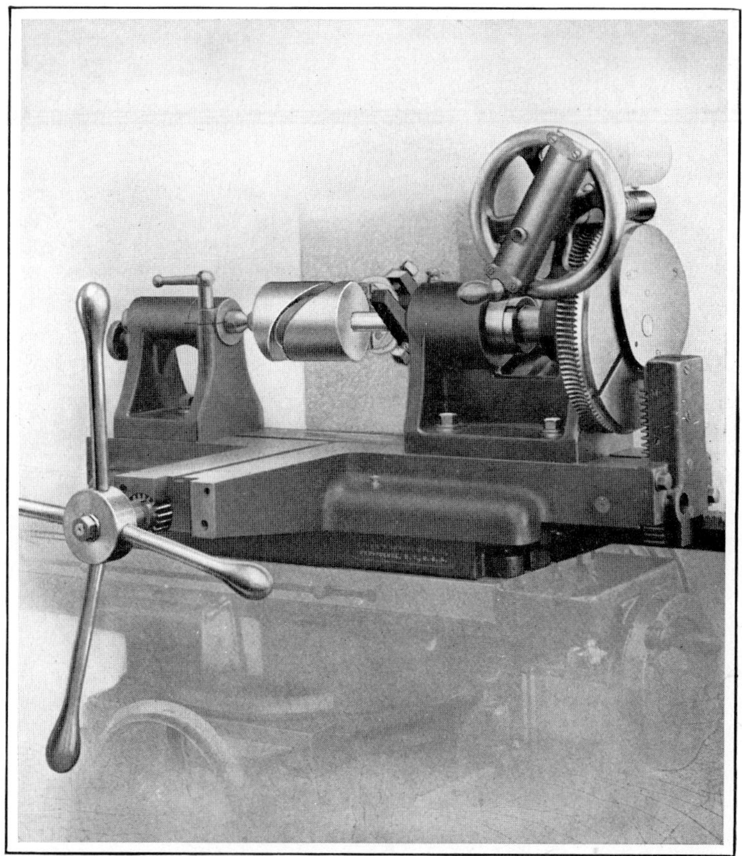

Cutting a Cylindrical Cam, Using Cam Cutting Attachment

For cutting a cylindrical cam, the head is bolted to the bed parallel to the table and the cam blank is supported on an arbor mounted on the attachment centres and dogged to the spindle. The table is raised to a point that brings the attachment centres at the same height as the axis of the spindle.

A spiral end mill is used for this operation and the necessary movement to feed the work is obtained from the attachment, the table remaining clamped in one position.

This view of the attachment shows very clearly the former on the outer end of the head.

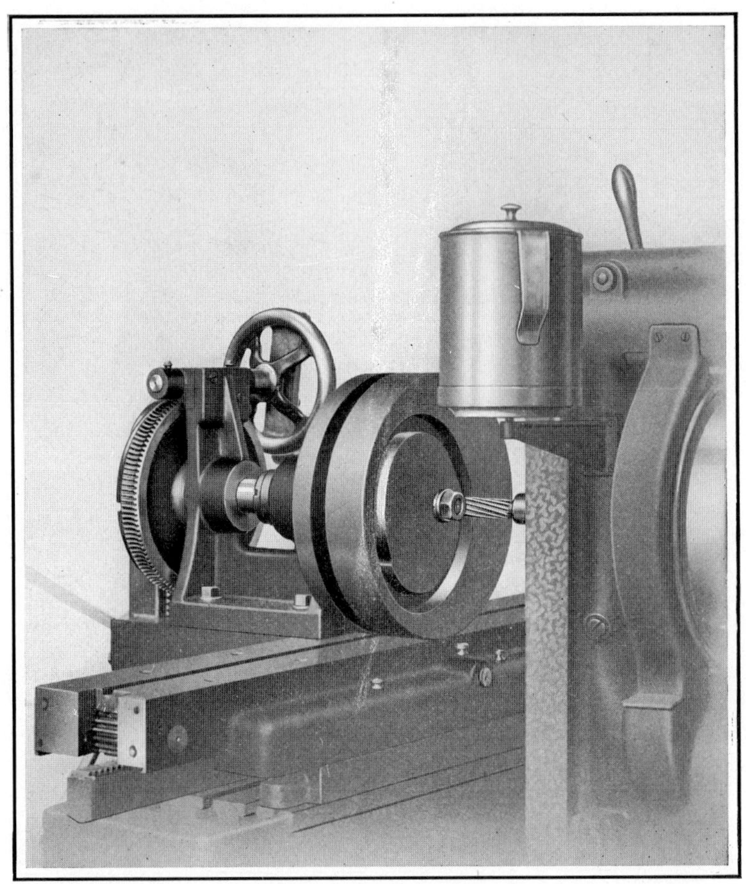

Cutting a Face Cam, Using the Cam Cutting Attachment

In this operation the head of the attachment is bolted to the bed at right angles to the table and the cam blank is fastened to the attachment spindle by means of a bolt. A peripheral cam would be milled in the same manner. The necessary rotative movement is obtained by hand feed, and the longitudinal movement to give the proper lead and shape to the cam is produced by the cam former and the mechanism of the attachment, as described in Chapter V.

A spiral end mill is used. The machine table remains clamped in one position.

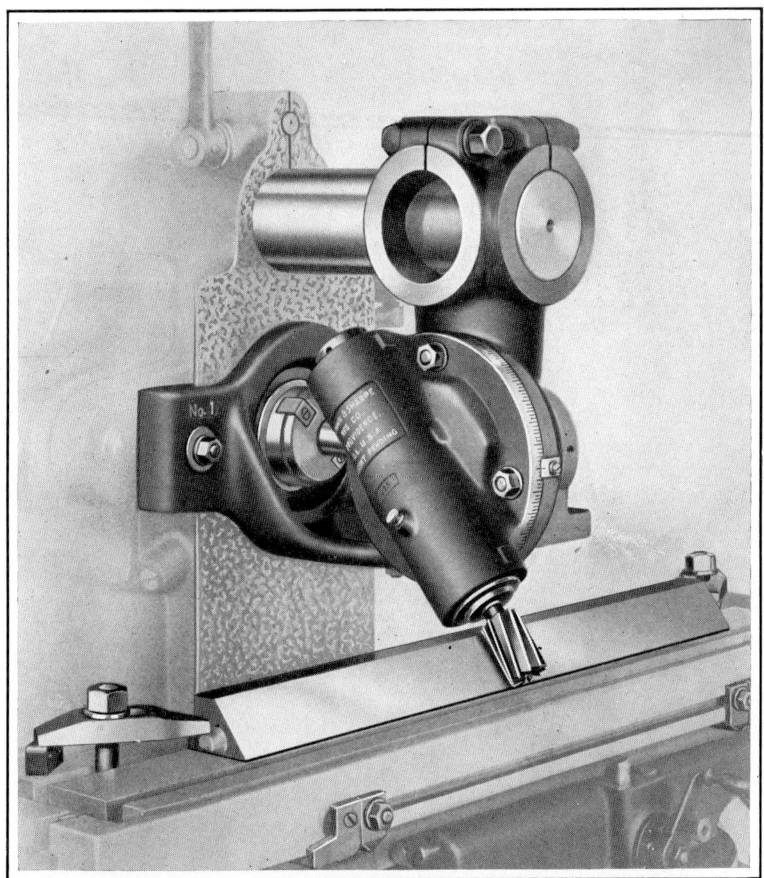

Milling Angular Gib, Using Compound Vertical Spindle Milling Attachment

Angular cutters are not always at hand that will produce the proper angle on angular strips, gibs, etc., and when this is the case, the value of a Compound Vertical Spindle Milling Attachment can be appreciated. This attachment can be swung to mill a wide variety of different angles, using an ordinary end mill. It can be used to mill an angle on a long gib, similar to that shown above, or the head can be removed, turned quarter way around and put back in place, and used to mill an angle on a piece where, for some reason, it is advantageous to feed the table transversely.

Milling Clutch Teeth

This operation is very similar in the way it is set up to the one of Milling Bolts previously described. The character of the cut, however, is lighter and the arbor is supported at the outer end in the arbor yoke bearing. A cutter of special form is used, and one tooth is finished at each cut, the cut beginning at the outside of blank and finishing in the centre.

Indexing in this case is accomplished with the regular index plates and crank as the number of teeth required cannot be indexed with the plate on the spindle nose.

Milling End Teeth in End Mill

When it is required to mill end teeth in an end mill, it may be done as shown in the illustration above.

The mill is held by its shank in a collet that is inserted in the spiral head spindle. The spiral head is adjusted to an angle to give the correct form to the teeth.

An angular cutter is used and the table is fed longitudinally. Indexing is accomplished with the index plates and crank in the usual way.

Oil is used, as the material of the end mill is tool steel.

Milling Squares for Wrench on Reamer Shank

A reamer of the type illustrated is necessarily rather long and cannot be accommodated on centres as a shorter piece would be. It is, therefore, passed through the hole in the spiral head spindle and is clamped in the chuck, while the wrench end is supported by the foot-stock centre.

An end mill is used and the work is fed vertically. To prevent longitudinal movement of table, the small clamping lever shown on the front of the saddle is set up. Where there are many pieces to be done, a more permanent method of fixing the table is by means of stops that fasten on to the V bearing at the bottom of the table and come against the side of the saddle.

Milling Tenon on Collet

A taper plug having a centre hole at the large end is driven into the hole in the collet, which is then mounted on the spiral head centres. A dog on the taper plug locks the collet to the spiral head spindle.

An end mill is used and the cutting is done with the teeth on the periphery. The rapid index plate is used to index the work and the table is fed longitudinally.

The table feed trip dog is set to insure milling both sides to the same length.

If a quantity of this work is to be done, formed straddle mills would be employed with an entirely different arrangement.

Milling Flutes in Taper Reamer

There are times when a shop requires a reamer of special size that cannot be procured readily, and in such cases one can be turned up and the flutes cut in the manner shown above. The spiral head is set at the angle of taper and the foot-stock centre is adjusted to correspond with it. The reamer blank is then mounted on the centres and dogged to the spiral head spindle.

A stock cutter, known as a reamer fluting cutter, is used and the table is fed longitudinally.

The procedure is the same for milling a straight reamer, except that the spiral head and foot-stock are set at zero.

Cutting a Spiral with End Mill

When a spiral slot with parallel sides is required an end mill should be employed and the job set up as shown above.

The spiral head centres are brought to a level with the centre of the machine spindle.

The table is at right angles to the spindle and the angle of the spiral is obtained by the combination of change gears used.

Either right- or left-hand spirals can be cut in this way by simply leaving out or interposing an intermediate gear in the train of change gears.

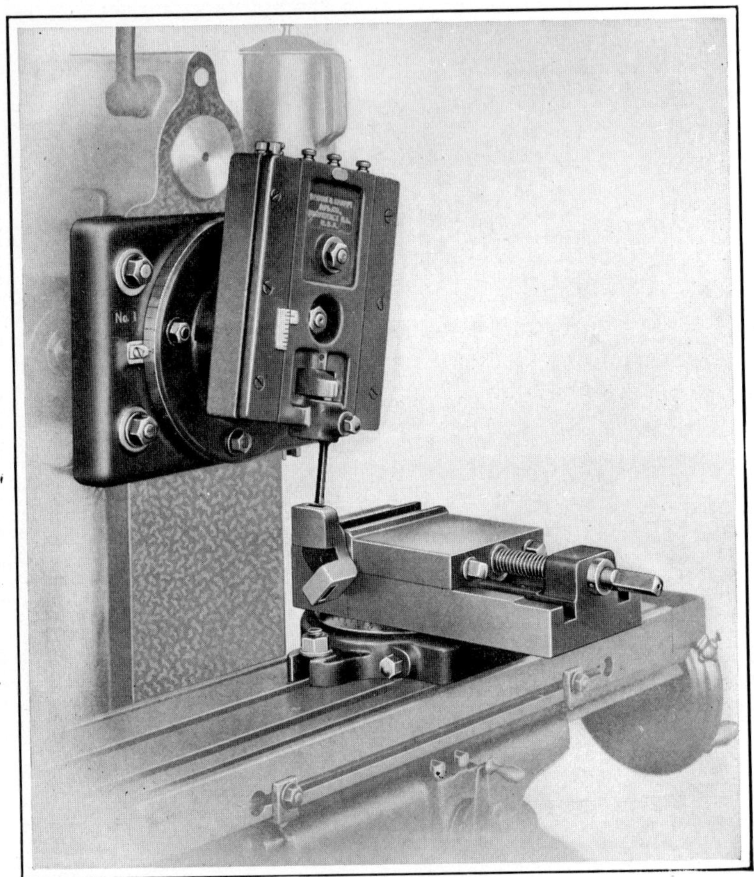

Cutting Slots in Screw Machine Tool, Using Slotting Attachment

The screw machine tool is held by its shank in a vise, and the slotting attachment is set at an angle so as to give the proper clearance to the cutter that is intended for use in the slot. A hole is drilled for starting the slot.

In slotting work, all necessary movements of the table are made by the hand feed.

The swivel vise is very useful in connection with the slotting attachment, for the work can be swung to any angle or indexed, if it is desired to make a special shaped slot.

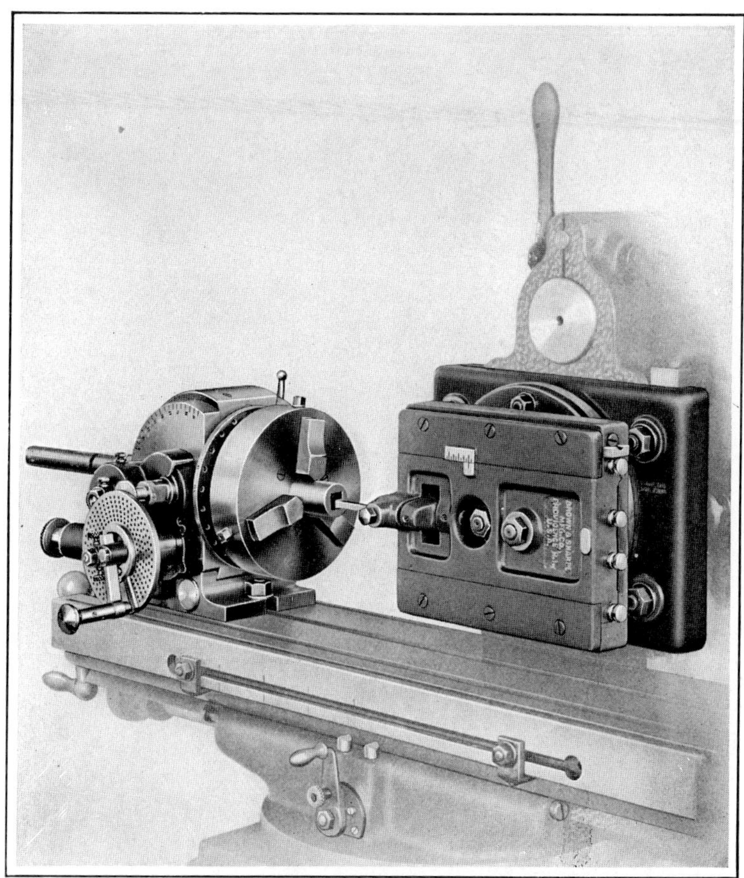

Slotting Square Hole in Extension Wrench

In this operation the piece of work is too long to be set in a vertical position; it is, therefore, passed through the spiral head spindle and is clamped in the chuck. The slotting attachment head is then set so that the tool moves in a path parallel to the top of the table.

The ability to swing the head from a vertical to a horizontal position is one of the features of the B. & S. attachment.

The piece of work is indexed by means of the rapid index plate. All necessary movements of the table are made by hand.

Milling Flutes of Twist Drill

This operation is very similar to that of cutting a spiral gear. The drill blank is mounted on the spiral head centres and fastened to the spindle with a dog. The spiral head is geared for the required lead and the necessary angle is obtained by swinging the swivel table.

A stock cutter of special form, known as a twist drill cutter, is employed and oil is used in cutting.

More complete information on this subject can be found in Chapter IV.

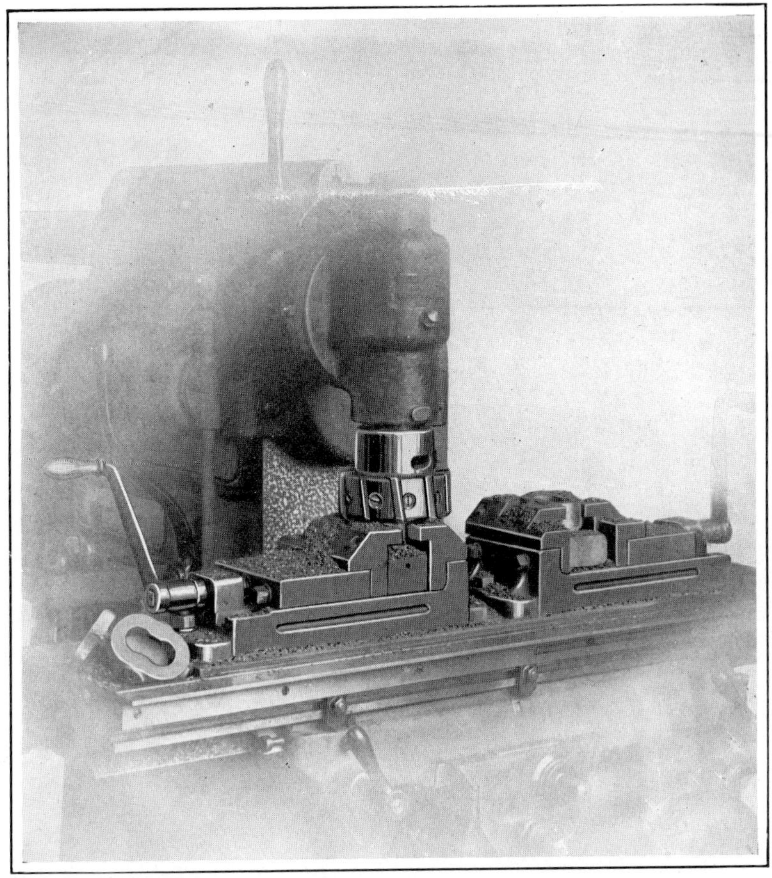

Face Milling Using a Standard Vertical Spindle Milling Attachment

The above operation on a No. 21 Automatic Milling Machine clearly illustrates the adaptability of the automatic milling machine to use with stock attachments.

An inserted tooth face milling cutter makes the cut on the pump bodies in both fixtures. At the finish of each cut the spindle is automatically stopped upon the reversal of the table, thus eliminating the possibility of marring the work. The table reverses and, at constant fast travel, brings the other fixture up to the cutter where the cutting feed is engaged and rotation of cutter begins.

The operation is completely automatic and is typical of the different jobs which can be handled by use of attachments. It is also of interest to note the simplicity of the fixtures, which are regular standard vises that have been fitted with special jaws.

Milling Jaws for Bolt Cutters on a No. 33 Automatic Milling Machine

On this job the ingenious design of the work fixtures enables a standard machine to be used for a difficult but not unusual cut. The direction of the cut being against the feed, the pieces are held in the fixture by the thrust of the cutters, which wedges the work against a pin and rib. Upon the completion of the cut, and when cutters have cleared the work, the pieces are automatically removed from the fixture in the following manner. Bolted to front of machine is an arm which acts as a cam for the lever extending from the side of the fixture. This lever operates a set of four spring plungers. By following the contour of the arm, the lever withdraws and locks these plungers, permitting the fixture to be loaded. On completion of cut, a trip dog releases the plungers, which spring forward, strike the pieces, and drive them from the fixture to the table of the machine.

Face Milling on a No. 33 Automatic Milling Machine

This operation on motor cages illustrates a possibility in the use of a special attachment designed for a face milling operation. While the part requires the use of both cutters, the attachment was designed to handle these cages in a variety of sizes, and for some cuts only the lower spindle is engaged.

Intermittent table travel is used. The cutting feed is engaged just before the cutter comes in contact with the casting, and continues until clearing the edge of a vertical set of feet. Fast travel is then engaged and the other pair of feet brought up to the cutters. When this cut is completed the table reverses at fast travel, bringing the other fixture up to the cutters, and the cycle of operations is repeated. The table dogs control the operation of table and spindle.

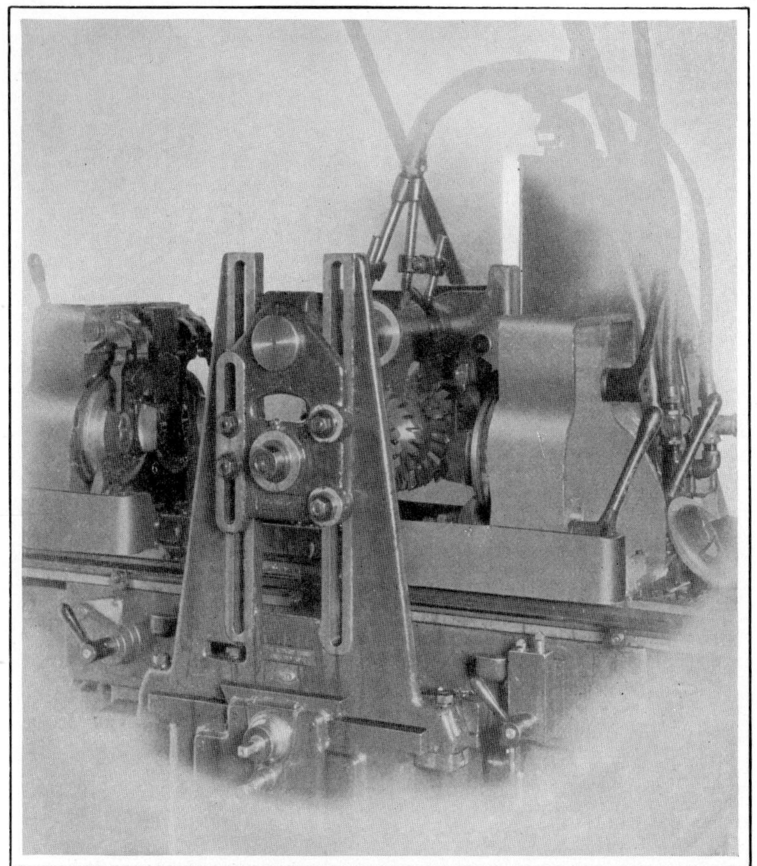

Slot Milling on a No. 33 Automatic Milling Machine (without Automatic Spindle)

Certain parts adaptable to automatic milling do not require the use of a machine with a reversible spindle. For work of this class the No. 33 Automatic Milling Machine (without Automatic Spindle) can be advantageously used. This machine has all the features of our regular automatics except the automatic spindle.

The operation shown on universal joint webs is typical of this class of work. The cut is a slot milling operation and, being on centres, can be milled with the spindle rotating continuously in one direction. The fixtures are of the quick-acting type, each holding two pieces, a short turn of the lever being sufficient to clamp the pieces firmly in position. Locating points are provided to facilitate placing the work in the proper position. There is ample time while the work in one fixture is being milled to reload the other.

The table travel is fully automatic in both directions and is controlled by the adjustable table dogs.

Straddle Milling Pipe Fittings on a No. 37 Automatic Duplex Milling Machine

The No. 37 Duplex is particularly valuable for straddle milling operations that cannot be accomplished on the other Automatic Milling Machines, due to the size of the part being milled, which would require the use of unusually large diameter cutters.

This operation illustrates the milling of a hex head on a pipe fitting. There is a fixture on each end of the table which holds three pieces. Three sets of cutters are used, two pairs on the upper spindle and one on the lower. The spindles rotate continuously and the work is fed to and from the cutters automatically. The fixtures are hand-indexed and, as each pair of cutters makes a single cut on each fitting, one rotation of the fixture completely mills three parts.

Form Milling on a No. OY Plain Milling Machine

This operation on a No. OY with a semi-automatic table is typical of the class of work which is ordinarily handled on these machines. The operation is form milling a part for a popular safety razor. Inasmuch as the travel of the table is controlled by a foot treadle, both hands of the operator are free to load and unload the fixture.

The adjustable table dogs which cause the engagement and release of the cutting feed can be clearly seen in the illustration. Also, on the right end of the table is the cylinder containing the coiled spring which actuates the return of the table to the loading position after the cut has been completed.

TABLES

INDEX TABLE 2 to 50

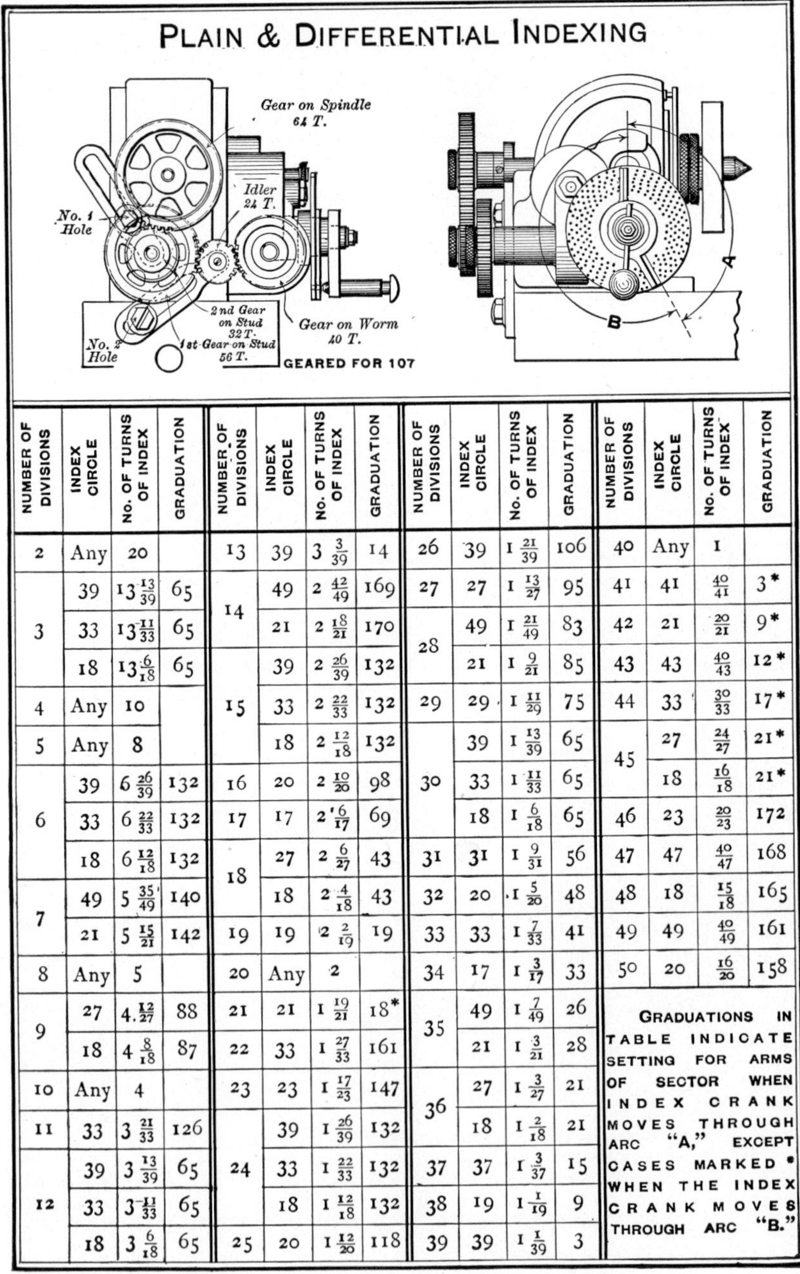

Number of Divisions	Index Circle	No. of Turns of Index	Graduation
2	Any	20	
3	39	$13\frac{13}{39}$	65
	33	$13\frac{11}{33}$	65
	18	$13\frac{6}{18}$	65
4	Any	10	
5	Any	8	
6	39	$6\frac{26}{39}$	132
	33	$6\frac{22}{33}$	132
	18	$6\frac{12}{18}$	132
7	49	$5\frac{35}{49}$	140
	21	$5\frac{15}{21}$	142
8	Any	5	
9	27	$4\frac{12}{27}$	88
	18	$4\frac{8}{18}$	87
10	Any	4	
11	33	$3\frac{21}{33}$	126
12	39	$3\frac{13}{39}$	65
	33	$3\frac{11}{33}$	65
	18	$3\frac{6}{18}$	65

Number of Divisions	Index Circle	No. of Turns of Index	Graduation
13	39	$3\frac{3}{39}$	14
14	49	$2\frac{42}{49}$	169
	21	$2\frac{18}{21}$	170
15	39	$2\frac{26}{39}$	132
	33	$2\frac{22}{33}$	132
	18	$2\frac{12}{18}$	132
16	20	$2\frac{10}{20}$	98
17	17	$2\frac{6}{17}$	69
18	27	$2\frac{6}{27}$	43
	18	$2\frac{4}{18}$	43
19	19	$2\frac{2}{19}$	19
20	Any	2	
21	21	$1\frac{19}{21}$	18*
22	33	$1\frac{27}{33}$	161
23	23	$1\frac{17}{23}$	147
24	39	$1\frac{26}{39}$	132
	33	$1\frac{22}{33}$	132
	18	$1\frac{12}{18}$	132
25	20	$1\frac{12}{20}$	118

Number of Divisions	Index Circle	No. of Turns of Index	Graduation
26	39	$1\frac{21}{39}$	106
27	27	$1\frac{13}{27}$	95
28	49	$1\frac{21}{49}$	83
	21	$1\frac{9}{21}$	85
29	29	$1\frac{11}{29}$	75
30	39	$1\frac{13}{39}$	65
	33	$1\frac{11}{33}$	65
	18	$1\frac{6}{18}$	65
31	31	$1\frac{9}{31}$	56
32	20	$1\frac{5}{20}$	48
33	33	$1\frac{7}{33}$	41
34	17	$1\frac{3}{17}$	33
35	49	$1\frac{7}{49}$	26
	21	$1\frac{3}{21}$	28
36	27	$1\frac{3}{27}$	21
	18	$1\frac{2}{18}$	21
37	37	$1\frac{3}{37}$	15
38	19	$1\frac{1}{19}$	9
39	39	$1\frac{1}{39}$	3

Number of Divisions	Index Circle	No. of Turns of Index	Graduation
40	Any	1	
41	41	$\frac{40}{41}$	3*
42	21	$\frac{20}{21}$	9*
43	43	$\frac{40}{43}$	12*
44	33	$\frac{30}{33}$	17*
45	27	$\frac{24}{27}$	21*
	18	$\frac{16}{18}$	21*
46	23	$\frac{20}{23}$	172
47	47	$\frac{40}{47}$	168
48	18	$\frac{15}{18}$	165
49	49	$\frac{40}{49}$	161
50	20	$\frac{16}{20}$	158

Graduations in table indicate setting for arms of sector when index crank moves through arc "A," except cases marked * when the index crank moves through arc "B."

INDEX TABLE 51 to 92.

Number of Divisions	Index Circle	No. of Turns of Index	Graduation	Gear on Worm	No. 1 Hole: 1st Gear on Stud	No. 1 Hole: 2nd Gear on Stud	Gear on Spindle	Idlers: No. 1 Hole	Idlers: No. 2 Hole
51	17	14/17	33*	24			48	24	44
52	39	30/39	152						
53	49	35/49	140	56	40	24	72		
53	21	15/21	142	56	40	24	72		
54	27	20/27	147						
55	33	24/33	144						
56	49	35/49	140						
56	21	15/21	142						
57	49	35/49	140	56			40	24	44
57	21	15/21	142	56			40	24	44
58	29	20/29	136						
59	39	26/39	132	48			32	44	
59	33	22/33	132	48			32	44	
59	18	12/18	132	48			32	44	
60	39	26/39	132						
60	33	22/33	132						
60	18	12/18	132						
61	39	26/39	132	48			32	24	44
61	33	22/33	132	48			32	24	44
61	18	12/18	132	48			32	24	44
62	31	20/31	127						
63	39	26/39	132	24			48	24	44
63	33	22/33	132	24			48	24	44
63	18	12/18	132	24			48	24	44
64	16	10/16	123						
65	39	24/39	121						
66	33	20/33	120						
67	49	28/49	112	28			48	44	
67	21	12/21	113	28			48	44	
68	17	10/17	116						

Number of Divisions	Index Circle	No. of Turns of Index	Graduation	Gear on Worm	No. 1 Hole: 1st Gear on Stud	No. 1 Hole: 2nd Gear on Stud	Gear on Spindle	Idlers: No. 1 Hole	Idlers: No. 2 Hole
69	20	12/20	118	40			56	24	44
70	49	28/49	112						
70	21	12/21	113						
71	27	15/27	110	72			40	24	
71	18	10/18	109	72			40	24	
72	27	15/27	110						
72	18	10/18	109						
73	49	28/49	112	28			48	24	44
73	21	12/21	113	28			48	24	44
74	37	20/37	107						
75	15	8/15	105						
76	19	10/19	103						
77	20	10/20	98	32			48	44	
78	39	20/39	101						
79	20	10/20	98	48			24	44	
80	20	10/20	98						
81	20	10/20	98	48			24	24	44
82	41	20/41	96						
83	26	10/20	98	32			48	24	44
84	21	10/21	94						
85	17	8/17	92						
86	43	20/43	91						
87	15	7/15	92	40			24	24	44
88	33	15/33	89						
89	27	12/27	88	72			32	44	
89	18	8/18	87	72			32	44	
90	27	12/27	88						
90	18	8/18	87						
91	39	18/39	91	24			48	24	44
92	23	10/23	86						

INDEX TABLE 93 to 125.

Number of Divisions	Index Circle	No. of Turns of Index	Graduation	Gear on Worm	No. 1 Hole: 1st Gear on Stud	No. 1 Hole: 2nd Gear on Stud	Gear on Spindle	Idlers: No. 1 Hole	Idlers: No. 2 Hole
93	27	$\frac{12}{27}$	88	24			32	24	44
	18	$\frac{8}{18}$	87	24			32	24	44
94	47	$\frac{20}{47}$	83						
95	19	$\frac{8}{19}$	82						
96	49	$\frac{21}{49}$	83	28			32	24	44
	21	$\frac{9}{21}$	85	28			32	24	44
97	20	$\frac{8}{20}$	78	40			48	44	
98	49	$\frac{20}{49}$	79						
99	20	$\frac{8}{20}$	78	56	28	40	32		
100	20	$\frac{8}{20}$	78						
101	20	$\frac{8}{20}$	78	72	24	40	48		24
102	20	$\frac{8}{20}$	78	40			32	24	44
103	20	$\frac{8}{20}$	78	40			48	24	44
104	39	$\frac{15}{39}$	75						
105	21	$\frac{8}{21}$	75						
106	43	$\frac{16}{43}$	73	86	24	24	48		
107	20	$\frac{8}{20}$	78	40	56	32	64		24
108	27	$\frac{10}{27}$	73						
109	16	$\frac{6}{16}$	73	32			28	24	44
110	33	$\frac{12}{33}$	71						
111	39	$\frac{13}{39}$	65	24			72	32	
	33	$\frac{11}{33}$	65	24			72	32	
	18	$\frac{6}{18}$	65	24			72	32	
112	39	$\frac{13}{39}$	65	24			64	44	
	33	$\frac{11}{33}$	65	24			64	44	
	18	$\frac{6}{18}$	65	24			64	44	
113	39	$\frac{13}{39}$	65	24			56	44	
	33	$\frac{11}{33}$	65	24			56	44	
	18	$\frac{6}{18}$	65	24			56	44	

Number of Divisions	Index Circle	No. of Turns of Index	Graduation	Gear on Worm	No. 1 Hole: 1st Gear on Stud	No. 1 Hole: 2nd Gear on Stud	Gear on Spindle	Idlers: No. 1 Hole	Idlers: No. 2 Hole
114	39	$\frac{13}{39}$	65	24			48	44	
	33	$\frac{11}{33}$	65	24			48	44	
	18	$\frac{6}{18}$	65	24			48	44	
115	23	$\frac{8}{23}$	68						
116	29	$\frac{10}{29}$	68						
117	39	$\frac{13}{39}$	65	24			24	56	
	33	$\frac{11}{33}$	65	24			24	56	
	18	$\frac{6}{18}$	65	24			24	56	
118	39	$\frac{13}{39}$	65	48			32	44	
	33	$\frac{11}{33}$	65	48			32	44	
	18	$\frac{6}{18}$	65	48			32	44	
119	39	$\frac{13}{39}$	65	72			24	44	
	33	$\frac{11}{33}$	65	72			24	44	
	18	$\frac{6}{18}$	65	72			24	44	
120	39	$\frac{13}{39}$	65						
	33	$\frac{11}{33}$	65						
	18	$\frac{6}{18}$	65						
121	39	$\frac{13}{39}$	65	72			24	24	44
	33	$\frac{11}{33}$	65	72			24	24	44
	18	$\frac{6}{18}$	65	72			24	24	44
122	39	$\frac{13}{39}$	65	48			32	24	44
	33	$\frac{11}{33}$	65	48			32	24	44
	18	$\frac{6}{18}$	65	48			32	24	44
123	39	$\frac{13}{39}$	65	24			24	24	44
	33	$\frac{11}{33}$	65	24			24	24	44
	18	$\frac{6}{18}$	65	24			24	24	44
124	31	$\frac{10}{31}$	63						
125	39	$\frac{13}{39}$	65	24			40	24	44
	33	$\frac{11}{33}$	65	24			40	24	44
	18	$\frac{6}{18}$	65	24			40	24	44

INDEX TABLE 126 to 168.

Number of Divisions	Index Circle	No. of Turns of Index	Graduation	Gear on Worm	No. 1 Hole: 1st Gear on Stud	No. 1 Hole: 2nd Gear on Stud	Gear on Spindle	Idlers: No. 1 Hole	Idlers: No. 2 Hole
126	39	13/39	65	24			48	24	44
	33	11/33	65	24			48	24	44
	18	6/18	65	24			48	24	44
127	39	13/39	65	24			56	24	44
	33	11/33	65	24			56	24	44
	18	6/18	65	24			56	24	44
128	16	5/16	61						
129	39	13/39	65	24			72	24	44
	33	11/33	65	24			72	24	44
	18	6/18	65	24			72	24	44
130	39	12/39	60						
131	20	6/20	58	40			28	44	
132	33	10/33	59						
133	49	14/49	55	24			48	44	
	21	6/21	56	24			48	44	
134	49	14/49	55	28			48	44	
	21	6/21	56	28			48	44	
135	27	8/27	58						
136	17	5/17	57						
137	49	14/49	55	28			24	56	
	21	6/21	56	28			24	56	
138	49	14/49	55	56			32	44	
	21	6/21	56	56			32	44	
139	49	14/49	55	56	32	48	24		
	21	6/21	56	56	32	48	24		
140	49	14/49	55						
	21	6/21	56						
141	18	5/18	54	48			40	44	
142	49	14/49	55	56			32	24	44
	21	6/21	56	56			32	24	44

Number of Divisions	Index Circle	No. of Turns of Index	Graduation	Gear on Worm	No. 1 Hole: 1st Gear on Stud	No. 1 Hole: 2nd Gear on Stud	Gear on Spindle	Idlers: No. 1 Hole	Idlers: No. 2 Hole
143	49	14/49	55	28			24	24	44
	21	6/21	56	28			24	24	44
144	18	5/18	54						
145	29	8/29	54						
146	49	14/49	55	28			48	24	44
	21	6/21	56	28			48	24	44
147	49	14/49	55	24			48	24	44
	21	6/21	56	24			48	24	44
148	37	10/37	53						
149	49	14/49	55	28			72	24	44
	21	6/21	56	28			72	24	44
150	15	4/15	52						
151	20	5/20	48	32			72	44	
152	19	5/19	51						
153	20	5/20	48	32			56	44	
154	20	5/20	48	32			48	44	
155	31	8/31	50						
156	39	10/39	50						
157	20	5/20	48	32			24	56	
158	20	5/20	48	48			24	44	
159	20	5/20	48	64	32	56	28		
160	20	5/20	48						
161	20	5/20	48	64	32	56	28		24
162	20	5/20	48	48			24	24	44
163	20	5/20	48	32			24	24	44
164	41	10/41	47						
165	33	8/33	47						
166	20	5/20	48	32			48	24	44
167	20	5/20	48	32			56	24	44
168	21	5/21	47						

INDEX TABLE 169 to 214.

Number of Divisions	Index Circle	No. of Turns of Index	Graduation	Gear on Worm	No. 1 Hole		Gear on Spindle	Idlers	
					1st Gear on Stud	2nd Gear on Stud		No. 1 Hole	No. 2 Hole
169	20	$\frac{5}{20}$	48	32			72	24	44
170	17	$\frac{4}{17}$	45						
171	21	$\frac{5}{21}$	47	56			40	24	44
172	43	$\frac{10}{43}$	44						
173	27	$\frac{6}{27}$	43	72	56	32	64		
	18	$\frac{4}{18}$	43	72	56	32	64		
174	27	$\frac{6}{27}$	43	24			32	56	
	18	$\frac{4}{18}$	43	24			32	56	
175	27	$\frac{6}{27}$	43	72	40	32	64		
	18	$\frac{4}{18}$	43	72	40	32	64		
176	27	$\frac{6}{27}$	43	72	24	24	64		
	18	$\frac{4}{18}$	43	72	24	24	64		
177	27	$\frac{6}{27}$	43	72			48	24	
	18	$\frac{4}{18}$	43	72			48	24	
178	27	$\frac{6}{27}$	43	72			32	44	
	18	$\frac{4}{18}$	43	72			32	44	
179	27	$\frac{6}{27}$	43	72	24	48	32		
	18	$\frac{4}{18}$	43	72	24	48	32		
180	27	$\frac{6}{27}$	43						
	18	$\frac{4}{18}$	43						
181	27	$\frac{6}{27}$	43	72	24	48	32		24
	18	$\frac{4}{18}$	43	72	24	48	32		24
182	27	$\frac{6}{27}$	43	72			32	24	44
	18	$\frac{4}{18}$	43	72			32	24	44
183	27	$\frac{6}{27}$	43	48			32	24	44
	18	$\frac{4}{18}$	43	48			32	24	44
184	23	$\frac{5}{23}$	42						
185	37	$\frac{8}{37}$	42						
186	27	$\frac{6}{27}$	43	48			64	24	44
	18	$\frac{4}{18}$	43	48			64	24	44

Number of Divisions	Index Circle	No. of Turns of Index	Graduation	Gear on Worm	No. 1 Hole		Gear on Spindle	Idlers	
					1st Gear on Stud	2nd Gear on Stud		No. 1 Hole	No. 2 Hole
187	27	$\frac{6}{27}$	43	72	48	24	56		24
	18	$\frac{4}{18}$	43	72	48	24	56		24
188	47	$\frac{10}{47}$	40						
189	27	$\frac{6}{27}$	43	32			64	24	44
	18	$\frac{4}{18}$	43	32			64	24	44
190	19	$\frac{4}{19}$	40						
191	20	$\frac{4}{20}$	38	40			72	24	
192	20	$\frac{4}{20}$	38	40			64	44	
193	20	$\frac{4}{20}$	38	40			56	44	
194	20	$\frac{4}{20}$	38	40			48	44	
195	39	$\frac{8}{39}$	39						
196	49	$\frac{10}{49}$	38						
197	20	$\frac{4}{20}$	38	40			24	56	
198	20	$\frac{4}{20}$	38	56	28	40	32		
199	20	$\frac{4}{20}$	38	100	40	64	32		
200	20	$\frac{4}{20}$	38						
201	20	$\frac{4}{20}$	38	72	24	40	24		24
202	20	$\frac{4}{20}$	38	72	24	40	48		24
203	20	$\frac{4}{20}$	38	40			24	24	44
204	20	$\frac{4}{20}$	38	40			32	24	44
205	41	$\frac{8}{41}$	37						
206	20	$\frac{4}{20}$	38	40			48	24	44
207	20	$\frac{4}{20}$	38	40			56	24	44
208	20	$\frac{4}{20}$	38	40			64	24	44
209	20	$\frac{4}{20}$	38	40			72	24	44
210	21	$\frac{4}{21}$	37						
211	16	$\frac{3}{16}$	36	64			28	44	
212	43	$\frac{8}{43}$	35	86	24	24	48		
213	27	$\frac{5}{27}$	36	72			40	44	
214	20	$\frac{4}{20}$	38	40	56	32	64		24

INDEX TABLE 215 to 270.

NUMBER OF DIVISIONS	INDEX CIRCLE	No. OF TURNS OF INDEX	GRADUATION	GEAR ON WORM	No. 1 HOLE		GEAR ON SPINDLE	IDLERS	
					1ST GEAR ON STUD	2ND GEAR ON STUD		No. 1 HOLE	No. 2 HOLE
215	43	$\frac{8}{43}$	35						
216	27	$\frac{5}{27}$	36						
217	21	$\frac{4}{21}$	37	48			64	24	44
218	16	$\frac{3}{16}$	36	64			56	24	44
219	21	$\frac{4}{21}$	37	28			48	24	44
220	33	$\frac{6}{33}$	35						
221	17	$\frac{3}{17}$	33	24			24	56	
222	18	$\frac{3}{18}$	32	24			72	44	
223	43	$\frac{8}{43}$	35	86	48	24	64		24
224	18	$\frac{3}{18}$	32	24			64	44	
225	27	$\frac{5}{27}$	36	24			40	24	44
226	18	$\frac{3}{18}$	32	24			56	44	
227	49	$\frac{8}{49}$	30	56	64	28	72		
228	18	$\frac{3}{18}$	32	24			48	44	
229	18	$\frac{3}{18}$	32	24			44	48	
230	23	$\frac{4}{23}$	34						
231	18	$\frac{3}{18}$	32	32			48	44	
232	29	$\frac{5}{29}$	33						
233	18	$\frac{3}{18}$	32	48			56	44	
234	18	$\frac{3}{18}$	32	24			24	56	
235	47	$\frac{8}{47}$	32						
236	18	$\frac{3}{18}$	32	48			32	44	
237	18	$\frac{3}{18}$	32	48			24	44	
238	18	$\frac{3}{18}$	32	72			24	44	
239	18	$\frac{3}{18}$	32	72	24	64	32		
240	18	$\frac{3}{18}$	32						
241	18	$\frac{3}{18}$	32	72	24	64	32		24
242	18	$\frac{3}{18}$	32	72			24	24	44
243	18	$\frac{3}{18}$	32	64			32	24	44
244	18	$\frac{3}{18}$	32	48			32	24	44

NUMBER OF DIVISIONS	INDEX CIRCLE	No. OF TURNS OF INDEX	GRADUATION	GEAR ON WORM	No. 1 HOLE		GEAR ON SPINDLE	IDLERS	
					1ST GEAR ON STUD	2ND GEAR ON STUD		No. 1 HOLE	No. 2 HOLE
245	49	$\frac{8}{49}$	30						
246	18	$\frac{3}{18}$	32	24			24	24	44
247	18	$\frac{3}{18}$	32	48			56	24	44
248	31	$\frac{5}{31}$	31						
249	18	$\frac{3}{18}$	32	32			48	24	44
250	18	$\frac{3}{18}$	32	24			40	24	44
251	18	$\frac{3}{18}$	32	48	44	32	64		24
252	18	$\frac{3}{18}$	32	24			48	24	44
253	33	$\frac{5}{33}$	29	24			40	56	
254	18	$\frac{3}{18}$	32	24			56	24	44
255	18	$\frac{3}{18}$	32	48	40	24	72		24
256	18	$\frac{3}{18}$	32	24			64	24	44
257	49	$\frac{8}{49}$	30	56	48	28	64		24
258	43	$\frac{7}{43}$	31	32			64	24	44
259	49	$\frac{7}{49}$	26	24			72	44	
	21	$\frac{3}{21}$	28	24			72	44	
260	39	$\frac{6}{39}$	29						
261	29	$\frac{4}{29}$	26	48	64	24	72		
262	20	$\frac{3}{20}$	28	40			28	44	
263	49	$\frac{8}{49}$	30	56	64	28	72		24
264	33	$\frac{5}{33}$	29						
265	49	$\frac{7}{49}$	26	56	40	24	72		
	21	$\frac{3}{21}$	28	56	40	24	72		
266	49	$\frac{7}{49}$	26	32			64	44	
	21	$\frac{3}{21}$	28	32			64	44	
267	27	$\frac{4}{27}$	28	72			32	44	
268	49	$\frac{7}{49}$	26	28			48	44	
	21	$\frac{3}{21}$	28	28			48	44	
269	20	$\frac{3}{20}$	28	64	32	40	28		24
270	27	$\frac{4}{27}$	28						

INDEX TABLE 271 to 310

NUMBER OF DIVISIONS	INDEX CIRCLE	No. OF TURNS OF INDEX	GRADUATION	GEAR ON WORM	No. 1 HOLE		GEAR ON SPINDLE	IDLERS	
					1ST GEAR ON STUD	2ND GEAR ON STUD		No. 1 HOLE	No. 2 HOLE
271	49	$\frac{7}{49}$	26	56			72	24	
	21	$\frac{3}{21}$	28	56			72	24	
272	49	$\frac{7}{49}$	26	56			64	24	
	21	$\frac{3}{21}$	28	56			64	24	
273	49	$\frac{7}{49}$	26	24			24	56	
	21	$\frac{3}{21}$	28	24			24	56	
274	49	$\frac{7}{49}$	26	56			48	44	
	21	$\frac{3}{21}$	28	56			48	44	
275	49	$\frac{7}{49}$	26	56			40	44	
	21	$\frac{3}{21}$	28	56			40	44	
276	49	$\frac{7}{49}$	26	56			32	44	
	21	$\frac{3}{21}$	28	56			32	44	
277	49	$\frac{7}{49}$	26	56			24	44	
	21	$\frac{3}{21}$	28	56			24	44	
278	49	$\frac{7}{49}$	26	56	32	48	24		
	21	$\frac{3}{21}$	28	56	32	48	24		
279	27	$\frac{4}{27}$	28	24			32	24	44
280	49	$\frac{7}{49}$	26						
	21	$\frac{3}{21}$	28						
281	49	$\frac{7}{49}$	26	72	24	56	24		24
	21	$\frac{3}{21}$	28	72	24	56	24		24
282	43	$\frac{6}{43}$	26	86	24	24	56		
283	49	$\frac{7}{49}$	26	56			24	24	44
	21	$\frac{3}{21}$	28	56			24	24	44
284	49	$\frac{7}{49}$	26	56			32	24	44
	21	$\frac{3}{21}$	28	56			32	24	44
285	49	$\frac{7}{49}$	26	56			40	24	44
	21	$\frac{3}{21}$	28	56			40	24	44
286	49	$\frac{7}{49}$	26	56			48	24	44
	21	$\frac{3}{21}$	28	56			48	24	44

NUMBER OF DIVISIONS	INDEX CIRCLE	No. OF TURNS OF INDEX	GRADUATION	GEAR ON WORM	No. 1 HOLE		GEAR ON SPINDLE	IDLERS	
					1ST GEAR ON STUD	2ND GEAR ON STUD		No. 1 HOLE	No. 2 HOLE
287	49	$\frac{7}{49}$	26	24			24	24	44
	21	$\frac{3}{21}$	28	24			24	24	44
288	49	$\frac{7}{49}$	26	28			32	24	44
	21	$\frac{3}{21}$	28	28			32	24	44
289	49	$\frac{7}{49}$	26	56	24	24	72		24
	21	$\frac{3}{21}$	28	56	24	24	72		24
290	29	$\frac{4}{29}$	26						
291	15	$\frac{2}{15}$	25	40			48	44	
292	49	$\frac{7}{49}$	26	28			48	24	44
	21	$\frac{3}{21}$	28	28			48	24	44
293	15	$\frac{2}{15}$	25	48	32	40	56		
294	49	$\frac{7}{49}$	26	24			48	24	44
	21	$\frac{3}{21}$	28	24			48	24	44
295	15	$\frac{2}{15}$	25	48			32	44	
296	37	$\frac{5}{37}$	26						
297	33	$\frac{4}{33}$	23	28	48	24	56		
298	49	$\frac{7}{49}$	26	28			72	24	44
	21	$\frac{3}{21}$	28	28			72	24	44
299	23	$\frac{3}{23}$	25	24			24	56	
300	15	$\frac{2}{15}$	25						
301	43	$\frac{6}{43}$	26	24			48	24	44
302	16	$\frac{2}{16}$	24	32			72	24	
303	15	$\frac{2}{15}$	25	72	24	40	48		24
304	16	$\frac{2}{16}$	24	24			48	44	
305	15	$\frac{2}{15}$	25	48			32	24	44
306	15	$\frac{2}{15}$	25	40			32	24	44
307	15	$\frac{2}{15}$	25	72	48	40	56		24
308	16	$\frac{2}{16}$	24	32			48	44	
309	15	$\frac{2}{15}$	25	40			48	24	44
310	31	$\frac{4}{31}$	24						

INDEX TABLE 311 to 355

Number of Divisions	Index Circle	No. of Turns of Index	Graduation	Gear on Worm	No. 1 Hole: 1st Gear on Stud	No. 1 Hole: 2nd Gear on Stud	Gear on Spindle	Idlers: No. 1 Hole	Idlers: No. 2 Hole	Number of Divisions	Index Circle	No. of Turns of Index	Graduation	Gear on Worm	No. 1 Hole: 1st Gear on Stud	No. 1 Hole: 2nd Gear on Stud	Gear on Spindle	Idlers: No. 1 Hole	Idlers: No. 2 Hole
311	16	2/16	24	64	24	24	72			339	27	3/27	21	24			56	44	
312	39	5/39	24								18	2/18	21	24			56	44	
313	16	2/16	24	32			28	56		340	17	2/17	22						
314	16	2/16	24	32			24	56		341	43	5/43	21	86	24	32	40		
315	16	2/16	24	64			40	24		342	27	3/27	21	32			64	44	
316	16	2/16	24	64			32	44			18	2/18	21	32			64	44	
317	16	2/16	24	64			24	44		343	15	2/15	25	40	64	24	86		24
318	16	2/16	24	56	28	48	24			344	43	5/43	21						
319	29	4/29	26	48	64	24	72		24	345	27	3/27	21	24			40	56	
320	16	2/16	24								18	2/18	21	24			40	56	
321	16	2/16	24	72	24	64	24		24	346	27	3/27	21	72	56	32	64		
322	23	3/23	25	32			64	24	44		18	2/18	21	72	56	32	64		
323	16	2/16	24	64			24	24	44	347	43	5/43	21	86	24	32	40		24
324	16	2/16	24	64			32	24	44	348	27	3/27	21	24			32	56	
325	16	2/16	24	64			40	24	44		18	2/18	21	24			32	56	
326	16	2/16	24	32			24	24	44	349	27	3/27	21	72	44	24	48		
327	16	2/16	24	32			28	24	44		18	2/18	21	72	44	24	48		
328	41	5/41	23							350	27	3/27	21	72	40	32	64		
329	16	2/16	24	64	24	24	72		24		18	2/18	21	72	40	32	64		
330	33	4/33	23							351	27	3/27	21	24			24	56	
331	16	2/16	24	64	44	24	48		24		18	2/18	21	24			24	56	
332	16	2/16	24	32			48	24	44	352	27	3/27	21	72	24	24	64		
333	27	3/27	21	24			72	44			18	2/18	21	72	24	24	64		
	18	2/18	21	24			72	44		353	27	3/27	21	72	24	24	56		
334	16	2/16	24	32			56	24	44		18	2/18	21	72	24	24	56		
335	33	4/33	23	72	48	44	40		24	354	27	3/27	21	72			48	24	
336	16	2/16	24	32			64	24	44		18	2/18	21	72			48	24	
337	43	5/43	21	86	40	32	56			355	27	3/27	21	72			40	24	
338	16	2/16	24	32			72	24	44		18	2/18	21	72			40	24	

INDEX TABLE 356 to 399.

Number of Divisions	Index Circle	No. of Turns of Index	Graduation	Gear on Worm	No. 1 Hole: 1st Gear on Stud	No. 1 Hole: 2nd Gear on Stud	Gear on Spindle	Idlers: No. 1 Hole	Idlers: No. 2 Hole
356	27	3/27	21	72			32	24	
	18	2/18	21	72			32	24	
357	27	3/27	21	72			24	44	
	18	2/18	21	72			24	44	
358	27	3/27	21	72	32	48	24		
	18	2/18	21	72	32	48	24		
359	43	5/43	21	86	48	32	100		24
360	27	3/27	21						
	18	2/18	21						
361	19	2/19	19	32			64	44	
362	27	3/27	21	72	28	56	32		24
	18	2/18	21	72	28	56	32		24
363	27	3/27	21	72			24	24	44
	18	2/18	21	72			24	24	44
364	27	3/27	21	72			32	24	44
	18	2/18	21	72			32	24	44
365	20	2/20	18	32	48	24	56		
366	27	3/27	21	48			32	24	44
	18	2/18	21	48			32	24	44
367	27	3/27	21	72	24	24	56		24
	18	2/18	21	72	24	24	56		24
368	27	3/27	21	72	24	24	64		24
	18	2/18	21	72	24	24	64		24
369	41	4/41	18	32	56	28	64		
370	37	4/37	20						
371	21	2/21	18	32	56	24	64		
372	27	3/27	21	48			64	24	44
	18	2/18	21	48			64	24	44
373	20	2/20	18	40	48	32	72		

Number of Divisions	Index Circle	No. of Turns of Index	Graduation	Gear on Worm	No. 1 Hole: 1st Gear on Stud	No. 1 Hole: 2nd Gear on Stud	Gear on Spindle	Idlers: No. 1 Hole	Idlers: No. 2 Hole
374	27	3/27	21	72	56	32	64		24
	18	2/18	21	72	56	32	64		24
375	27	3/27	21	24			40	24	44
	18	2/18	21	24			40	24	44
376	47	5/47	19						
377	29	3/29	19	24			24	56	
378	27	3/27	21	32			64	24	44
	18	2/18	21	32			64	24	44
379	20	2/20	18	48	56	40	72		
380	19	2/19	19						
381	27	3/27	21	24			56	24	44
	18	2/18	21	24			56	24	44
382	20	2/20	18	40			72	24	
383	20	2/20	18	40			68*		
384	20	2/20	18	40			64	44	
385	20	2/20	18	32			48	44	
386	20	2/20	18	40			56	44	
387	43	4/43	15	32	56	28	64		
388	20	2/20	18	40			48	44	
389	20	2/20	18	40			44	56	
390	39	4/39	17						
391	20	2/20	18	48	24	40	72		
392	49	5/49	16						
393	20	2/20	18	40			28	44	
394	20	2/20	18	40			24	56	
395	20	2/20	18	64			32	44	
396	20	2/20	18	56	28	40	32		
397	20	2/20	18	64	24	40	32		
398	20	2/20	18	100	40	64	32		
399	21	2/21	18	32			64	44	

* SPECIAL GEAR.

INDEX TABLE

Plain and Differential Indexing for Divisions from 383 to 1008

Many of these divisions can be obtained by plain indexing and differential indexing, using the gears furnished with the machines. By the addition of eight special change gears all divisions from 383 to 1008 may be indexed.

The special change gears required have the following numbers of teeth: 46, 47, 52, 58, 68, 70, 76, 84.

INDEX TABLE 807 TO 912

Number of Divisions	Index Circle	No. of Turns of Index	Gear on Worm	No. 1 Hole		Gear on Spindle	Idlers	
				1st Gear on Stud	2nd Gear on Stud		No. 1 Hole	No. 2 Hole
807	20	$\frac{1}{20}$	64	32	40	28		24
808	20	$\frac{1}{20}$	72	24	40	48		24
809	20	$\frac{1}{20}$	64	24	40	48		24
810	20	$\frac{1}{20}$	48			24	24	44
811	20	$\frac{1}{20}$	64	32	40	44		24
812	20	$\frac{1}{20}$	40			24	24	44
813	21	$\frac{1}{21}$	56	24	24	72		
814	20	$\frac{1}{20}$	40			28	24	44
815	20	$\frac{1}{20}$	32			24	24	44
816	20	$\frac{1}{20}$	40			32	24	44
817	43	$\frac{2}{43}$	24			48	44	
818	20	$\frac{1}{20}$	40	24	32	48		24
819	39	$\frac{2}{39}$	24			48	24	44
820	41	$\frac{2}{41}$						
821	20	$\frac{1}{20}$	32	28	40	48		24
822	21	$\frac{1}{21}$	28			24	56	
823	39	$\frac{2}{39}$	52*	32	24	86		24
824	20	$\frac{1}{20}$	40			48	24	44
825	21	$\frac{1}{21}$	56			40	44	
826	21	$\frac{1}{21}$	48			32	44	
827	20	$\frac{1}{20}$	40	24	32	72		24
828	21	$\frac{1}{21}$	56			32	44	
829	21	$\frac{1}{21}$	72	24	28	44		
830	20	$\frac{1}{20}$	32			48	24	44
831	21	$\frac{1}{21}$	56			24	44	
832	20	$\frac{1}{20}$	40			64	24	44
833	20	$\frac{1}{20}$	40	44	32	48		24
834	21	$\frac{1}{21}$	56	32	48	24		
835	20	$\frac{1}{20}$	32			56	24	44
836	20	$\frac{1}{20}$	40			72	24	44
837	21	$\frac{1}{21}$	72	24	56	24		
838	43	$\frac{2}{43}$	86	44	24	48		†
839	43	$\frac{2}{43}$	86	48	32	56		
840	21	$\frac{1}{21}$						
841	43	$\frac{2}{43}$	86	24	24	76*		
842	20	$\frac{1}{20}$	48	56	40	72		24
843	21	$\frac{1}{21}$	72	24	56	24		24
844	20	$\frac{1}{20}$	40	44	32	64		24
845	20	$\frac{1}{20}$	32			72	24	44
846	43	$\frac{2}{43}$	86	24	24	56		
847	21	$\frac{1}{21}$	72			24	24	44
848	43	$\frac{2}{43}$	86	24	24	48		
849	21	$\frac{1}{21}$	56			24	24	44
850	21	$\frac{1}{21}$	72	48	56	40		24
851	21	$\frac{1}{21}$	72	24	28	44		24
852	21	$\frac{1}{21}$	56			32	24	44
853	43	$\frac{2}{43}$	86			28	24	
854	20	$\frac{1}{20}$	40	48	32	72		24
855	21	$\frac{1}{21}$	56			40	24	44
856	20	$\frac{1}{20}$	40	56	32	64		24
857	21	$\frac{1}{21}$	72	24	28	68*		24
858	21	$\frac{1}{21}$	28			24	24	44
859	21	$\frac{1}{21}$	56	32	48	76*		24
860	43	$\frac{2}{43}$						
861	21	$\frac{1}{21}$	24			24	24	44
862	21	$\frac{1}{21}$	72	44	28	48		24
863	20	$\frac{1}{20}$	40	56	32	72		24
864	21	$\frac{1}{21}$	28			32	24	44
865	21	$\frac{1}{21}$	56	32	48	100		24
866	20	$\frac{1}{20}$	40	44	24	72		24
867	21	$\frac{1}{21}$	56	24	24	72		24
868	21	$\frac{1}{21}$	48			64	24	44
869	43	$\frac{2}{43}$	86	24	48	72		24
870	21	$\frac{1}{21}$	28			40	24	44
871	43	$\frac{2}{43}$	86	24	24	44		24
872	20	$\frac{1}{20}$	40	48	24	72		24
873	21	$\frac{1}{21}$	56	48	24	44		24
874	23	$\frac{1}{23}$	32			64	44	
875	43	$\frac{2}{43}$	86	40	48	72		24
876	21	$\frac{1}{21}$	28			48	24	44
877	23	$\frac{1}{23}$	46*	24	24	86		
878	43	$\frac{2}{43}$	86	24	24	72		24
879	43	$\frac{2}{43}$	86	24	24	76*		24
880	43	$\frac{2}{43}$	32	64	86	40		24
881	43	$\frac{2}{43}$	86	48	32	56		24
882	21	$\frac{1}{21}$	24			48	24	44
883	21	$\frac{1}{21}$	48	32	28	86		24
884	20	$\frac{1}{20}$	40	56	24	72		24
885	43	$\frac{2}{43}$	86	24	24	100		24
886	20	$\frac{1}{20}$	40	48	24	86		24
887	43	$\frac{2}{43}$	86	48	32	72		24
888	21	$\frac{1}{21}$	56	48	24	64		24
889	21	$\frac{1}{21}$	24			56	24	44
890	43	$\frac{2}{43}$	86	40	24	72		24
891	23	$\frac{1}{23}$	46*			58*	44	
892	43	$\frac{2}{43}$	86	48	24	64		24
893	43	$\frac{2}{43}$	86	44	24	72		24
894	21	$\frac{1}{21}$	28			72	24	44
895	43	$\frac{2}{43}$	86	56	40	100		24
896	20	$\frac{1}{20}$	40	64	24	72		24
897	23	$\frac{1}{23}$	24			24	56	
898	23	$\frac{1}{23}$	46*			44	56	
899	23	$\frac{1}{23}$	46*	28	32	48		
900	43	$\frac{2}{43}$	86	64	40	100		24
901	23	$\frac{1}{23}$	48	24	46*	76*		
902	43	$\frac{2}{43}$	86	56	24	72		24
903	43	$\frac{2}{43}$	24			48	24	44
904	47	$\frac{2}{47}$	47			72		24
905	43	$\frac{2}{43}$	86	72	40	100		24
906	47	$\frac{2}{47}$	47			68*		24
907	23	$\frac{1}{23}$	48	24	46*	52*		
908	49	$\frac{2}{49}$	56	64	28	72		
909	23	$\frac{1}{23}$	48	24	46*	44		
910	49	$\frac{2}{49}$	28	40	32	64		
911	23	$\frac{1}{23}$	46*	48	64	24		
912	21	$\frac{1}{21}$	56	64	24	72		24

SPECIAL GEARS:
46, 47, 52, 58, 68, 70, 76, 84

† BOLT FOR 1ST AND 2ND STUD GEARS IN NO. 2 HOLE
* SPECIAL GEAR

INDEX TABLE 913 TO 1008

Number of Divisions	Index Circle	No. of Turns of Index	Gear on Worm	No. 1 Hole: 1st Gear on Stud	No. 1 Hole: 2nd Gear on Stud	Gear on Spindle	Idlers: No. 1 Hole	Idlers: No. 2 Hole
913	23	$\frac{1}{23}$	48	24	46*	28		
914	23	$\frac{1}{23}$	48	24	46*	24		
915	21	$\frac{1}{21}$	56	48	24	100		24
916	21	$\frac{1}{21}$	28	32	24	76*		24
917	49	$\frac{2}{49}$	28			72	44	
918	21	$\frac{1}{21}$	28	64	32	52*		24
919	47	$\frac{2}{47}$	64	48	47*	56		
920	23	$\frac{1}{23}$						
921	21	$\frac{1}{21}$	32	48	28	72		24
922	49	$\frac{2}{49}$	56	58*	28	64		
923	49	$\frac{2}{49}$	56	48	28	76*		
924	49	$\frac{2}{49}$	28			64	44	
925	21	$\frac{1}{21}$	28	40	24	68*		24
926	21	$\frac{1}{21}$	56	64	24	86		24
927	23	$\frac{1}{23}$	48	24	46*	28		24
928	21	$\frac{1}{21}$	28	44	24	64		24
929	23	$\frac{1}{23}$	32	24	46*	24		24
930	49	$\frac{2}{49}$	56	32	28	100		
931	49	$\frac{2}{49}$	24			48	44	
932	49	$\frac{2}{49}$	56	48	28	64		
933	23	$\frac{1}{23}$	48	24	46*	52*		24
934	23	$\frac{1}{23}$	46*	24	24	28		24
935	49	$\frac{2}{49}$	56	40	28	72		
936	49	$\frac{2}{49}$	56	44	28	64		
937	49	$\frac{2}{49}$	56	32	28	86		
938	49	$\frac{2}{49}$	28			48	44	
939	21	$\frac{1}{21}$	28	44	24	72		24
940	47	$\frac{2}{47}$						
941	23	$\frac{1}{23}$	46*	28	32	48		24
942	49	$\frac{2}{49}$	56	32	28	76*		
943	23	$\frac{1}{23}$	24			24	24	48
944	49	$\frac{2}{49}$	56	32	28	72		
945	49	$\frac{2}{49}$	28			40	44	
946	49	$\frac{2}{49}$	56	32	28	68*		
947	49	$\frac{2}{49}$	56	44	28	48		
948	49	$\frac{2}{49}$	56	32	28	64		
949	23	$\frac{1}{23}$	46*	24	24	58*		24
950	49	$\frac{2}{49}$	56	40	28	48		
951	49	$\frac{2}{49}$	56	32	28	58*		
952	49	$\frac{2}{49}$	56			64	24	
953	49	$\frac{2}{49}$	56	24	28	72		
954	49	$\frac{2}{49}$	56	32	28	52*		
955	23	$\frac{1}{23}$	46*	40	32	56		24
956	49	$\frac{2}{49}$	56	24	28	64		
957	49	$\frac{2}{49}$	56	32	28	46*		
958	49	$\frac{2}{49}$	56	32	28	44		
959	49	$\frac{2}{49}$	28			24	56	
960	49	$\frac{2}{49}$	56	32	28	40		
961	47	$\frac{2}{47}$	47*	24	32	56		24
962	49	$\frac{2}{49}$	56	24	28	48		
963	23	$\frac{1}{23}$	46*	24	24	86		24
964	23	$\frac{1}{23}$	46*	44	24	48		24
965	49	$\frac{2}{49}$	56	24	28	40		
966	49	$\frac{2}{49}$	56			32	44	
967	23	$\frac{1}{23}$	46*	47*	24	48		24
968	49	$\frac{2}{49}$	56	24	28	32		
969	21	$\frac{1}{21}$	28	48	24	86		24
970	23	$\frac{1}{23}$	46*	24	24	100		24
971	23	$\frac{1}{23}$	46*	48	32	68*		24
972	27	$\frac{1}{27}$	32	56	28	64		
973	49	$\frac{2}{49}$	56	32	48	24		
974	23	$\frac{1}{23}$	46*	48	32	72		24
975	27	$\frac{1}{27}$	24	40	24	56		
976	23	$\frac{1}{23}$	46*	48	24	56		24
977	23	$\frac{1}{23}$	46*	48	32	76*		24
978	23	$\frac{1}{23}$	46*	58*	32	64		24
979	47	$\frac{2}{47}$	47*	48	32	52*		24
980	49	$\frac{2}{49}$						
981	27	$\frac{1}{27}$	24	44	24	48		
982	47	$\frac{2}{47}$	47*	48	32	56		24
983	23	$\frac{1}{23}$	46*	56	32	72		24
984	23	$\frac{1}{23}$	46*	48	24	64		24
985	23	$\frac{1}{23}$	46*	52*	40	100		24
986	29	$\frac{1}{29}$	32	64	24	72		
987	49	$\frac{2}{49}$	56	24	48	32		24
988	23	$\frac{1}{23}$	46*	48	24	68*		24
989	49	$\frac{2}{49}$	56	24	28	24		24
990	27	$\frac{1}{27}$	32	40	24	64		
991	49	$\frac{2}{49}$	70*	40	56	44		24
992	49	$\frac{2}{49}$	56	24	28	32		24
993	49	$\frac{2}{49}$	70*	40	56	52*		24
994	49	$\frac{2}{49}$	56			32	24	44
995	49	$\frac{2}{49}$	56	24	28	40		24
996	27	$\frac{1}{27}$	48	56	24	64		
997	49	$\frac{2}{49}$	70*	40	56	68*		24
998	49	$\frac{2}{49}$	56	24	28	48		24
999	27	$\frac{1}{27}$	24			72	44	
1000	49	$\frac{2}{49}$	56	32	28	40		24
1001	49	$\frac{2}{49}$	28			24	24	44
1002	49	$\frac{2}{49}$	56	32	28	44		24
1003	49	$\frac{2}{49}$	56	32	28	46*		24
1004	49	$\frac{2}{49}$	56	32	28	48		24
1005	27	$\frac{1}{27}$	72	48	24	100		
1006	23	$\frac{1}{23}$	46*	64	32	86		24
1007	49	$\frac{2}{49}$	56	24	28	72		24
1008	49	$\frac{2}{49}$	56			64	24	24

SPECIAL GEARS:
46, 47, 52, 58, 68, 70, 76, 84

* SPECIAL GEAR

TABLE OF APPROXIMATE ANGLES FOR CUTTING SPIRALS

$$\text{TANGENT OF ANGLE OF SPIRAL} = \frac{\text{CIRCUMFERENCE OF CUTTER, DRILL, OR MILL}}{\text{LEAD IN INCHES TO ONE TURN}}$$

C = CIRCUMFERENCE OF CUTTER, DRILL, OR MILL
L = LEAD IN INCHES TO ONE TURN
T = TANGENT OF ANGLE OF SPIRAL

$$T = \frac{C}{L} \qquad L = \frac{C}{T}$$

NOS. OF TEETH IN GEARS FURNISHED WITH MACHINE
24(2) 28 32 40 44 48 56 64 72 86 100

$$\text{THE LEAD IN INCHES TO ONE TURN} = \frac{10 \times \text{GEAR ON WORM} \times \text{2ND GEAR ON STUD}}{\text{GEAR ON SCREW} \times \text{1ST GEAR ON STUD}}$$

Gear on Worm	1st Gear on Stud	2nd Gear on Stud	Gear on Screw	Lead in Inches to One Turn	Diameter of Cutter, Drill, or Mill																											
					1/8"	1/4"	3/8"	1/2"	5/8"	3/4"	7/8"	1"	1 1/4"	1 1/2"	1 3/4"	2"	2 1/4"	2 1/2"	2 3/4"	3"	3 1/4"	3 1/2"	3 3/4"	4"	4 1/4"	4 1/2"	4 3/4"	5"	5 1/4"	5 1/2"	5 3/4"	6"
24	72	28	86	1.085	20	36	47¼																									
24	72	32	86	1.240	17½	32¼	43½	51¾																								
24	72	40	100	1.333	16½	30½	41½	49¾																								
24	48	28	100	1.400	15¾	29¼	40	48¼																								
24	64	40	100	1.500	14¾	27¾	38¼	46¼	52½																							
28	56	32	100	1.600	13¾	26¼	36¼	44½	50¾																							
24	72	44	86	1.706	13	24¾	34½	42½	49																							
24	64	48	100	1.800	12¼	23½	33¼	41	47½	52½																						
24	40	32	100	1.920	11½	22¼	31½	39¼	45¾	50¾																						
28	64	40	86	2.035	11	21	30	37¾	44	49¼																						
24	72	56	86	2.171	10¼	20	28½	35¾	42	47¼	51¾																					
24	64	44	72	2.292	9¾	19	27¼	34½	40½	45¾	50¼																					
28	64	56	100	2.450	9	17¾	25¾	32¾	38¾	44	48¼	52																				
40	86	56	100	2.605	8½	16¾	24¼	31	37	42	46½	50¼																				
40	56	28	72	2.778	8	15¾	23	29½	35¼	40¼	44¾	48½																				
24	56	44	64	2.946	7½	15	21¾	28	33¾	38¾	43	46¾																				
24	86	72	64	3.140	7	14	20½	26½	32	37	41¼	45	51¼																			
28	56	48	72	3.333	6¾	13¼	19½	25¼	30½	35¼	39½	43¼	49¾																			
48	44	28	86	3.552	6¼	12½	18¼	23¾	29	33½	37¾	41½	47¾	53																		
44	56	48	100	3.771	6	11¾	17¼	22½	27½	32	36	39¾	46¼	51¼																		
72	100	48	86	4.019	5½	11	16¼	21¼	26	30½	34¼	38	44¼	49½																		
64	48	32	100	4.267	5¼	10½	15½	20¼	24¾	29	32¾	36¼	42½	47¾	52¼																	
56	48	28	72	4.537	5	9¾	14½	19	23½	27½	31¼	34¾	41	46	50½																	
56	64	40	72	4.861	4½	9¼	13½	18	22	25¾	29½	32¾	39	44	48½	52¼																

EXAMPLE ILLUSTRATING USE OF TABLE

DIAMETER OF CUTTER, DRILL, OR MILL.......... = 1¼
LEAD IN INCHES TO ONE TURN.................... = 3.140
REQUIRED ANGLE TO NEAREST QUARTER DEGREE TO SET SADDLE OF UNIVERSAL MILLING MACHINE = 51¼°

TABLE OF APPROXIMATE ANGLES FOR CUTTING SPIRALS

$$\text{TANGENT OF ANGLE OF SPIRAL} = \frac{\text{CIRCUMFERENCE OF CUTTER, DRILL, OR MILL}}{\text{LEAD IN INCHES TO ONE TURN}}$$

C=CIRCUMFERENCE OF CUTTER, DRILL, OR MILL
L=LEAD IN INCHES TO ONE TURN
T=TANGENT OF ANGLE OF SPIRAL

$T=\frac{C}{L}$ $L=\frac{C}{T}$

NOS. OF TEETH IN GEARS FURNISHED WITH MACHINE
24(2) 28 32 40 44 48 56 64 72 86 100

$$\text{THE LEAD IN INCHES TO ONE TURN} = \frac{10 \times \text{GEAR ON WORM} \times \text{2ND GEAR ON STUD}}{\text{GEAR ON SCREW} \times \text{1ST GEAR ON STUD}}$$

Gear on Worm	1st Gear on Stud	2nd Gear on Stud	Gear on Screw	Lead in Inches to One Turn	Diameter of Cutter, Drill, or Mill																											
					⅛"	¼"	⅜"	½"	⅝"	¾"	⅞"	1"	1¼"	1½"	1¾"	2"	2¼"	2½"	2¾"	3"	3¼"	3½"	3¾"	4"	4¼"	4½"	4¾"	5"	5¼"	5½"	5¾"	6"
56	48	44	100	5.133	4¼	8¾	13	17	21	24¾	28¼	31½	37½	42½	47	50¾																
86	44	28	100	5.473	4	8¼	12¼	16	19¾	23¼	26¾	29¾	35¾	40¾	45	49	52¼															
100	48	24	86	5.814	3¾	7¾	11½	15	18¾	22	25¼	28½	34	39	43½	47¼	50½															
72	56	48	100	6.171	3¾	7¼	10¾	14¼	17¾	21	24	27	32½	37¼	41¾	45½	48¾	51¾														
72	56	44	86	6.578	3½	6¾	10¼	13½	16½	19¾	22¾	25½	30¾	35½	40	43¾	47	50	52¾													
56	32	40	100	7.000	3¼	6½	9½	12¾	15¾	18½	21½	24¼	29¼	34	38¼	42	45¼	48¼	51													
56	28	32	86	7.442	3	6	9	12	14¾	17½	20¼	23	27¾	32¼	36½	40¼	43½	46½	49¼	51¾												
72	40	44	100	7.920	2¾	5¾	8½	11¼	14	16½	19¼	21¾	26¼	30¾	34¾	38½	41¾	44¾	47½	50	52¼											
56	32	48	100	8.400	2¾	5¼	8	10½	13¼	15¾	18	20½	25	29¼	33¼	36¾	40	43	45¾	48¼	50½	52½										
86	32	24	72	8.959	2½	5	7½	10	12¼	14¾	17	19¼	23¾	27¾	31½	35	38¼	41¼	44	46½	48¾	50¾	52¾									
64	48	40	56	9.524	2¼	4¾	7	9¼	11¾	14	16	18¼	22½	26¼	30	33½	36½	39½	42¼	44¾	47	49	51	52¾								
100	44	32	72	10.101	2¼	4½	6¾	8¾	11	13	15¼	17¼	21¼	25	28½	31¾	35	37¾	40½	43	45¼	47½	49½	51¼	53							
86	40	32	64	10.750	2	4¼	6¼	8¼	10¼	12¼	14¼	16¼	20	23¾	27	30¼	33¼	36¼	38¾	41¼	43½	45¾	47½	49½	51¼	52¾						
86	48	64	100	11.467	2	4	5¾	7¾	9¾	11½	13½	15¼	19	22¼	25½	28¾	31¾	34½	37	39½	41¾	43¾	45¾	47½	49¼	51	52½					
72	44	64	86	12.178	1¾	3¾	5½	7¼	9¼	11	12¾	14½	18	21¼	24¼	27¼	30¼	32¾	35¼	37¾	40	42	44	46	47¾	49¼	50¾	52¼				
56	24	40	72	12.963	1¾	3½	5¼	7	8½	10¼	12	13½	16¾	20	23	25¾	28½	31¼	33¾	36	38¼	40¼	42¼	44	45¾	47½	49	50½	51½	51¾		
86	40	64	100	13.760	1¾	3¼	5	6½	8	9¾	11¼	12¾	16	19	21¾	24½	27¼	29¾	32	34½	36½	38½	40½	42½	44¼	45¾	47¼	48¾	50¼	51½	52¾	
86	44	48	64	14.659	1½	3	4½	6	7¾	9¼	10½	12	15	17¾	20½	23¼	25¾	28¼	30½	32¾	34¾	36¾	38¾	40½	42¼	44	45½	47	48¼	49¾	51	52
64	32	56	72	15.556	1½	3	4¼	5¾	7¼	8½	10	11½	14¼	16¾	19½	22	24½	26¾	29	31¼	33¼	35¼	37¼	39	40¾	42¼	43¾	45¼	46¾	48	49¼	50½
72	40	44	48	16.500	1¼	2¾	4	5½	6¾	8¼	9½	10¾	13½	16	18½	20¾	23¼	25½	27¾	29¾	31¾	33¾	35½	37¼	39	40½	42	43½	45	46¼	47½	48¾
100	44	56	72	17.677	1¼	2½	3¾	5	6¼	7½	8¾	10	12½	15	17¼	19½	21¾	24	26	28	30	31¾	33¾	35½	37	38¾	40¼	41½	43	44¼	45½	46¾
86	28	44	72	18.770	1¼	2½	3½	4¾	6	7¼	8¼	9½	11¾	14	16¼	18½	20¾	22¾	24¾	26¾	28½	30¼	32	33¾	35½	37	38½	40	41¼	42½	44	45
100	28	48	86	19.934	1¼	2¼	3½	4½	5½	6¾	7¾	9	11¼	13¼	15½	17½	19½	21½	23½	25¼	27	28¾	30½	32¼	33¾	35¼	36¾	38¼	39½	41	42¼	43½
86	32	44	56	21.12	1	2¼	3¼	4¼	5¼	6¼	7½	8½	10½	12½	14½	16½	18½	20½	22¼	24	25¾	27½	29¼	30¾	32¼	33¾	35¼	36¾	38	39¼	40½	41¾

TABLE OF APPROXIMATE ANGLES FOR CUTTING SPIRALS

$$\text{TANGENT OF ANGLE OF SPIRAL} = \frac{\text{CIRCUMFERENCE OF CUTTER, DRILL, OR MILL}}{\text{LEAD IN INCHES TO ONE TURN}}$$

C = CIRCUMFERENCE OF CUTTER, DRILL, OR MILL
L = LEAD IN INCHES TO ONE TURN
T = TANGENT OF ANGLE OF SPIRAL

$T = \frac{C}{L}$ $L = \frac{C}{T}$

NOS. OF TEETH IN GEARS FURNISHED WITH MACHINE
24(2) 28 32 40 44 48 56 64 72 86 100

$$\text{THE LEAD IN INCHES TO ONE TURN} = \frac{10 \times \text{GEAR ON WORM} \times \text{2ND GEAR ON STUD}}{\text{GEAR ON SCREW} \times \text{1ST GEAR ON STUD}}$$

Gear on Worm	1st Gear on Stud	2nd Gear on Stud	Gear on Screw	Lead in Inches to One Turn	Diameter of Cutter, Drill, or Mill																											
					⅛″	¼″	⅜″	½″	⅝″	¾″	⅞″	1″	1¼″	1½″	1¾″	2″	2¼″	2½″	2¾″	3″	3¼″	3½″	3¾″	4″	4¼″	4½″	4¾″	5″	5¼″	5½″	5¾″	6″
72	28	56	64	22.50	1	2	3	4	5	6	7	8	10	11¾	13¾	15½	17½	19¼	21	22¾	24½	26	27¾	29¼	30¾	32¼	33½	35	36¼	37½	38¾	40
64	40	72	48	24.00	1	2	2¾	3¾	4¾	5½	6½	7½	9¼	11	13	14¾	16½	18¼	19¾	21½	23	24½	26¼	27½	29	30½	31¾	33¼	34½	35¾	37	38¼
100	64	72	44	25.57	1	1¾	2¾	3½	4½	5¼	6¼	7¼	8¾	10½	12¼	13¾	15½	17	18¾	20¼	21¾	23¼	24¾	26¼	27½	29	30¼	31½	32¾	34	35¼	36½
100	72	86	44	27.15		1¾	2½	3¼	4¼	5	5¾	6½	8¼	9¾	11½	13	14½	16¼	17¾	19¼	20½	22	23½	24¾	26¼	27½	28¾	30	31¼	32½	33¾	34¾
86	40	64	48	28.67		1½	2¼	3¼	4	4¾	5½	6¼	7¾	9¼	10¾	12¼	13¾	15¼	16¾	18¼	19½	21	22¼	23¾	25	26¼	27½	28¾	30	31	32¼	33¼
86	32	64	56	30.71		1½	2¼	3	3¾	4½	5	5¾	7¼	8¾	10¼	11½	13	14¼	15¾	17	18½	19¾	21	22¼	23½	24¾	26	27	28¼	29¼	30½	31½
72	32	64	44	32.73		1¼	2	2¾	3½	4	4¾	5½	6¾	8¼	9½	10¾	12¼	13½	14¾	16	17¼	18½	19¾	21	22¼	23¼	24½	25¾	26¾	27¾	29	30
100	24	40	48	34.72		1¼	2	2½	3¼	4	4½	5¼	6½	7¾	9	10¼	11½	12¾	14	15¼	16½	17½	18¾	20	21	22¼	23¼	24¼	25½	26½	27½	28½
100	24	64	72	37.04		1¼	1¾	2½	3	3¾	4¼	4¾	6	7¼	8½	9¾	10¾	12	13¼	14¼	15½	16½	17¾	18¾	19¾	21	22	23	24	25	26	27
100	28	44	40	39.29		1¼	1¾	2¼	2¾	3½	4	4½	5¾	6¾	8	9	10¼	11¼	12½	13½	14½	15¾	16¾	17¾	18¾	19¾	20¾	21¾	22¾	23¾	24¾	25½
86	24	56	48	41.81		1	1½	2¼	2¾	3¼	3¾	4¼	5¼	6½	7½	8½	9½	10¾	11¾	12¾	13¾	14¾	15¾	16¾	17¾	18¾	19¾	20½	21½	22½	23¼	24¼
100	28	40	32	44.64		1	1½	2	2½	3	3½	4	5	6	7	8	9	10	11	12	13	13¾	14¾	15¾	16¾	17½	18½	19½	20¼	21¼	22	23
100	28	64	48	47.62		1	1½	2	2¼	2¾	3¼	3¾	4¾	5¾	6½	7½	8½	9¼	10¼	11¼	12	13	14	14¾	15¾	16½	17½	18¼	19	20	20¾	21½
86	28	72	44	50.26		1	1¼	1¾	2¼	2¾	3¼	3½	4½	5¼	6¼	7¼	8	9	9¾	10½	11½	12¼	13¼	14	14¾	15¾	16½	17¼	18¼	19	19¾	20½
100	28	48	32	53.57			1¼	1¾	2	2½	3	3¼	4½	5	5¾	6¾	7	8¼	9¼	10	10¾	11½	12½	13¼	14	14¾	15½	16¼	17	17¾	18¾	19½
100	28	64	40	57.14			1¼	1½	2	2¼	2¾	3¼	4	4¾	5½	6¼	7	7¾	8½	9¼	10¼	11	11¾	12½	13¼	14	14¾	15¼	16	16¾	17½	18¼
100	24	64	44	60.61			1	1½	1¾	2¼	2½	3	3¾	4½	5¼	6	6¾	7½	8	8¾	9½	10¼	11	11¾	12½	13¼	13¾	14½	15¼	16	16½	17¼
100	28	86	48	63.99				1½	1¾	2	2½	2¾	3½	4¼	5	5½	6¼	7	7¾	8½	9	9¾	10½	11	11¾	12½	13	13¾	14½	15	15¾	16½
72	24	64	28	68.57				1¼	1¾	2	2¼	2½	3¼	4	4½	5¼	6	6½	7¼	7¾	8½	9	9¾	10½	11	11¾	12¼	13	13½	14¼	14¾	15¼
86	24	64	32	71.67				1¼	1½	2	2¼	2½	3¼	3¾	4½	5	5¾	6¼	6¾	7½	8	8¾	9¼	10	10½	11¼	11¾	12¼	13	13½	14¼	14¾
100	24	72	40	75.00				1¼	1½	1¾	2	2½	3	3½	4¼	4¾	5½	6	6½	7¼	7¾	8¼	9	9½	10	10¾	11¼	11¾	12½	13	13½	14
100	24	64	32	83.33				1	1¼	1½	2	2¼	2¾	3¼	3¾	4¼	4¾	5½	6	6½	7	7½	8	8½	9	9½	10¼	10¾	11¼	11¾	12¼	12¾
100	24	86	40	89.59				1	1¼	1½	1¾	2	2½	3	3½	4	4½	5	5½	6	6½	7	7½	8	8½	9	9½	10	10½	11	11½	12
100	24	64	28	95.24					1¼	1½	1¾	2	2¼	2¾	3¼	3¾	4¼	4¾	5¼	5¾	6	6½	7	7½	8	8½	9	9¼	9¾	10¼	10¾	11¼

TABLE OF LEADS

This table contains all the leads that can be obtained with any possible combination of the change gears furnished with Universal Milling Machines made by Brown & Sharpe Mfg. Co., even though some of the leads are not available for use on account of the gears interfering or not reaching. Combinations of gears that are too small in diameter to reach for right-hand spirals can generally be used for left-hand spirals, as the reverse gear is then required and will enable the gears to reach. For further information regarding the use of these tables, see Chapter IV.

The change gears that are furnished with the machines have the following numbers of teeth: 24 (2 gears), 28, 32, 40, 44, 48, 56, 64, 72, 86 and 100.

TABLE OF LEADS, .670″ TO 2.182″

	DRIVEN	DRIVER	DRIVEN	DRIVER		DRIVEN	DRIVER	DRIVEN	DRIVER		DRIVEN	DRIVER	DRIVEN	DRIVER
LEAD IN INCHES	GEAR ON WORM	1ST GEAR ON STUD	2ND GEAR ON STUD	GEAR ON SCREW	LEAD IN INCHES	GEAR ON WORM	1ST GEAR ON STUD	2ND GEAR ON STUD	GEAR ON SCREW	LEAD IN INCHES	GEAR ON WORM	1ST GEAR ON STUD	2ND GEAR ON STUD	GEAR ON SCREW
.670	24	86	24	100	1.527	24	44	28	100	1.886	24	56	44	100
.781	24	86	28	100	1.550	24	72	40	86	1.905	24	56	32	72
.800	24	72	24	100	1.556	28	72	40	100	1.919	24	64	44	86
.893	24	86	32	100	1.563	24	86	56	100	1.920	24	40	32	100
.900	24	64	24	100	1.563	28	86	48	100	1.925	28	64	44	100
.930	24	72	24	86	1.595	24	56	32	86	1.944	24	48	28	72
.933	24	72	28	100	1.600	24	48	32	100	1.944	28	64	32	72
1.029	24	56	24	100	1.600	28	56	32	100	1.954	24	40	28	86
1.042	28	86	32	100	1.600	24	72	48	100	1.956	32	72	44	100
1.047	24	64	24	86	1.607	24	56	24	64	1.990	28	72	44	86
1.050	24	64	28	100	1.628	24	48	28	86	1.993	24	56	40	86
1.067	24	72	32	100	1.628	28	64	32	86	2.000	24	40	24	72
1.085	24	72	28	86	1.637	32	86	44	100	2.000	24	48	40	100
1.116	24	86	40	100	1.650	24	64	44	100	2.000	28	56	40	100
1.196	24	56	24	86	1.667	24	56	28	72	2.000	32	64	40	100
1.200	24	48	24	100	1.667	24	48	24	72	2.009	24	86	72	100
1.200	24	56	28	100	1.667	24	64	32	72	2.030	24	44	32	86
1.200	24	64	32	100	1.674	24	40	24	86	2.035	28	64	40	86
1.221	24	64	28	86	1.680	24	40	28	100	2.036	28	44	32	100
1.228	24	86	44	100	1.706	24	72	44	86	2.045	24	44	24	64
1.240	24	72	32	86	1.711	28	72	44	100	2.047	40	86	44	100
1.244	28	72	32	100	1.714	24	56	40	100	2.057	24	28	24	100
1.250	24	64	24	72	1.744	24	64	40	86	2.057	24	56	48	100
1.302	28	86	40	100	1.745	24	44	32	100	2.067	32	72	40	86
1.309	24	44	24	100	1.750	28	64	40	100	2.083	24	64	40	72
1.333	24	72	40	100	1.776	24	44	28	86	2.084	28	86	64	100
1.340	24	86	48	100	1.778	32	72	40	100	2.084	32	86	56	100
1.371	24	56	32	100	1.786	24	86	64	100	2.093	24	64	48	86
1.395	24	48	24	86	1.786	32	86	48	100	2.093	24	32	24	86
1.395	24	56	28	86	1.800	24	64	48	100	2.100	24	64	56	100
1.395	24	64	32	86	1.800	24	32	24	100	2.100	28	64	48	100
1.400	24	48	28	100	1.809	28	72	40	86	2.100	24	32	28	100
1.400	28	64	32	100	1.818	24	44	24	72	2.121	24	44	28	72
1.429	24	56	24	72	1.823	28	86	56	100	2.133	24	72	64	100
1.433	28	86	44	100	1.860	28	56	32	86	2.133	32	72	48	100
1.440	24	40	24	100	1.861	24	72	48	86	2.143	24	56	32	64
1.447	28	72	32	86	1.861	24	48	32	86	2.143	24	48	24	56
1.458	24	64	28	72	1.867	28	48	32	100	2.171	24	72	56	86
1.467	24	72	44	100	1.867	24	72	56	100	2.171	28	48	32	86
1.488	32	86	40	100	1.867	28	72	48	100	2.171	28	72	48	86
1.500	24	64	40	100	1.875	24	48	24	64	2.178	28	72	56	100
1.522	24	44	24	86	1.875	24	56	28	64	2.182	24	44	40	100

TABLE OF LEADS, 2.188″ TO 3.080″

	DRIVEN	DRIVER	DRIVEN	DRIVER		DRIVEN	DRIVER	DRIVEN	DRIVER		DRIVEN	DRIVER	DRIVEN	DRIVER
LEAD IN INCHES	GEAR ON WORM	1ST GEAR ON STUD	2ND GEAR ON STUD	GEAR ON SCREW	LEAD IN INCHES	GEAR ON WORM	1ST GEAR ON STUD	2ND GEAR ON STUD	GEAR ON SCREW	LEAD IN INCHES	GEAR ON WORM	1ST GEAR ON STUD	2ND GEAR ON STUD	GEAR ON SCREW
2.188	24	48	28	64	2.500	24	48	28	56	2.800	24	24	28	100
2.193	24	56	44	86	2.500	28	56	32	64	2.800	32	64	56	100
2.200	24	48	44	100	2.500	24	64	48	72	2.800	24	48	56	100
2.200	28	56	44	100	2.500	24	48	32	64	2.812	24	32	24	64
2.200	32	64	44	100	2.500	24	32	24	72	2.828	28	44	32	72
2.222	24	48	32	72	2.514	32	56	44	100	2.843	40	72	44	86
2.222	28	56	32	72	2.532	28	72	56	86	2.845	32	72	64	100
2.233	40	86	48	100	2.537	24	44	40	86	2.849	28	64	56	86
2.233	24	40	32	86	2.546	28	44	40	100	2.857	24	48	32	56
2.238	28	64	44	86	2.558	32	64	44	86	2.857	24	56	48	72
2.240	28	40	32	100	2.558	28	56	44	86	2.857	24	28	24	72
2.250	24	40	24	64	2.558	24	48	44	86	2.865	44	86	56	100
2.274	32	72	44	86	2.567	28	48	44	100	2.867	86	72	24	100
2.286	32	56	40	100	2.571	24	40	24	56	2.880	24	40	48	100
2.292	24	64	44	72	2.593	28	48	32	72	2.894	28	72	64	86
2.326	32	64	40	86	2.605	28	40	32	86	2.894	32	72	56	86
2.326	24	48	40	86	2.605	40	86	56	100	2.909	32	44	40	100
2.326	28	56	40	86	2.618	24	44	48	100	2.917	24	64	56	72
2.333	28	48	40	100	2.619	24	56	44	72	2.917	28	64	48	72
2.333	24	40	28	72	2.625	24	40	28	64	2.917	28	48	32	64
2.338	24	44	24	56	2.640	24	40	44	100	2.917	24	32	28	72
2.344	28	86	72	100	2.658	32	56	40	86	2.924	32	56	44	86
2.368	28	44	32	86	2.667	40	72	48	100	2.933	44	72	48	100
2.381	32	86	64	100	2.667	32	48	40	100	2.934	32	48	44	100
2.381	24	56	40	72	2.667	24	40	32	72	2.946	24	56	44	64
2.386	24	44	28	64	2.674	28	64	44	72	2.950	28	44	40	86
2.392	24	56	48	86	2.678	24	56	40	64	2.977	40	86	64	100
2.392	24	28	24	86	2.679	32	86	72	100	2.984	28	48	44	86
2.400	28	56	48	100	2.700	24	64	72	100	3.000	24	40	28	56
2.400	32	64	48	100	2.713	28	48	40	86	3.000	24	40	32	64
2.424	24	44	32	72	2.727	24	44	32	64	3.000	24	32	40	100
2.431	28	64	40	72	2.727	24	44	28	56	3.000	40	64	48	100
2.442	24	32	28	86	2.727	24	44	24	48	3.000	24	40	24	48
2.442	28	64	48	86	2.743	24	56	64	100	3.030	24	44	40	72
2.442	24	64	56	86	2.743	32	56	48	100	3.044	24	44	48	86
2.445	40	72	44	100	2.743	24	28	32	100	3.055	28	44	48	100
2.450	28	64	56	100	2.750	40	64	44	100	3.055	24	44	56	100
2.456	44	86	48	100	2.778	32	64	40	72	3.056	32	64	44	72
2.481	32	72	48	86	2.778	24	48	40	72	3.056	28	56	44	72
2.481	24	72	64	86	2.778	40	56	28	72	3.056	24	48	44	72
2.489	32	72	56	100	2.791	28	56	48	86	3.070	24	40	44	86
2.489	28	72	64	100	2.791	32	64	48	86	3.080	28	40	44	100

TABLE OF LEADS, 3.086″ TO 3.896

	DRIVEN	DRIVER	DRIVEN	DRIVER		DRIVEN	DRIVER	DRIVEN	DRIVER		DRIVEN	DRIVER	DRIVEN	DRIVER
LEAD IN INCHES	GEAR ON WORM	1ST GEAR ON STUD	2ND GEAR ON STUD	GEAR ON SCREW	LEAD IN INCHES	GEAR ON WORM	1ST GEAR ON STUD	2ND GEAR ON STUD	GEAR ON SCREW	LEAD IN INCHES	GEAR ON WORM	1ST GEAR ON STUD	2ND GEAR ON STUD	GEAR ON SCREW
3.086	24	56	72	100	3.349	48	40	24	86	3.637	48	44	24	72
3.101	40	72	48	86	3.360	56	40	24	100	3.646	40	48	28	64
3.101	32	48	40	86	3.360	48	40	28	100	3.655	40	56	44	86
3.111	28	40	32	72	3.383	32	44	40	86	3.657	64	56	32	100
3.111	40	72	56	100	3.403	28	64	56	72	3.663	72	64	28	86
3.117	24	44	32	56	3.409	24	44	40	64	3.667	40	48	44	100
3.125	28	56	40	64	3.411	32	48	44	86	3.667	44	40	24	72
3.125	24	48	40	64	3.411	44	72	48	86	3.673	24	28	24	56
3.126	48	86	56	100	3.422	44	72	56	100	3.684	44	86	72	100
3.140	24	86	72	64	3.428	24	40	32	56	3.686	86	56	24	100
3.143	40	56	44	100	3.429	40	28	24	100	3.704	32	48	40	72
3.150	28	100	72	64	3.429	40	56	48	100	3.721	24	24	32	86
3.175	32	56	40	72	3.438	24	48	44	64	3.721	64	48	24	86
3.182	28	44	32	64	3.438	28	56	44	64	3.721	64	56	28	86
3.182	24	44	28	48	3.488	40	64	48	86	3.733	48	72	56	100
3.189	32	56	48	86	3.488	40	32	24	86	3.733	56	48	32	100
3.189	24	28	32	86	3.491	64	44	24	100	3.733	64	48	28	100
3.190	24	86	64	56	3.491	48	44	32	100	3.733	28	24	32	100
3.198	40	64	44	86	3.492	32	56	44	72	3.750	24	32	24	48
3.200	28	100	64	56	3.500	40	64	56	100	3.750	24	32	28	56
3.200	24	100	64	48	3.500	28	32	40	100	3.750	28	56	48	64
3.200	24	24	32	100	3.500	28	40	32	64	3.763	86	64	28	100
3.214	24	56	48	64	3.500	24	40	28	48	3.771	44	56	48	100
3.214	24	32	24	56	3.520	32	40	44	100	3.772	24	28	44	100
3.214	24	28	24	64	3.535	28	44	40	72	3.799	56	48	28	86
3.225	24	100	86	64	3.552	56	44	24	86	3.809	24	28	32	72
3.241	28	48	40	72	3.552	48	44	28	86	3.810	64	56	24	72
3.256	24	24	28	86	3.556	40	72	64	100	3.810	32	56	48	72
3.256	24	86	56	48	3.564	56	44	28	100	3.818	24	40	28	44
3.256	32	64	56	86	3.565	28	48	44	72	3.819	40	64	44	72
3.267	28	48	56	100	3.571	24	48	40	56	3.822	86	72	32	100
3.273	24	40	24	44	3.571	32	56	40	64	3.837	24	32	44	86
3.275	44	86	64	100	3.572	48	86	64	100	3.837	44	64	48	86
3.281	24	32	28	64	3.582	44	40	28	86	3.840	64	40	24	100
3.300	44	64	48	100	3.588	72	56	24	86	3.840	32	40	48	100
3.300	44	32	24	100	3.600	72	48	24	100	3.850	44	64	56	100
3.308	32	72	64	86	3.600	72	64	32	100	3.850	28	32	44	100
3.333	32	64	48	72	3.600	72	56	28	100	3.876	24	72	100	86
3.333	28	56	48	72	3.600	48	32	24	100	3.889	32	64	56	72
3.333	28	48	32	56	3.618	56	72	40	86	3.889	56	48	24	72
3.345	28	100	86	72	3.636	24	44	32	48	3.889	24	24	28	72
3.349	40	86	72	100	3.636	28	44	32	56	3.896	24	44	40	56

TABLE OF LEADS, 3.907″ TO 4.778″

	DRIVEN	DRIVER	DRIVEN	DRIVER		DRIVEN	DRIVER	DRIVEN	DRIVER		DRIVEN	DRIVER	DRIVEN	DRIVER
LEAD IN INCHES	GEAR ON WORM	1ST GEAR ON STUD	2ND GEAR ON STUD	GEAR ON SCREW	LEAD IN INCHES	GEAR ON WORM	1ST GEAR ON STUD	2ND GEAR ON STUD	GEAR ON SCREW	LEAD IN INCHES	GEAR ON WORM	1ST GEAR ON STUD	2ND GEAR ON STUD	GEAR ON SCREW
3.907	28	40	48	86	4.200	48	64	56	100	4.480	56	40	32	100
3.907	56	40	24	86	4.200	56	32	24	100	4.480	64	40	28	100
3.911	44	72	64	100	4.200	28	32	48	100	4.500	72	64	40	100
3.920	28	40	56	100	4.200	72	48	28	100	4.500	48	40	24	64
3.927	72	44	24	100	4.242	28	44	32	48	4.500	24	32	24	40
3.929	32	56	44	64	4.242	28	44	48	72	4.522	100	72	28	86
3.929	24	48	44	56						4.537	56	48	28	72
3.977	28	44	40	64	4.242	24	44	56	72	4.545	24	44	40	48
3.979	44	72	56	86	4.253	64	56	32	86	4.546	28	44	40	56
3.987	24	28	40	86	4.264	40	48	44	86	4.546	32	44	40	64
3.987	40	56	48	86	4.267	64	48	32	100	4.548	44	72	64	86
4.000	24	40	32	48	4.267	48	72	64	100	4.558	56	40	28	86
4.000	28	40	32	56	4.278	28	40	44	72	4.567	72	44	24	86
4.000	24	24	40	100	4.286	24	28	24	48	4.572	40	56	64	100
4.000	24	40	48	72	4.286	24	28	32	64	4.572	32	28	40	100
4.011	28	48	44	64	4.286	32	56	48	64	4.582	72	44	28	100
4.019	72	86	48	100	4.300	86	56	28	100	4.583	44	64	48	72
4.040	32	44	40	72	4.300	86	64	32	100	4.583	44	32	24	72
4.059	32	44	48	86	4.300	86	48	24	100	4.584	32	48	44	64
4.060	64	44	24	86	4.320	72	40	24	100	4.584	28	48	44	56
4.070	28	32	40	86	4.341	48	72	56	86	4.651	40	24	24	86
4.070	40	64	56	86	4.341	56	48	32	86	4.655	64	44	32	100
4.073	64	44	28	100	4.342	64	48	28	86	4.667	28	40	32	48
4.073	56	44	32	100	4.342	28	24	32	86	4.667	40	24	28	100
4.074	32	48	44	72	4.361	100	64	24	86	4.667	56	40	24	72
4.091	24	44	48	64	4.363	24	40	32	44	4.667	48	40	28	72
4.091	24	32	24	44	4.364	40	44	48	100	4.667	40	48	56	100
4.093	32	40	44	86	4.365	40	56	44	72	4.675	24	28	24	44
4.114	48	28	24	100	4.375	24	24	28	64	4.675	48	44	24	56
4.114	72	56	32	100	4.375	24	32	28	48	4.687	40	32	24	64
4.125	24	40	44	64	4.375	56	48	24	64	4.688	56	86	72	100
4.135	40	72	64	86	4.386	24	28	44	86	4.691	86	44	24	100
4.144	56	44	28	86	4.386	44	56	48	86	4.714	44	40	24	56
4.167	28	48	40	56	4.400	24	24	44	100	4.736	64	44	28	86
4.167	40	64	48	72	4.444	64	56	28	72	4.736	56	44	32	86
4.167	32	48	40	64	4.444	24	24	32	72	4.762	40	28	24	72
4.167	24	32	40	72	4.444	64	48	24	72	4.762	40	48	32	56
4.167	56	86	64	100	4.465	64	40	24	86	4.762	40	56	48	72
4.186	72	64	32	86	4.466	48	40	32	86	4.773	24	32	28	44
4.186	48	32	24	86	4.477	44	32	28	86	4.773	56	44	24	64
4.186	72	48	24	86	4.477	56	64	44	86	4.773	48	44	28	64
4.186	72	56	28	86	4.479	86	64	24	72	4.778	86	72	40	100

TABLE OF LEADS, 4.784″ TO 5.733″

	DRIVEN	DRIVER	DRIVEN	DRIVER		DRIVEN	DRIVER	DRIVEN	DRIVER		DRIVEN	DRIVER	DRIVEN	DRIVER
LEAD IN INCHES	GEAR ON WORM	1ST GEAR ON STUD	2ND GEAR ON STUD	GEAR ON SCREW	LEAD IN INCHES	GEAR ON WORM	1ST GEAR ON STUD	2ND GEAR ON STUD	GEAR ON SCREW	LEAD IN INCHES	GEAR ON WORM	1ST GEAR ON STUD	2ND GEAR ON STUD	GEAR ON SCREW
4.784	72	56	32	86	5.116	44	24	24	86	5.358	64	86	72	100
4.785	48	28	24	86	5.119	86	56	24	72	5.375	86	64	40	100
4.800	48	24	24	100	5.120	64	40	32	100	5.400	72	32	24	100
4.800	56	28	24	100	5.133	56	48	44	100	5.400	72	64	48	100
4.800	64	32	24	100	5.134	44	24	28	100	5.413	64	44	32	86
4.800	72	48	32	100	5.142	72	56	40	100	5.426	40	24	28	86
4.813	44	40	28	64	5.143	24	28	24	40	5.427	40	48	56	86
4.821	72	56	24	64	5.143	24	40	48	56	5.444	56	40	28	72
4.849	32	44	48	72	5.156	44	32	24	64	5.455	48	44	28	56
4.849	64	44	24	72	5.160	86	40	24	100	5.455	32	44	48	64
4.861	40	32	28	72	5.168	100	72	32	86	5.469	40	32	28	64
4.861	56	64	40	72	5.185	28	24	32	72	5.473	86	44	28	100
4.884	48	64	56	86	5.186	64	48	28	72	5.486	64	28	24	100
4.884	72	48	28	86	5.186	56	48	32	72	5.486	48	28	32	100
4.884	48	32	28	86	5.195	32	44	40	56	5.486	48	56	64	100
4.884	56	32	24	86	5.209	100	64	24	72	5.500	44	40	24	48
4.889	32	40	44	72	5.210	64	40	28	86	5.500	44	40	32	64
4.898	24	28	32	56	5.210	56	40	32	86	5.500	40	32	44	100
4.900	56	32	28	100	5.226	86	64	28	72	5.500	44	40	28	56
4.911	40	56	44	64	5.233	72	64	40	86	5.556	40	24	24	72
4.914	86	56	32	100	5.236	72	44	32	100	5.568	56	44	28	64
4.950	56	44	28	72	5.238	44	28	24	72	5.581	64	32	24	86
4.950	72	64	44	100	5.238	32	48	44	56	5.581	56	28	24	86
4.961	64	48	32	86	5.238	44	56	48	72	5.581	72	48	32	86
4.961	64	72	48	86	5.250	24	32	28	40	5.582	48	24	24	86
4.978	56	72	64	100	5.250	56	40	24	64	5.600	56	24	24	100
4.984	100	56	24	86	5.250	48	40	28	64	5.600	48	24	28	100
5.000	24	24	28	56	5.256	86	72	44	100	5.600	64	32	28	100
5.000	24	24	32	64	5.280	48	40	44	100	5.625	48	32	24	64
5.000	48	32	24	72	5.303	28	44	40	48	5.625	72	48	24	64
5.017	86	48	28	100	5.316	40	28	32	86	5.625	72	56	28	64
5.023	72	40	24	86	5.316	40	56	64	86	5.657	56	44	32	72
5.029	44	28	32	100	5.328	72	44	28	86	5.657	72	56	44	100
5.029	64	56	44	100	5.333	40	24	32	100	5.657	64	44	28	72
5.040	72	40	28	100	5.333	64	40	24	72	5.698	56	32	28	86
5.074	40	44	48	86	5.333	32	40	48	72	5.714	48	28	24	72
5.080	64	56	32	72	5.333	40	48	64	100	5.714	24	28	32	48
5.088	100	64	28	86	5.347	44	64	56	72	5.714	24	24	32	56
5.091	56	44	40	100	5.348	44	32	28	72	5.714	64	48	24	56
5.091	28	40	32	44	5.357	40	28	24	64	5.730	40	48	44	64
5.093	40	48	44	72	5.357	40	32	24	56	5.733	86	48	32	100
5.105	28	48	56	64	5.357	40	56	48	64	5.733	86	72	48	100

TABLE OF LEADS, 5.756" TO 6.757"

	DRIVEN	DRIVER	DRIVEN	DRIVER		DRIVEN	DRIVER	DRIVEN	DRIVER		DRIVEN	DRIVER	DRIVEN	DRIVER
LEAD IN INCHES	GEAR ON WORM	1ST GEAR ON STUD	2ND GEAR ON STUD	GEAR ON SCREW	LEAD IN INCHES	GEAR ON WORM	1ST GEAR ON STUD	2ND GEAR ON STUD	GEAR ON SCREW	LEAD IN INCHES	GEAR ON WORM	1ST GEAR ON STUD	2ND GEAR ON STUD	GEAR ON SCREW
5.756	72	64	44	86	6.089	72	44	32	86	6.417	44	40	28	48
5.759	86	56	24	64	6.109	56	44	48	100	6.429	24	28	24	32
5.760	72	40	32	100	6.112	24	24	44	72	6.429	48	28	24	64
5.788	64	72	56	86	6.122	40	28	24	56	6.429	48	32	24	56
5.814	100	64	32	86	6.125	56	40	28	64	6.429	72	48	24	56
5.814	100	56	28	86	6.137	72	44	24	64	6.429	72	56	32	64
5.814	100	48	24	86	6.140	48	40	44	86	6.450	86	64	48	100
5.818	64	44	40	100	6.143	86	56	40	100	6.450	86	32	24	100
5.833	28	24	24	48	6.160	56	40	44	100	6.460	100	72	40	86
5.833	32	24	28	64						6.465	64	44	32	72
5.833	56	32	24	72	6.171	72	56	48	100	6.482	56	48	40	72
5.833	48	32	28	72	6.172	72	28	24	100	6.482	40	24	28	72
5.833	56	48	32	64	6.202	40	24	32	86	6.512	56	24	24	86
5.833	56	64	48	72	6.202	64	48	40	86	6.512	64	32	28	86
5.847	64	56	44	86	6.222	64	40	28	72	6.512	48	24	28	86
5.848	44	28	32	86	6.222	56	40	32	72	6.515	86	44	24	72
5.861	72	40	28	86	6.234	32	28	24	44	6.533	56	24	28	100
5.867	44	24	32	100	6.234	64	44	24	56	6.545	48	40	24	44
5.867	64	48	44	100	6.234	48	44	32	56	6.545	72	44	40	100
5.893	44	32	24	56	6.250	24	24	40	64	6.548	44	48	40	56
5.893	44	28	24	64	6.250	40	32	24	48	6.563	56	32	24	64
5.893	48	56	44	64	6.250	40	32	28	56	6.563	72	48	28	64
5.912	86	64	44	100	6.255	86	44	32	100	6.563	48	32	28	64
5.920	56	44	40	86	6.279	72	64	48	86	6.578	72	56	44	86
5.926	64	48	32	72	6.279	72	32	24	86	6.600	48	32	44	100
5.952	100	56	24	72	6.286	44	40	32	56	6.600	72	48	44	100
5.954	64	40	32	86	6.286	44	28	40	100	6.645	100	56	32	86
5.969	44	24	28	86	6.300	72	32	28	100	6.667	64	48	28	56
5.969	56	48	44	86	6.300	72	64	56	100	6.667	32	24	28	56
5.972	86	48	24	72	6.343	100	44	24	86	6.667	32	24	24	48
5.972	86	56	28	72	6.350	40	28	32	72	6.667	48	24	24	72
5.972	86	64	32	72	6.350	64	56	40	72	6.667	56	28	24	72
5.980	72	56	40	86	6.364	56	44	24	48	6.667	64	32	24	72
6.000	48	40	28	56	6.364	56	44	32	64	6.689	86	72	56	100
6.000	48	40	32	64	6.364	24	24	28	44	6.697	100	56	24	64
6.000	48	32	40	100	6.379	64	28	24	86	6.698	72	40	32	86
6.000	72	48	40	100	6.379	48	28	32	86	6.719	86	48	24	64
6.016	44	32	28	64	6.379	64	56	48	86	6.719	86	56	28	64
6.020	86	40	28	100	6.396	44	32	40	86	6.720	56	40	48	100
6.061	40	44	32	48	6.400	64	24	24	100	6.735	44	28	24	56
6.061	48	44	40	72	6.400	48	24	32	100	6.750	72	40	24	64
6.077	100	64	28	72	6.400	56	28	32	100	6.757	86	56	44	100

TABLE OF LEADS, 6.766″ TO 7.883″

	DRIVEN	DRIVER	DRIVEN	DRIVER		DRIVEN	DRIVER	DRIVEN	DRIVER		DRIVEN	DRIVER	DRIVEN	DRIVER
LEAD IN INCHES	GEAR ON WORM	1ST GEAR ON STUD	2ND GEAR ON STUD	GEAR ON SCREW	LEAD IN INCHES	GEAR ON WORM	1ST GEAR ON STUD	2ND GEAR ON STUD	GEAR ON SCREW	LEAD IN INCHES	GEAR ON WORM	1ST GEAR ON STUD	2ND GEAR ON STUD	GEAR ON SCREW
6.766	64	44	40	86	7.159	72	44	28	64	7.525	86	32	28	100
6.784	100	48	28	86	7.163	56	40	44	86	7.525	86	64	56	100
6.806	56	32	28	72	7.167	86	40	24	72	7.543	48	28	44	100
6.818	40	32	24	44	7.167	86	48	40	100	7.576	100	44	24	72
6.818	48	44	40	64	7.176	72	28	24	86	7.597	56	24	28	86
6.822	44	24	32	86	7.176	72	56	48	86	7.601	86	44	28	72
6.822	64	48	44	86	7.200	72	24	24	100	7.611	72	44	40	86
6.825	86	56	32	72	7.268	100	64	40	86	7.619	64	48	32	56
6.857	32	28	24	40	7.272	64	44	28	56	7.619	64	56	48	72
6.857	64	40	24	56	7.273	32	24	24	44	7.620	64	28	24	72
6.857	48	40	32	56	7.273	64	44	24	48	7.620	48	28	32	72
6.857	48	28	40	100	7.292	56	48	40	64	7.636	56	40	24	44
6.875	44	24	24	64	7.292	40	32	28	48	7.636	48	40	28	44
6.875	44	32	24	48	7.292	40	24	28	64	7.639	44	32	40	72
6.875	44	32	28	56	7.310	44	28	40	86	7.644	86	72	64	100
6.880	86	40	32	100	7.314	64	28	32	100	7.657	56	32	28	64
6.944	100	48	24	72	7.325	72	32	28	86	7.674	72	48	44	86
6.944	100	64	32	72	7.326	72	64	56	86	7.675	48	32	44	86
6.945	100	56	28	72	7.330	86	44	24	64	7.679	86	48	24	56
6.968	86	48	28	72	7.333	44	24	40	100	7.679	86	56	32	64
6.977	48	32	40	86	7.333	48	40	44	72	7.680	64	40	48	100
6.977	100	40	24	86	7.334	44	40	32	48	7.700	56	32	44	100
6.977	72	48	40	86	7.347	48	28	24	56	7.714	72	40	24	56
6.982	64	44	48	100	7.371	86	56	48	100	7.752	100	48	32	86
6.984	44	28	32	72	7.372	86	28	24	100	7.752	100	72	48	86
6.984	64	56	44	72	7.400	100	44	28	86	7.778	32	24	28	48
7.000	28	24	24	40	7.408	40	24	32	72	7.778	56	24	24	72
7.000	56	40	24	48	7.408	64	48	40	72	7.778	48	24	28	72
7.000	56	40	32	64	7.424	56	44	28	48	7.778	64	32	28	72
7.000	56	32	40	100	7.442	64	24	24	86	7.792	40	28	24	44
7.013	72	44	24	56	7.442	48	24	32	86	7.792	48	44	40	56
7.040	64	40	44	100	7.442	56	28	32	86	7.813	100	48	24	64
7.071	56	44	40	72	7.465	86	64	40	72	7.813	100	56	28	64
					7.467	64	24	28	100	7.815	56	40	48	86
7.104	56	44	48	86						7.818	86	44	40	100
7.106	100	72	44	86	7.467	56	24	32	100	7.838	86	48	28	64
7.111	64	40	32	72	7.467	64	48	56	100	7.855	72	44	48	100
7.130	44	24	28	72	7.500	48	24	24	64	7.857	44	24	24	56
7.130	56	48	44	72	7.500	56	28	24	64	7.857	44	28	24	48
7.143	40	28	32	64	7.500	48	32	28	56	7.872	44	28	32	64
7.143	40	28	24	48	7.500	72	48	28	56	7.875	72	40	28	64
7.143	40	24	24	56	7.500	72	48	32	64	7.883	86	48	44	100

TABLE OF LEADS, 7.920″ TO 9.302″

LEAD IN INCHES	DRIVEN GEAR ON WORM	DRIVER 1ST GEAR ON STUD	DRIVEN 2ND GEAR ON STUD	DRIVER GEAR ON SCREW	LEAD IN INCHES	DRIVEN GEAR ON WORM	DRIVER 1ST GEAR ON STUD	DRIVEN 2ND GEAR ON STUD	DRIVER GEAR ON SCREW	LEAD IN INCHES	DRIVEN GEAR ON WORM	DRIVER 1ST GEAR ON STUD	DRIVEN 2ND GEAR ON STUD	DRIVER GEAR ON SCREW
7.920	72	40	44	100	8.333	48	32	40	72	8.772	48	28	44	86
7.936	100	56	32	72	8.333	100	40	24	72	8.800	48	24	44	100
7.954	40	32	28	44	8.334	40	24	28	56	8.800	64	32	44	100
7.955	56	44	40	64	8.361	86	40	28	72	8.800	56	28	44	100
7.963	86	48	32	72	8.372	72	24	24	86	8.838	100	44	28	72
7.974	48	28	40	86	8.377	86	44	24	56	8.839	72	56	44	64
7.994	100	64	44	86	8.400	72	24	28	100	8.889	64	24	24	72
8.000	64	32	40	100	8.400	56	32	48	100	8.889	56	28	32	72
8.000	32	24	24	40	8.400	72	48	56	100	8.889	48	24	32	72
8.000	64	40	24	48	8.437	72	32	24	64	8.909	56	40	28	44
8.000	64	40	28	56	8.457	100	44	32	86	8.929	100	48	24	56
8.000	56	28	40	100	8.484	32	24	28	44	8.929	100	56	32	64
8.000	48	24	40	100	8.485	64	44	28	48	8.930	64	40	48	86
8.021	44	32	28	48	8.485	56	44	32	48	8.953	56	32	44	86
8.021	44	24	28	64	8.485	56	44	48	72	8.959	86	48	28	56
8.021	56	48	44	64	8.506	64	28	32	86	8.959	86	32	24	72
8.035	72	56	40	64	8.523	100	44	24	64	8.959	86	64	48	72
8.063	86	40	24	64	8.527	44	24	40	86	8.959	86	48	28	56
8.081	64	44	40	72	8.532	86	56	40	72	8.960	64	40	56	100
8.102	100	48	28	72	8.534	64	24	32	100	8.980	44	28	32	56
8.119	64	44	48	86	8.552	86	44	28	64	9.000	48	32	24	40
8.140	56	32	40	86	8.556	56	40	44	72	9.000	72	40	24	48
8.140	100	40	28	86	8.572	64	32	24	56	9.000	72	40	28	56
8.145	64	44	56	100	8.572	48	28	32	64	9.000	72	40	32	64
8.148	64	48	44	72	8.572	48	24	24	56	9.000	72	32	40	100
8.149	44	24	32	72	8.572	72	48	32	56	9.044	100	72	56	86
8.163	40	28	32	56	8.594	44	32	40	64	9.074	56	24	28	72
8.167	56	40	28	48	8.600	86	24	24	100	9.091	40	24	24	44
8.182	48	32	24	44	8.640	72	40	48	100	9.115	100	48	28	64
8.182	72	44	24	48	8.681	100	64	40	72	9.134	72	44	48	86
8.182	72	44	28	56	8.682	64	24	28	86	9.137	100	56	44	86
8.182	72	44	32	64	8.682	56	24	32	86	9.143	64	40	32	56
8.186	64	40	44	86	8.682	64	48	56	86	9.143	64	28	40	100
8.212	86	64	44	72	8.687	86	44	32	72	9.164	72	44	56	100
8.229	72	28	32	100	8.721	100	32	24	86	9.167	44	24	24	48
8.229	72	56	64	100	8.721	100	64	48	86	9.167	44	24	28	56
8.250	44	32	24	40	8.727	48	40	32	44	9.167	44	24	32	64
8.250	48	40	44	64	8.730	44	28	40	72	9.167	48	32	44	72
8.306	100	56	40	86	8.750	28	24	24	32	9.210	72	40	44	86
8.312	64	44	32	56	8.750	56	32	24	48	9.214	86	40	24	56
8.333	40	24	24	48	8.750	56	24	24	64	9.260	100	48	32	72
8.333	40	24	32	64	8.750	48	24	28	64	9.302	48	24	40	86

TABLE OF LEADS, 9.303″ TO 10.477″

Lead in Inches	Driven Gear on Worm	Driver 1st Gear on Stud	Driven 2nd Gear on Stud	Driver Gear on Screw	Lead in Inches	Driven Gear on Worm	Driver 1st Gear on Stud	Driven 2nd Gear on Stud	Driver Gear on Screw	Lead in Inches	Driven Gear on Worm	Driver 1st Gear on Stud	Driven 2nd Gear on Stud	Driver Gear on Screw
9.303	56	28	40	86	9.675	86	64	72	100	10.101	100	44	32	72
9.303	64	32	40	86	9.690	100	48	40	86	10.159	64	28	32	72
9.303	100	40	32	86	9.697	64	48	32	44	10.175	100	32	28	86
9.333	64	40	28	48	9.697	64	44	48	72	10.175	100	64	56	86
9.333	56	40	32	48	9.723	40	24	28	48	10.182	64	40	28	44
9.333	56	24	40	100	9.723	56	32	40	72	10.182	56	40	32	44
9.333	56	40	48	72	9.723	100	40	28	72	10.186	44	24	40	72
9.334	32	24	28	40	9.741	100	44	24	56	10.209	56	24	28	64
9.351	48	28	24	44	9.768	72	48	56	86	10.209	56	32	28	48
9.351	72	44	32	56	9.768	56	32	48	86	10.228	72	44	40	64
9.375	48	32	40	64	9.768	72	24	28	86	10.233	48	24	44	86
9.375	100	40	24	64	9.773	86	44	24	48	10.233	56	28	44	86
9.375	72	48	40	64	9.773	86	44	28	56	10.233	64	32	44	86
9.382	86	44	48	100	9.773	86	44	32	64	10.238	86	28	24	72
9.385	86	56	44	72	9.778	64	40	44	72	10.238	86	48	32	56
9.406	86	40	28	64	9.796	64	28	24	56	10.238	86	56	48	72
9.428	44	28	24	40	9.796	48	28	32	56	10.267	56	24	44	100
9.429	48	40	44	56	9.818	72	40	24	44	10.286	48	28	24	40
9.460	86	40	44	100	9.822	44	32	40	56	10.286	72	40	32	56
9.472	64	44	56	86	9.822	44	28	40	64	10.286	72	28	40	100
9.524	40	28	32	48	9.828	86	28	32	100	10.312	48	32	44	64
9.524	40	24	32	56	9.828	86	56	64	100	10.313	72	48	44	64
9.524	48	28	40	72	9.844	72	32	28	64	10.320	86	40	48	100
9.524	64	48	40	56	9.900	72	32	44	100	10.336	100	72	64	86
9.545	72	44	28	48	9.921	100	56	40	72	10.370	64	24	28	72
9.546	56	32	24	44	9.923	64	24	32	86	10.370	56	24	32	72
9.546	48	32	28	44	9.943	100	44	28	64	10.371	64	48	56	72
9.547	56	44	48	64	9.954	86	48	40	72	10.390	40	28	32	44
9.549	100	64	44	72	9.967	100	56	48	86	10.390	64	44	40	56
9.556	86	40	32	72	9.967	100	28	24	86	10.417	100	32	24	72
9.569	72	28	32	86	10.000	56	28	24	48	10.417	100	48	28	56
9.569	72	56	64	86	10.000	48	24	28	56	10.417	100	48	32	64
9.598	86	56	40	64	10.000	64	32	24	48	10.417	100	64	48	72
9.600	72	24	32	100	10.000	64	32	28	56	10.419	64	40	56	86
9.600	56	28	48	100	10.000	56	28	32	64	10.451	86	32	28	72
9.600	64	32	48	100	10.000	48	24	32	64	10.451	86	64	56	72
9.600	72	48	64	100	10.033	86	24	28	100	10.467	72	32	40	86
9.625	44	32	28	40	10.033	86	48	56	100	10.473	72	44	64	100
9.625	56	40	44	64	10.046	72	40	48	86	10.476	44	24	32	56
9.643	72	32	24	56	10.057	64	28	44	100	10.476	44	28	32	48
9.643	72	28	24	64	10.078	86	32	24	64	10.477	48	28	44	72
9.643	72	56	48	64	10.080	72	40	56	100	10.477	64	48	44	56

TABLE OF LEADS, 10.500″ TO 12.272″

	DRIVEN	DRIVER	DRIVEN	DRIVER		DRIVEN	DRIVER	DRIVEN	DRIVER		DRIVEN	DRIVER	DRIVEN	DRIVER
LEAD IN INCHES	GEAR ON WORM	1ST GEAR ON STUD	2ND GEAR ON STUD	GEAR ON SCREW	LEAD IN INCHES	GEAR ON WORM	1ST GEAR ON STUD	2ND GEAR ON STUD	GEAR ON SCREW	LEAD IN INCHES	GEAR ON WORM	1ST GEAR ON STUD	2ND GEAR ON STUD	GEAR ON SCREW
10.500	56	32	24	40	11.111	48	24	40	72	11.667	64	32	28	48
10.500	48	32	28	40	11.111	56	28	40	72	11.667	56	32	48	72
10.500	72	40	28	48	11.111	64	32	40	72	11.667	56	24	32	64
10.500	56	40	48	64	11.111	100	40	32	72	11.688	72	44	40	56
10.558	86	56	44	64	11.137	56	32	28	44	11.695	64	28	44	86
10.571	100	44	40	86	11.160	100	56	40	64	11.719	100	32	24	64
10.606	56	44	40	48	11.163	72	24	32	86	11.721	72	40	56	86
10.606	40	24	28	44	11.163	56	28	48	86	11.728	86	40	24	44
10.631	64	28	40	86	11.163	72	48	64	86	11.733	64	24	44	100
10.655	72	44	56	86	11.163	64	32	48	86	11.757	86	32	28	64
10.659	100	48	44	86	11.169	86	44	32	56	11.785	72	48	44	56
10.667	64	40	48	72	11.198	86	48	40	64	11.786	44	28	24	32
10.667	64	24	40	100	11.200	56	24	48	100	11.786	48	32	44	56
10.667	64	40	32	48	11.200	64	32	56	100	11.786	48	28	44	64
10.694	44	24	28	48	11.225	44	28	40	56	11.825	86	32	44	100
10.694	56	32	44	72	11.250	72	24	24	64	11.852	64	24	32	72
10.713	40	28	24	32	11.250	72	32	24	48	11.905	100	28	24	72
10.714	48	32	40	56	11.250	72	32	28	56	11.905	100	48	32	56
10.714	48	28	40	64	11.313	64	44	56	72	11.905	100	56	48	72
10.714	100	40	24	56	11.314	72	28	44	100	11.938	56	24	44	86
10.714	72	48	40	56	11.363	100	44	24	48	11.944	86	24	24	72
10.750	86	40	24	48	11.363	100	44	28	56	11.960	72	28	40	86
10.750	86	40	28	56	11.363	100	44	32	64	12.000	48	24	24	40
10.750	86	40	32	64	11.401	86	44	28	48	12.000	56	28	24	40
10.750	86	32	40	100	11.429	32	24	24	28	12.000	64	32	24	40
10.800	72	32	48	100	11.429	64	28	24	48	12.000	72	40	32	48
10.853	56	24	40	86	11.429	64	24	24	56	12.000	72	24	40	100
10.859	86	44	40	72	11.429	48	24	32	56	12.031	56	32	44	64
10.909	72	44	32	48	11.454	72	40	28	44	12.040	86	40	56	100
10.909	56	28	24	44	11.459	44	24	40	64	12.121	40	24	32	44
10.909	48	24	24	44	11.459	44	32	40	48	12.121	64	44	40	48
10.909	64	32	24	44	11.467	86	24	32	100	12.153	100	32	28	72
10.913	100	56	44	72	11.467	86	48	64	100	12.153	100	64	56	72
10.937	56	32	40	64	11.512	72	32	44	86	12.178	72	44	64	86
10.937	100	40	28	64	11.518	86	28	24	64	12.216	86	44	40	64
10.945	86	44	56	100	11.518	86	32	24	56	12.222	44	24	32	48
10.949	86	48	44	72	11.518	86	56	48	64	12.222	48	24	44	72
10.972	64	28	48	100	11.520	72	40	64	100	12.222	56	28	44	72
11.000	44	24	24	40	11.574	100	48	40	72	12.222	64	32	44	72
11.021	72	28	24	56	11.629	100	24	24	86	12.245	48	28	40	56
11.057	86	56	72	100	11.638	64	40	32	44	12.250	56	32	28	40
11.111	40	24	32	48	11.667	56	24	24	48	12.272	72	32	24	44

TABLE OF LEADS, 12.272″ TO 14.322″

LEAD IN INCHES	DRIVEN GEAR ON WORM	DRIVER 1ST GEAR ON STUD	DRIVEN 2ND GEAR ON STUD	DRIVER GEAR ON SCREW	LEAD IN INCHES	DRIVEN GEAR ON WORM	DRIVER 1ST GEAR ON STUD	DRIVEN 2ND GEAR ON STUD	DRIVER GEAR ON SCREW	LEAD IN INCHES	DRIVEN GEAR ON WORM	DRIVER 1ST GEAR ON STUD	DRIVEN 2ND GEAR ON STUD	DRIVER GEAR ON SCREW
12.272	72	44	48	64	12.900	86	32	48	100	13.566	100	48	56	86
12.277	100	56	44	64	12.900	86	48	72	100	13.611	56	24	28	48
12.286	86	28	40	100	12.963	56	24	40	72	13.636	48	32	40	44
12.286	86	40	32	56	12.987	100	44	32	56	13.636	100	40	24	44
12.318	86	48	44	64	13.020	100	48	40	64	13.636	72	44	40	48
12.343	72	28	48	100	13.024	56	24	48	86	13.643	64	24	44	86
12.375	72	40	44	64	13.024	64	32	56	86	13.650	86	28	32	72
12.403	64	24	40	86	13.030	86	44	32	48	13.650	86	56	64	72
12.444	64	40	56	72	13.030	86	44	48	72	13.672	100	32	28	64
12.468	64	28	24	44	13.062	64	28	32	56	13.682	86	40	28	44
12.468	48	28	32	44	13.082	100	64	72	86	13.713	64	40	48	56
12.468	64	44	48	56	13.090	72	40	32	44	13.715	64	28	24	40
12.500	40	24	24	32	13.096	44	28	40	48	13.715	48	28	32	40
12.500	48	24	40	64	13.096	44	24	40	56	13.750	44	24	24	32
12.500	56	28	40	64	13.125	72	32	28	48	13.750	48	24	44	64
12.500	100	40	24	48	13.125	72	24	28	64	13.750	56	28	44	64
12.500	100	40	28	56	13.125	56	32	48	64	13.760	86	40	64	100
12.500	100	40	32	64	13.125	72	48	56	64	13.889	100	24	24	72
12.542	86	40	28	48	13.139	86	40	44	72	13.933	86	48	56	72
12.508	86	44	64	100	13.157	72	28	44	86	13.935	86	24	28	72
12.558	72	32	48	86	13.163	86	28	24	56	13.953	72	24	40	86
12.571	64	40	44	56	13.200	72	24	44	100	13.953	100	40	48	86
12.572	44	28	32	40	13.258	100	44	28	48	13.960	86	44	40	56
12.600	72	32	56	100	13.289	100	28	32	86	13.968	64	28	44	72
12.627	100	44	40	72	13.289	100	56	64	86	14.000	56	24	24	40
12.686	100	44	48	86	13.333	64	24	24	48	14.000	48	24	28	40
12.698	64	28	40	72	13.333	64	24	28	56	14.000	64	32	28	40
12.727	64	32	28	44	13.333	56	28	32	48	14.025	72	44	48	56
12.728	56	24	24	44	13.333	56	28	48	72	14.026	72	28	24	44
12.728	48	24	28	44	13.333	64	32	48	72	14.063	72	32	40	64
12.732	100	48	44	72	13.393	100	56	48	64	14.071	86	44	72	100
12.758	64	28	48	86	13.393	100	28	24	64	14.078	86	48	44	56
12.791	100	40	44	86	13.393	100	32	24	56	14.142	72	40	44	56
12.798	86	48	40	56	13.396	72	40	64	86	14.204	100	44	40	64
12.800	64	28	56	100	13.437	86	32	28	56	14.260	56	24	44	72
12.800	64	24	48	100	13.438	86	24	24	64	14.286	40	24	24	28
12.834	56	40	44	48	13.438	86	32	24	48	14.286	48	24	40	56
12.834	44	24	28	40	13.469	48	28	44	56	14.286	64	32	40	56
12.857	72	28	32	64	13.500	72	32	24	40	14.286	100	40	32	56
12.857	72	24	24	56	13.500	72	40	48	64	14.318	72	32	28	44
12.857	72	28	24	48	13.514	86	28	44	100	14.319	72	44	56	64
12.858	48	28	24	32	13.566	100	24	28	86	14.322	100	48	44	64

TABLE OF LEADS, 14.333″ TO 16.914″

	DRIVEN	DRIVER	DRIVEN	DRIVER		DRIVEN	DRIVER	DRIVEN	DRIVER		DRIVEN	DRIVER	DRIVEN	DRIVER
LEAD IN INCHES	GEAR ON WORM	1ST GEAR ON STUD	2ND GEAR ON STUD	GEAR ON SCREW	LEAD IN INCHES	GEAR ON WORM	1ST GEAR ON STUD	2ND GEAR ON STUD	GEAR ON SCREW	LEAD IN INCHES	GEAR ON WORM	1ST GEAR ON STUD	2ND GEAR ON STUD	GEAR ON SCREW
14.333	86	40	32	48	15.238	64	28	48	72	15.989	100	32	44	86
14.333	86	24	40	100	15.239	64	28	32	48	16.000	64	24	24	40
14.333	86	40	48	72	15.239	64	24	32	56	16.000	48	24	32	40
14.352	72	28	48	86	15.272	56	40	48	44	16.000	56	28	32	40
14.400	72	24	48	100	15.278	44	24	40	48	16.042	56	24	44	64
14.400	72	28	56	100	15.279	100	40	44	72	16.042	56	32	44	48
14.400	72	32	64	100	15.306	100	28	24	56	16.043	44	24	28	32
14.536	100	32	40	86	15.349	72	24	44	86	16.071	72	32	40	56
14.545	64	24	24	44	15.357	86	28	24	48	16.071	72	28	40	64
14.545	48	24	32	44	15.357	86	24	24	56	16.125	86	32	24	40
14.545	56	28	32	44	15.357	86	28	32	64	16.125	86	40	48	64
14.583	56	32	40	48	15.429	72	40	48	56	16.204	100	24	28	72
14.583	56	24	40	64	15.429	72	28	24	40	16.204	100	48	56	72
14.583	100	40	28	48	15.469	72	32	44	64	16.233	100	44	40	56
14.584	40	24	28	32	15.480	86	40	72	100	16.280	100	40	56	86
14.651	72	32	56	86	15.504	100	48	64	86	16.288	86	44	40	48
14.659	86	44	48	64	15.504	100	24	32	86	16.296	64	24	44	72
14.659	86	32	24	44	15.556	64	32	56	72	16.327	64	28	40	56
14.667	64	40	44	48	15.556	64	24	28	48	16.333	56	24	28	40
14.668	44	24	32	40	15.556	56	24	32	48	16.364	72	24	24	44
14.694	72	28	32	56	15.556	32	24	28	24	16.370	100	48	44	56
14.743	86	28	48	100	15.556	56	24	48	72	16.423	86	32	44	72
14.780	86	40	44	64	15.584	48	28	40	44	16.456	72	28	64	100
14.800	100	44	56	86	15.625	100	24	24	64	16.500	72	40	44	48
14.815	64	24	40	72	15.625	100	32	24	48	16.500	48	32	44	40
14.849	56	24	28	44	15.625	100	32	28	56	16.612	100	28	40	86
14.880	100	48	40	56	15.636	86	40	32	44	16.623	64	28	32	44
14.884	64	28	56	86	15.677	86	32	28	48	16.667	56	28	40	48
14.884	64	24	48	86	15.677	86	24	28	64	16.667	64	32	40	48
14.931	86	32	40	72	15.677	86	48	56	64	16.667	100	40	32	48
14.933	64	24	56	100	15.714	44	24	24	28	16.667	100	40	48	72
14.950	100	56	72	86	15.714	48	24	44	56	16.722	86	40	56	72
15.000	48	24	24	32	15.714	64	32	44	56	16.744	72	24	48	86
15.000	56	28	24	32	15.750	72	32	28	40	16.744	72	28	56	86
15.000	72	24	24	48	15.750	72	40	56	64	16.744	72	32	64	86
15.000	72	24	28	56	15.767	86	24	44	100	16.752	86	44	48	56
15.000	72	24	32	64	15.873	100	56	64	72	16.753	86	28	24	44
15.000	56	28	48	64	15.874	100	28	32	72	16.797	86	32	40	64
15.050	86	32	56	100	15.909	100	40	28	44	16.800	72	24	56	100
15.150	100	44	32	48	15.909	56	32	40	44	16.875	72	32	48	64
15.151	100	44	48	72	15.925	86	48	64	72	16.892	86	40	44	56
15.202	86	44	56	72	15.926	86	24	32	72	16.914	100	44	64	86

TABLE OF LEADS, 16.969″ TO 20.20″

	DRIVEN	DRIVER	DRIVEN	DRIVER		DRIVEN	DRIVER	DRIVEN	DRIVER		DRIVEN	DRIVER	DRIVEN	DRIVER
LEAD IN INCHES	GEAR ON WORM	1ST GEAR ON STUD	2ND GEAR ON STUD	GEAR ON SCREW	LEAD IN INCHES	GEAR ON WORM	1ST GEAR ON STUD	2ND GEAR ON STUD	GEAR ON SCREW	LEAD IN INCHES	GEAR ON WORM	1ST GEAR ON STUD	2ND GEAR ON STUD	GEAR ON SCREW
16.969	64	44	56	48	17.918	86	32	48	72	19.091	72	24	28	44
16.970	64	24	28	44	17.959	64	28	44	56	19.096	100	32	44	72
16.970	56	24	32	44	18.000	72	24	24	40	19.111	86	40	64	72
17.045	100	32	24	44	18.181	56	28	40	44	19.136	72	28	64	86
17.046	100	44	48	64	18.181	64	32	40	44	19.197	86	32	40	56
17.062	86	28	40	72	18.181	100	40	32	44	19.197	86	28	40	64
17.101	86	44	56	64	18.182	48	24	40	44	19.200	72	24	64	100
17.102	86	32	28	44	18.229	100	32	28	48	19.250	56	32	44	40
17.141	64	32	48	56	18.229	100	24	28	64	19.285	72	32	48	56
17.143	64	28	24	32	18.229	100	48	56	64	19.285	72	28	48	64
17.144	48	24	24	28	18.273	100	28	44	86	19.286	72	28	24	32
17.144	72	28	32	48	18.285	64	28	32	40	19.350	86	32	72	100
17.144	72	24	32	56	18.333	56	28	44	48	19.380	100	24	40	86
17.144	72	48	64	56	18.333	64	32	44	48	19.394	64	24	32	44
17.188	100	40	44	64	18.367	72	28	40	56	19.444	40	24	28	24
17.200	86	32	64	100	18.428	86	28	24	40	19.444	56	24	40	48
17.200	86	28	56	100	18.428	86	40	48	56	19.444	100	40	56	72
17.200	86	24	48	100	18.476	86	32	44	64	19 480	100	28	24	44
17.275	86	56	72	64	18.519	100	24	32	72	19.480	100	44	48	56
17.361	100	32	40	72	18.519	100	48	64	72	19.531	100	32	40	64
17.364	64	24	56	86	18.605	100	40	64	86	19.535	72	24	56	86
17.373	86	44	64	72	18.663	100	64	86	72	19.545	86	24	24	44
17.442	100	32	48	86	18.667	64	24	28	40	19.590	64	28	48	56
17.442	100	48	72	86	18.667	56	24	32	40	19.635	72	40	48	44
17.454	64	40	48	44	18.667	64	40	56	48	19.642	100	40	44	56
17.500	56	24	24	32	18.700	72	44	64	56	19.643	44	28	40	32
17.500	48	24	28	32	18.700	72	28	32	44	19.656	86	28	64	100
17.500	72	24	28	48	18.750	100	32	24	40	19.687	72	32	56	64
17.500	56	24	48	64	18.750	72	24	40	64	19.710	86	40	44	48
17.550	86	28	32	56	18.750	72	32	40	48	19.840	100	28	40	72
17.677	100	44	56	72	18.750	100	40	48	64	19.886	100	44	56	64
17.679	72	32	44	56	18.770	86	28	44	72	19.887	100	32	28	44
17.679	72	28	44	64	18.812	86	32	28	40	19.908	86	24	40	72
17.778	64	24	32	48	18.812	86	40	56	64	19.934	100	28	48	86
17.778	64	24	48	72	18.858	48	28	44	40	20.00	72	24	32	48
17.778	64	28	56	72	18.939	100	44	40	48	20.00	64	24	24	32
17.858	100	24	24	56	19.029	100	44	72	86	20.00	56	24	24	28
17.858	100	28	32	64	19.048	40	24	32	28	20.07	86	24	56	100
17.858	100	28	24	48	19.048	64	24	40	56	20.09	100	56	72	64
17.917	86	24	32	64	19.048	64	28	40	48	20.16	86	48	72	64
17.917	86	24	28	56	19.090	56	32	48	44	20.16	86	32	48	64
17.918	86	24	24	48	19.090	72	44	56	48	20.20	100	44	64	72

TABLE OF LEADS, 20.20″ TO 24.55″

	DRIVEN	DRIVER	DRIVEN	DRIVER		DRIVEN	DRIVER	DRIVEN	DRIVER		DRIVEN	DRIVER	DRIVEN	DRIVER
LEAD IN INCHES	GEAR ON WORM	1ST GEAR ON STUD	2ND GEAR ON STUD	GEAR ON SCREW	LEAD IN INCHES	GEAR ON WORM	1ST GEAR ON STUD	2ND GEAR ON STUD	GEAR ON SCREW	LEAD IN INCHES	GEAR ON WORM	1ST GEAR ON STUD	2ND GEAR ON STUD	GEAR ON SCREW
					21.43	100	28	24	40	23.04	86	32	48	56
20.20	72	28	44	56	21.48	100	32	44	64	23.04	86	28	48	64
20.35	100	32	56	86	21.50	86	24	24	40	23.04	86	28	24	32
20.36	64	40	56	44	21.82	72	44	64	48	23.14	100	24	40	72
20.41	100	28	32	56	21.82	100	28	44	72	23.26	100	32	64	86
20.42	56	24	28	32	21.82	64	32	48	44	23.26	100	28	56	86
20.45	72	32	40	44	21.82	56	28	48	44	23.26	100	24	48	86
20.48	86	48	64	56	21.82	72	24	32	44	23.33	64	32	56	48
20.48	86	28	48	72	21.88	100	40	56	64	23.33	48	24	28	24
20.48	86	28	32	48	21.88	100	32	28	40	23.33	64	24	28	32
20.48	86	24	32	56	21.90	86	24	44	72	23.38	72	28	40	44
20.57	72	40	64	56	21.94	86	28	40	56	23.44	100	48	72	64
20.57	72	28	32	40	21.99	86	44	72	64	23.44	100	32	48	64
20.63	72	32	44	48	22.00	64	32	44	40	23.45	86	40	48	44
20.63	72	24	44	64	22.00	48	24	44	40	23.52	86	32	56	64
20.74	64	24	56	72	22.00	56	28	44	40	23.57	72	28	44	48
20.78	64	28	40	44	22.04	72	28	48	56	23.57	72	24	44	56
20.83	100	32	48	72	22.11	86	28	72	100	23.57	48	28	44	32
20.83	100	24	32	64	22.22	100	40	64	72					
20.83	100	24	28	56	22.22	40	24	32	24	23.81	100	48	64	56
20.83	100	24	24	48	22.22	64	24	40	48	23.81	100	28	48	72
20.90	86	32	56	72	22.32	72	24	64	86	23.81	100	28	32	48
20.90	86	24	28	48	22.32	100	32	40	56	23.81	100	24	32	56
20.93	100	40	72	86	22.32	100	28	40	64	23.89	86	32	64	72
20.95	64	28	44	48	22.34	86	44	64	56	23.89	86	28	56	72
20.95	64	24	44	56	22.34	86	28	32	44	23.89	86	24	48	72
20.95	44	24	32	28	22.40	86	32	40	48	23.89	86	24	32	48
21.00	56	32	48	40	22.40	86	24	40	64	24.00	64	40	72	48
21.00	72	40	56	48	22.50	72	24	48	64	24.00	72	24	32	40
21.00	72	24	28	40	22.50	72	24	24	32	24.00	56	28	48	40
21.12	86	32	44	56	22.50	72	28	56	64	24.00	64	32	48	40
21.12	86	28	44	64	22.73	100	24	24	44	24.00	100	56	86	64
21.21	56	24	40	44	22.80	86	48	56	44	24.13	86	28	44	56
21.32	100	24	44	86	22.80	86	24	28	44	24.19	86	40	72	64
21.33	100	56	86	72	22.86	64	24	24	28	24.24	64	24	40	44
21.33	64	24	32	40	22.86	48	24	32	28	24.31	100	32	56	72
21.39	44	24	28	24	22.86	64	24	48	56	24.31	100	24	28	48
21.39	56	24	44	48	22.91	72	44	56	40	24.43	86	32	40	44
21.43	100	40	48	56	22.92	100	40	44	48	24.44	44	24	32	24
21.43	72	28	40	48	22.92	44	24	40	32	24.44	64	24	44	48
21.43	72	24	40	56	22.93	86	24	64	100	24.54	72	32	48	44
21.43	48	28	40	32	23.04	86	56	72	48	24.55	100	32	44	56

TABLE OF LEADS, 24.55″ TO 31.11″

Lead in Inches	Driven Gear on Worm	Driver 1st Gear on Stud	Driven 2nd Gear on Stud	Driver Gear on Screw	Lead in Inches	Driven Gear on Worm	Driver 1st Gear on Stud	Driven 2nd Gear on Stud	Driver Gear on Screw	Lead in Inches	Driven Gear on Worm	Driver 1st Gear on Stud	Driven 2nd Gear on Stud	Driver Gear on Screw
24.55	100	28	44	64	26.52	100	24	28	44	28.57	100	56	64	40
24.57	86	40	64	56	26.58	100	28	64	86	28.57	48	28	40	24
24.57	86	28	32	40	26.67	64	28	56	48	28.57	64	32	40	28
24.64	86	24	44	64	26.67	56	24	32	28	28.57	100	28	32	40
24.64	86	32	44	48	26.67	48	24	32	24	28.64	72	44	56	32
24.75	72	32	44	40	26.79	100	48	72	56	28.65	100	32	44	48
24.88	100	72	86	48	26.79	100	32	48	56	28.65	100	24	44	64
24.93	64	28	48	44	26.79	100	28	48	64	28.67	86	40	64	48
25.00	72	24	40	48	26.79	100	28	24	32	28.67	86	24	32	40
25.00	48	24	40	32	26.88	86	28	56	64	29.09	64	24	48	44
25.00	56	28	40	32	26.88	86	24	48	64	29.09	64	28	56	44
25.00	100	24	24	40	26.88	86	24	24	32	29.17	100	40	56	48
25.08	86	24	28	40	27.00	72	32	48	40	29.17	56	24	40	32
25.09	86	40	56	48	27.13	100	24	56	86	29.17	100	24	28	40
25.13	86	44	72	56	27.15	100	44	86	72	29.22	100	56	72	44
25.14	64	28	44	40	27.22	56	24	28	24	29.32	86	48	72	44
25.45	64	44	56	32	27.27	100	40	48	44	29.32	86	32	48	44
25.45	56	24	48	44	27.27	72	24	40	44	29.34	64	24	44	40
25.46	100	24	44	72	27.30	86	28	64	72	29.39	72	28	64	56
25.51	100	28	40	56	27.34	100	32	56	64	29.56	86	32	44	40
25.57	100	64	72	44	27.36	86	40	56	44	29.76	100	28	40	48
25.60	86	28	40	48	27.43	64	28	48	40	29.76	100	24	40	56
25.60	86	24	40	56	27.50	56	32	44	28	29.86	100	40	86	72
25.67	56	24	44	40	27.50	48	24	44	32	29.86	86	24	40	48
25.71	72	24	48	56	27.50	72	24	44	48	29.90	100	28	72	86
25.71	72	56	64	32	27.64	86	40	72	56	30.00	56	28	48	32
25.72	72	24	24	28	27.78	100	32	64	72	30.00	72	32	64	48
25.80	86	24	72	100	27.78	100	28	56	72	30.00	72	28	56	48
25.97	100	44	64	56	27.78	100	24	48	72	30.23	86	32	72	64
25.97	100	28	32	44	27.78	100	24	32	48	30.30	100	48	64	44
26.04	100	32	40	48	27.87	86	24	56	72	30.30	100	24	32	44
26.04	100	24	40	64	27.92	86	28	40	44	30.48	64	24	32	28
26.06	86	44	64	48	28.00	100	64	86	48	30.54	100	44	86	64
26.06	86	24	32	44	28.00	64	32	56	40	30.56	44	24	40	24
26.16	100	32	72	86	28.00	56	24	48	40	30.61	100	28	48	56
26.18	72	40	64	44	28.05	72	28	48	44	30.71	86	24	48	56
26.19	44	24	40	28	28.06	100	28	44	56	30.71	86	32	64	56
26.25	72	32	56	48	28.13	100	40	72	64	30.72	86	24	24	28
26.25	72	24	56	64	28.15	86	28	44	48	30.86	72	28	48	40
26.25	72	24	28	32	28.15	86	24	44	56	31.01	100	24	64	86
26.33	86	28	48	56	28.29	72	28	44	40	31.11	64	24	56	48
26.52	100	44	56	48	28.41	100	32	40	44	31.11	56	24	32	24

TABLE OF LEADS, 31.11″ TO 41.99″

	DRIVEN	DRIVER	DRIVEN	DRIVER		DRIVEN	DRIVER	DRIVEN	DRIVER		DRIVEN	DRIVER	DRIVEN	DRIVER
LEAD IN INCHES	GEAR ON WORM	1ST GEAR ON STUD	2ND GEAR ON STUD	GEAR ON SCREW	LEAD IN INCHES	GEAR ON WORM	1ST GEAR ON STUD	2ND GEAR ON STUD	GEAR ON SCREW	LEAD IN INCHES	GEAR ON WORM	1ST GEAR ON STUD	2ND GEAR ON STUD	GEAR ON SCREW
31.11	64	24	28	24	34.09	100	44	48	32	37.50	72	24	40	32
31.25	100	28	56	64	34.20	86	44	56	32	37.63	86	32	56	40
31.25	100	24	48	64	34.29	72	48	64	28	37.88	100	24	40	44
31.25	100	24	24	32	34.29	72	24	64	56	38.10	64	24	40	28
31.27	86	40	64	44	34.29	64	32	48	28	38.18	72	24	56	44
31.35	86	32	56	48	34.29	72	24	32	28	38.20	100	24	44	48
31.35	86	24	56	64	34.38	100	32	44	40	38.39	100	40	86	56
31.36	86	24	28	32	34.55	86	32	72	56	38.39	86	28	40	32
31.43	64	28	44	32	34.55	86	28	72	64	38.57	72	28	48	32
31.43	48	24	44	28	34.72	100	24	40	48	38.89	56	24	40	24
31.50	72	32	56	40	34.88	100	24	72	86	38.96	100	28	48	44
31.75	100	72	64	28	34.90	100	56	86	44	39.09	86	32	64	44
31.82	100	44	56	40	35.00	72	24	56	48	39.09	86	28	56	44
31.85	86	24	64	72	35.00	56	24	48	32	39.09	86	24	48	44
31.99	100	56	86	48	35.00	72	24	28	24	39.29	100	28	44	40
32.00	64	28	56	40	35.10	86	28	64	56	39.42	86	24	44	40
32.00	64	24	48	40	35.16	100	32	72	64					
32.09	56	24	44	32	35.18	86	44	72	40	39.49	86	28	72	56
32.14	100	56	72	40	35.36	72	32	44	28	39.77	100	32	56	44
32.14	72	28	40	32	35.56	64	24	32	24	40.00	72	24	64	48
32.25	86	48	72	40	35.71	100	32	64	56	40.00	64	28	56	32
32.25	86	40	48	32	35.71	100	24	48	56	40.00	64	24	48	32
32.41	100	24	56	72	35.72	100	24	24	28	40.00	56	24	48	28
32.47	100	28	40	44	35.83	86	32	64	48	40.00	72	24	32	24
32.58	86	24	40	44	35.83	86	28	56	48	40.18	100	32	72	56
32.73	72	32	64	44	36.00	72	32	64	40	40.18	100	28	72	64
32.73	72	28	56	44	36.00	72	28	56	40	40.31	86	32	72	48
32.73	72	24	48	44	36.00	72	24	48	40	40.31	86	24	72	64
32.74	100	28	44	48	36.36	100	44	64	40	40.72	100	44	86	48
32.74	100	24	44	56	36.46	100	48	56	32	40.82	100	28	64	56
32.85	86	24	44	48	36.46	100	24	56	64	40.91	100	40	72	44
33.00	72	24	44	40	36.46	100	24	28	32	40.95	86	28	64	48
33.33	100	24	32	40	36.67	48	24	44	24	40.95	86	24	64	56
33.33	100	48	64	40	36.67	64	24	44	32	40.96	86	24	32	28
33.33	64	24	40	32	36.67	56	24	44	28	41.14	72	28	64	40
33.33	56	24	40	28	36.86	86	28	48	40	41.25	72	24	44	32
33.33	48	24	40	24	37.04	100	24	64	72	41.67	100	32	64	48
33.51	86	28	48	44	37.33	100	32	86	72	41.67	100	28	56	48
33.59	100	64	86	40	37.33	64	24	56	40	41.81	86	24	56	48
33.79	86	28	44	40	37.40	72	28	64	44	41.81	86	24	28	24
33.94	64	24	56	44	37.50	100	48	72	40	41.91	64	24	44	28
34.09	100	48	72	44	37.50	100	32	48	40	41.99	100	32	86	64

TABLE OF LEADS, 42.00″ TO 74.65″

	DRIVEN	DRIVER	DRIVEN	DRIVER		DRIVEN	DRIVER	DRIVEN	DRIVER		DRIVEN	DRIVER	DRIVEN	DRIVER
LEAD IN INCHES	GEAR ON WORM	1ST GEAR ON STUD	2ND GEAR ON STUD	GEAR ON SCREW	LEAD IN INCHES	GEAR ON WORM	1ST GEAR ON STUD	2ND GEAR ON STUD	GEAR ON SCREW	LEAD IN INCHES	GEAR ON WORM	1ST GEAR ON STUD	2ND GEAR ON STUD	GEAR ON SCREW
42.00	72	24	56	40	48.00	72	24	64	40	56.31	86	24	44	28
					48.38	86	32	72	40	57.14	100	28	64	40
42.23	86	28	44	32	48.61	100	24	56	48	57.30	100	24	44	32
42.66	100	28	86	72	48.61	100	24	28	24	57.33	86	24	64	40
42.78	56	24	44	24	48.86	100	40	86	44	58.33	100	24	56	40
42.86	100	28	48	40	48.89	64	24	44	24	58.44	100	28	72	44
42.86	72	24	40	28	49.11	100	28	44	32	58.64	86	24	72	44
43.00	86	32	64	40	49.14	86	28	64	40	59.53	100	24	40	28
43.00	86	28	56	40	49.27	86	24	44	32	59.72	86	24	40	24
43.00	86	24	48	40	49.77	100	24	86	72	60.00	72	24	64	32
43.64	72	24	64	44	50.00	100	28	56	40	60.00	72	24	56	28
43.75	100	32	56	40	50.00	100	24	48	40	60.00	72	24	48	24
43.98	86	32	72	44	50.00	72	24	40	24	60.61	100	24	64	44
44.44	64	24	40	24	50.00	100	32	64	40	61.08	100	32	86	44
44.64	100	28	40	32	50.17	86	24	56	40	61.43	86	28	64	32
44.68	86	28	64	44	50.26	86	28	72	44	61.43	86	24	48	28
44.79	100	40	86	48	51.14	100	32	72	44	62.22	64	24	56	24
44.79	86	24	40	32	51.19	86	24	40	28	62.50	100	24	72	48
45.00	72	28	56	32	51.43	72	28	64	32	62.50	100	28	56	32
45.00	72	24	48	32	51.43	72	24	48	28	62.50	100	24	48	32
45.45	100	32	64	44	51.95	100	28	64	44	62.71	86	24	56	32
45.45	100	24	48	44	52.08	100	24	40	32	63.99	100	28	86	48
45.46	100	28	56	44	52.12	86	24	64	44	63.99	100	24	86	56
45.61	86	24	56	44	52.50	72	24	56	32	64.29	100	28	72	40
45.72	64	24	48	28	53.03	100	24	56	44	64.50	86	24	72	40
45.84	100	24	44	40	53.33	64	24	56	28	65.48	100	24	44	28
45.92	100	28	72	56	53.33	64	24	48	24	65.70	86	24	44	24
46.07	86	28	72	48	53.57	100	28	72	48	66.67	100	24	64	40
46.07	86	24	72	56	53.57	100	24	72	56	67.19	100	32	86	40
46.07	86	28	48	32						68.18	100	24	72	44
46.67	64	24	56	32	53.57	100	28	48	32	68.57	72	24	64	28
46.67	56	24	48	24	53.75	86	24	72	48	69.11	86	28	72	32
46.88	100	32	72	48	53.75	86	24	48	32	69.44	100	24	40	24
46.88	100	24	72	64	53.75	86	28	56	32	69.80	100	28	86	44
47.15	72	24	44	28	54.85	100	28	86	56	70.00	72	24	56	24
47.62	100	28	64	48	55.00	72	24	44	24	71.43	100	28	64	32
47.62	100	24	64	56	55.28	86	28	72	40	71.43	100	24	48	28
47.62	100	24	32	28	55.56	100	24	32	24	71.67	86	24	64	32
47.78	86	24	64	48	55.56	100	24	64	48	71.67	86	24	56	28
47.78	86	24	32	24	55.99	100	24	86	64	71.67	86	24	48	24
47.99	100	32	86	56	55.99	100	32	86	48	72.92	100	24	56	32
47.99	100	28	86	64	56.25	100	32	72	40	74.65	100	24	86	48

TABLE OF LEADS, 75.00″ TO 149.31″

	DRIVEN	DRIVER	DRIVEN	DRIVER		DRIVEN	DRIVER	DRIVEN	DRIVER		DRIVEN	DRIVER	DRIVEN	DRIVER
LEAD IN INCHES	GEAR ON WORM	1ST GEAR ON STUD	2ND GEAR ON STUD	GEAR ON SCREW	LEAD IN INCHES	GEAR ON WORM	1ST GEAR ON STUD	2ND GEAR ON STUD	GEAR ON SCREW	LEAD IN INCHES	GEAR ON WORM	1ST GEAR ON STUD	2ND GEAR ON STUD	GEAR ON SCREW
75.00	100	24	72	40										
76.39	100	24	44	24										
76.79	100	28	86	40										
80.00	72	24	64	24										
80.36	100	28	72	32										
80.63	86	24	72	32										
81.44	100	24	86	44										
81.90	86	24	64	28										
83.33	100	24	64	32										
83.33	100	24	56	28										
83.33	100	24	48	24										
83.61	86	24	56	24										
89.59	100	24	86	40										
92.14	86	24	72	28										
93.75	100	24	72	32										
95.24	100	24	64	28										
95.56	86	24	64	24										
95.98	100	28	86	32										
97.22	100	24	56	24										
107.14	100	24	72	28										
107.50	86	24	72	24										
111.11	100	24	64	24										
111.98	100	24	86	32										
125.00	100	24	72	24										
127.98	100	24	86	28										
149.31	100	24	86	24										

Double Compounding of Gearing, or the Use of Six Change Gears. In milling machine work, it is often necessary to obtain longer or more accurate leads than are possible by the use of four change gears. Therefore, the table of gear ratios on the opposite page is given to supplement the ordinary table of leads and permit the quick selection of the other two change gears.

The table of gear ratios is based upon the change gears furnished with Brown & Sharpe Universal Milling Machines. These change gears are as follows: 24 (2), 28, 32, 40, 44, 48, 56, 64, 72, 86, 100. Occasionally in determining the most accurate lead, the proper change gears will necessitate the use of two gears with the same number of teeth. Inasmuch as there are no two gears with the same number of teeth (with the exception of two gears with 24 teeth) it will be necessary to employ the next nearest gear ratio, resulting in a lead very close to the one desired.

Determining the Proper Change Gears to Use when Six Change Gears are Necessary.

Example: To find the proper change gears for gashing a hob with a lead of 167.5″.

Referring to the Table of Leads we find that 149.31″ is the longest obtainable with four regular change gears. Assuming that a greater degree of accuracy is desired, divide the lead desired (167.5) by the decimal equivalent 4.1667 given in the table on the opposite page and we have 40.1997″. The decimal equivalent 4.1667 is taken, as it corresponds to the first gear ratio (100 : 24) given for lead 149.31″ in the table of leads. The nearest lead to 40.1997 (which was found above) listed in the table of leads is 40.18″. Inasmuch as two 100 tooth gears are required to obtain this lead, it is necessary to try the next gear ratio.

Dividing 167.5 by 3.5833 (the decimal equivalent of the next ratio), we have 46.7446. Referring to the Table of Leads it will be found that the nearest lead is 46.67, for which the change gears are $\frac{64}{24}$ and $\frac{56}{32}$.

Adding the two gears from the Table of Ratios and to the driven gears the constant 10 (which is the constant of the lead of the machine), we have

$$\frac{64 \times 56 \times \mathbf{86} \times 10}{24 \times 32 \times \mathbf{24}} = 167.2222$$

Thus the six change gears 64, 24, 56, 32, 86 and 24 will give a lead of 167.2222. The error of lead .2778″ or the difference between the lead desired and the lead obtained is for this length of lead practically negligible and is considered near enough for all practical purposes.

TABLE OF RATIOS OF TWO GEARS WITH THEIR DECIMAL EQUIVALENTS

RATIO	DEC. EQUIV.	RATIO	DEC. EQUIV.	RATIO	DEC. EQUIV.
100:24	4.1667	100:72	1.3889	28:40	.7000
86:24	3.5833	44:32	1.3750	44:64	.6875
100:28	3.5714	86:64	1.3438	48:72	.6667
100:32	3.1250	64:48	1.3333	32:48	.6667
86:28	3.0714	32:24	1.3333	56:86	.6512
72:24	3.0000	72:56	1.2857	64:100	.6400
86:32	2.6875	56:44	1.2727	28:44	.6364
64:24	2.6667	40:32	1.2500	40:64	.6250
72:28	2.5714	48:40	1.2000	44:72	.6111
100:40	2.5000	86:72	1.1944	24:40	.6000
56:24	2.3333	56:48	1.1667	28:48	.5833
64:28	2.2857	28:24	1.1667	32:56	.5714
100:44	2.2727	100:86	1.1628	56:100	.5600
72:32	2.2500	64:56	1.1429	48:86	.5581
86:40	2.1500	32:28	1.1429	40:72	.5556
100:48	2.0833	72.64	1.1250	24:44	.5455
48:24	2.0000	44:40	1.1000	44:86	.5116
56:28	2.0000	48:44	1.0909	24:48	.5000
64:32	2.0000	44:48	.9167	28:56	.5000
86:44	1.9545	40:44	.9091	32:64	.5000
44:24	1.8333	64:72	.8889	48:100	.4800
72:40	1.8000	56:64	.8750	40:86	.4651
86:48	1.7917	28:32	.8750	32:72	.4444
100:56	1.7857	86:100	.8600	44:100	.4400
56:32	1.7500	48:56	.8571	28:64	.4375
48:28	1.7143	24:28	.8571	24:56	.4286
40:24	1.6667	72:86	.8372	40:100	.4000
72:44	1.6364	40:48	.8333	28:72	.3889
64:40	1.6000	32:40	.8000	24:64	.3750
44:28	1.5714	44:56	.7857	32:86	.3721
100:64	1.5625	56:72	.7778	24:72	.3333
86:56	1.5357	24:32	.7500	28:86	.3256
48:32	1.5000	48:64	.7500	32:100	.3200
72:48	1.5000	64:86	.7442	28:100	.2800
64:44	1.4545	32:44	.7273	24:86	.2791
40:28	1.4286	72:100	.7200	24:100	.2400
56:40	1.4000	40:56	.7143		

TABLES OF LEADS FOR CAM LOBES

Obtained with Spiral Head and a Vertical Spindle Milling Attachment Set at an Angle

The method of using the Spiral Head and a Vertical Spindle Milling Attachment for cutting the lobes of cams is described in Chapter IX, and the following tables have been worked out to enable the machine to be set up without the necessity of figuring the leads and settings.

In compiling these tables, we have employed the same combinations of change gears as those in the "Table of Approximate Angles for Cutting Spirals," all of which will reach without interfering. The practical leads obtainable with each set of change gears have been grouped together so that when a machine is set for any lead, and it is desired to change to another lead, the operator can quickly determine whether the required lead is available without changing the gears already on. As this is often the case in this work, the saving in time that is effected is readily appreciated.

A selection of cam leads from 0 to 20″ is listed, and it should be understood that these are the leads or amount of rise in a complete circle, not the amount of rise of a lobe in a fractional part of the circumference. From the amount of rise of the lobe it will be necessary before using these tables to calculate the lead or rise if the lobe were continued the full circumference. This is easily found as explained on page 171.

In using these tables to set up a machine to mill any required lead, the column under the heading "Approximate Lead" is first followed down until the range of leads is found which embraces the required one. Then follow the horizontal line across until the nearest dimension to the exact lead required is found. At the top of the column containing this dimension will be found the required combination of change gears, and in the next two columns at the right, and in line with the dimension selected, will be found the angles at which to set the spiral head and vertical milling attachment.

Example: Required, the change gears and angles at which to set the spiral head and vertical milling attachment to cut a cam with a lead of .1476″.

Following down the first column we find .145–50, which embraces the required lead. Following this line across horizontally we find .1474″, which is sufficiently near to .1476″ for all practical purposes. At the top of the column containing .1474″ is the proper combination of change gears, 24, 86, 32, and 100, and in the two columns at the right and in line with .1474″ are the necessary angles; 9 1/2° for spiral head, and 80 1/2° for vertical milling attachment.

When the machine is already set for a given lead and it is desired to know whether another required lead can be obtained without changing the gears, proceed as follows:

Example: Machine is set with a combination of gears, 24, 72, 32, and 86, and a lead of .1080″ is required.

Follow down the column of exact leads that are given under the combination of change gears for which the machine is set until .1081″ is found. This is sufficiently near to .1080″ for all practical purposes. Hence it is possible to obtain this lead without changing the gears, by setting the spiral head at 5° and the vertical milling attachment at 85°.

In milling cams in this way an angle of greater than 80° with the spiral head, which is the greatest angle listed in these tables, should be avoided to prevent going beyond the range of the spiral head.

A vertical spindle milling attachment with offset spindle, as shown on page 77, is preferable for this work, as it will reach nearer to the spiral head spindle when milling small cams with the head set nearly vertical.

We also manufacture an extension by the use of which the spiral head can be moved farther in on the table to bring the spiral head and vertical spindle attachment spindles nearer together.

The standard end mill is of sufficient length for practically all leads on ordinary screw machine cams, for long leads usually extend over only a partial turn of the cam.

The mill should be of the same diameter as the roll to be used with the cam, and, in laying out cam, work from the centre of the roll.

The change gears that are furnished with Universal Milling Machines have the following numbers of teeth: 24 (2 gears), 28, 32, 40, 44, 48, 56, 64, 72, 86 and 100.

LEADS FROM .000 TO .150

Approximate Lead	Gear on Worm 24, 1st on Stud 86, 2nd on Stud 24, Gear on Screw 100	Angle to Set Spiral Head (Degrees)	Angle to Set Vertical Att. (Degrees)	Gear on Worm 24, 1st on Stud 86, 2nd on Stud 28, Gear on Screw 100	Angle to Set Spiral Head (Degrees)	Angle to Set Vertical Att. (Degrees)	Gear on Worm 24, 1st on Stud 86, 2nd on Stud 32, Gear on Screw 100	Angle to Set Spiral Head (Degrees)	Angle to Set Vertical Att. (Degrees)	Gear on Worm 24, 1st on Stud 72, 2nd on Stud 28, Gear on Screw 86	Angle to Set Spiral Head (Degrees)	Angle to Set Vertical Att. (Degrees)
.000-05	.0029	1/4	89 3/4	.0034	1/4	89 3/4	.0039	1/4	89 3/4	.0047	1/4	89 3/4
.005-10	.0088	3/4	89 1/4	.0068	1/2	89 1/2	.0078	1/2	89 1/2	.0095	1/2	89 1/2
.010-15	.0117	1	89	.0102	3/4	89 1/4	.0117	3/4	89 1/4	.0142	3/4	89 1/4
.015-20	.0175	1 1/2	88 1/2	.0170	1 1/4	88 3/4	.0195	1 1/4	88 3/4	.0189	1	89
.020-25	.0234	2	88	.0205	1 1/2	88 1/2	.0234	1 1/2	88 1/2	.0237	1 1/4	88 3/4
.025-30	.0263	2 1/4	87 3/4	.0273	2	88	.0273	1 3/4	88 1/4	.0284	1 1/2	88 1/2
.030-35	.0321	2 3/4	87 1/4	.0341	2 1/2	87 1/2	.0312	2	88	.0331	1 3/4	88 1/4
.035-40	.0351	3	87	.0375	2 3/4	87 1/4	.0390	2 1/2	87 1/2	.0379	2	88
.040-45	.0409	3 1/2	86 1/2	.0443	3 1/4	86 3/4	.0428	2 3/4	87 1/4	.0426	2 1/4	87 3/4
.045-50	.0497	4 1/4	85 3/4	.0477	3 1/2	86 1/2	.0467	3	87	.0473	2 1/2	87 1/2
.050-55	.0526	4 1/2	85 1/2	.0511	3 3/4	86 1/4	.0545	3 1/2	86 1/2	.0521	2 3/4	87 1/4
.055-60	.0584	5	85	.0579	4 1/4	85 3/4	.0584	3 3/4	86 1/4	.0568	3	87
.060-65	.0642	5 1/2	84 1/2	.0613	4 1/2	85 1/2	.0623	4	86	.0615	3 1/4	86 3/4
.065-70	.0671	5 3/4	84 1/4	.0681	5	85	.0662	4 1/4	85 3/4	.0662	3 1/2	86 1/2
.070-75	.0700	6	84	.0749	5 1/2	84 1/2	.0739	4 3/4	85 1/4	.0710	3 3/4	86 1/4
.075-80	.0758	6 1/2	83 1/2	.0782	5 3/4	84 1/4	.0778	5	85	.0757	4	86
.080-85	.0846	7 1/4	82 3/4	.0816	6	84	.0817	5 1/4	84 3/4	.0804	4 1/4	85 3/4
.085-90	.0875	7 1/2	82 1/2	.0884	6 1/2	83 1/2	.0895	5 3/4	84 1/4	.0899	4 3/4	85 1/4
.090-95	.0932	8	82	.0918	6 3/4	83 1/4	.0933	6	84	.0946	5	85
.095-00	.0961	8 1/4	81 3/4	.0952	7	83	.0972	6 1/4	83 3/4	.0993	5 1/4	84 3/4
.100-05	.1048	9	81	.1020	7 1/2	82 1/2	.1011	6 1/2	83 1/2	.1040	5 1/2	84 1/2
.105-10	.1077	9 1/4	80 3/4	.1053	7 3/4	82 1/4	.1088	7	83	.1087	5 3/4	84 1/4
.110-15	.1106	9 1/2	80 1/2	.1121	8 1/4	81 3/4	.1127	7 1/4	82 3/4	.1134	6	84
.115-20	.1163	10	80	.1155	8 1/2	81 1/2	.1166	7 1/2	82 1/2	.1181	6 1/4	83 3/4
.120-25	.1221	10 1/2	79 1/2	.1222	9	81	.1204	7 3/4	82 1/4	.1228	6 1/2	83 1/2
.125-30	.1250	10 3/4	79 1/4	.1289	9 1/2	80 1/2	.1281	8 1/4	81 3/4	.1275	6 3/4	83 1/4
.130-35	.1336	11 1/2	78 1/2	.1323	9 3/4	80 1/4	.1320	8 1/2	81 1/2	.1322	7	83
.135-40	.1393	12	78	.1356	10	80	.1397	9	81	.1369	7 1/4	82 3/4
.140-45	.1421	12 1/4	77 3/4	.1424	10 1/2	79 1/2	.1435	9 1/4	80 3/4	.1416	7 1/2	82 1/2
.145-50	.1450	12 1/2	77 1/2	.1491	11	79	.1474	9 1/2	80 1/2	.1463	7 3/4	82 1/4

Approximate Lead	Gear on Worm 24, 1st on Stud 72, 2nd on Stud 32, Gear on Screw 86	Angle to Set Spiral Head (Degrees)	Angle to Set Vertical Att. (Degrees)	Gear on Worm 24, 1st on Stud 72, 2nd on Stud 40, Gear on Screw 100	Angle to Set Spiral Head (Degrees)	Angle to Set Vertical Att. (Degrees)	Gear on Worm 24, 1st on Stud 48, 2nd on Stud 28, Gear on Screw 100	Angle to Set Spiral Head (Degrees)	Angle to Set Vertical Att. (Degrees)	Gear on Worm 24, 1st on Stud 64, 2nd on Stud 40, Gear on Screw 100	Angle to Set Spiral Head (Degrees)	Angle to Set Vertical Att. (Degrees)
.000-05												
.005-10	.0054	1/4	89 3/4	.0058	1/4	89 3/4	.0061	1/4	89 3/4	.0065	1/4	89 3/4
.010-15	.0108	1/2	89 1/2	.0116	1/2	89 1/2	.0122	1/2	89 1/2	.0131	1/2	89 1/2
.015-20	.0162	3/4	89 1/4	.0174	3/4	89 1/4	.0183	3/4	89 1/4	.0196	3/4	89 1/4
.020-25	.0216	1	89	.0233	1	89	.0244	1	89			
.025-30	.0271	1 1/4	88 3/4	.0291	1 1/4	88 3/4				.0262	1	89
.030-35	.0327	1 1/2	88 1/2	.0349	1 1/2	88 1/2	.0305	1 1/4	88 3/4	.0327	1 1/4	88 3/4
.035-40	.0379	1 3/4	88 1/4				.0367	1 1/2	88 1/2	.0393	1 1/2	88 1/2
.040-45	.0433	2	88	.0407	1 3/4	88 1/4	.0428	1 3/4	88 1/4			
.045-50	.0487	2 1/4	87 3/4	.0465	2	88	.0489	2	88	.0458	1 3/4	88 1/4
.050-55	.0541	2 1/2	87 1/2	.0524	2 1/4	87 3/4				.0524	2	88
.055-60	.0595	2 3/4	87 1/4	.0582	2 1/2	87 1/2	.0550	2 1/4	87 3/4	.0589	2 1/4	87 3/4
.060-65	.0649	3	87	.0640	2 3/4	87 1/4	.0611	2 1/2	87 1/2			
.065-70				.0698	3	87	.0672	2 3/4	87 1/4	.0654	2 1/2	87 1/2
.070-75	.0703	3 1/4	86 3/4				.0733	3	87	.0720	2 3/4	87 1/4
.075-80	.0757	3 1/2	86 1/2	.0756	3 1/4	86 3/4	.0794	3 1/4	86 3/4	.0785	3	87
.080-85	.0811	3 3/4	86 1/4	.0814	3 1/2	86 1/2						
.085-90	.0865	4	86	.0872	3 3/4	86 1/4	.0855	3 1/2	86 1/2	.0850	3 1/4	86 3/4
.090-95	.0919	4 1/4	85 3/4	.0930	4	86	.0916	3 3/4	86 1/4	.0916	3 1/2	86 1/2
.095-00	.0973	4 1/2	85 1/2	.0988	4 1/4	85 3/4	.0978	4	86	.0981	3 3/4	86 1/4
.100-05	.1027	4 3/4	85 1/4	.1046	4 1/2	85 1/2	.1038	4 1/4	85 3/4	.1046	4	86
.105-10	.1081	5	85				.1098	4 1/2	85 1/2			
.110-15	.1135	5 1/4	84 3/4	.1104	4 3/4	85 1/4				.1112	4 1/4	85 3/4
.115-20	.1188	5 1/2	84 1/2	.1162	5	85	.1159	4 3/4	85 1/4	.1177	4 1/2	85 1/2
.120-25	.1242	5 3/4	84 1/4	.1220	5 1/4	84 3/4	.1220	5	85	.1242	4 3/4	85 1/4
.125-30	.1296	6	84	.1278	5 1/2	84 1/2	.1281	5 1/4	84 3/4			
.130-35				.1336	5 3/4	84 1/4	.1342	5 1/2	84 1/2	.1307	5	85
.135-40	.1350	6 1/4	83 3/4	.1393	6	84				.1372	5 1/4	84 3/4
.140-45	.1404	6 1/2	83 1/2				.1403	5 3/4	84 1/4	.1438	5 1/2	84 1/2
.145-50	.1458	6 3/4	83 1/4	.1452	6 1/4	83 3/4	.1463	6	84			